Indian Summer

By
Ceri Stone

Indian Summer
First Edition
Published by DreamStar Books, December 2003

Lasyard House
Underhill Street
Bridgnorth
Shropshire
WV16 4BB
Tel: 00 1746 761298
e-mail: dreamstar@jakarna.co.uk

Set in 'Garamond'

Printed and bound in Great Britain by Antony Rowe Ltd

Mum and Dad
My parents: My Heroes

Acknowledgements

This story has taken an arduous seven years to finally see the light of day and although every word printed is mine a few special people deserve a huge thank you. Although the blood, the sweat and the tears all belonged to me these people picked me up when I was low, provided encouragement when I was unsure of the whole thing and they were an inspiration when I needed guidance. For this I am in their debt.

Mum and Dad: For allowing me to use their computer, putting a roof over my head, tolerating my mood swings as I wrote and never once asking what I was doing. For all those hours when I locked myself away in the spare room I wasn't just looking for porn on the Internet and this book is the result of their warmth, guidance and unflinching support. I hope they see it as worthwhile. They are the greatest parents a man could wish for.

David and Caroline Goodman, alias Beaker and Caz: For their unswerving loyalty and friendship, especially Caz for reading the book and not shattering my dreams, but instead providing me with even greater enthusiasm. Beaker and the kids for never failing to make me laugh.

Nicola Simpkin: For her support, criticism and help. She is a true friend who I haven't set eyes on for almost nine years. Watch out for her bestseller next year.

Paul and Jo: Never were there finer siblings in this land.

Mark from Books4Publishing: Thanks for the encouragement, advice and persistence.

Leslie Thomas: The reason I first put pen to paper without being told to. His stories changed my life.

About the author

Ceri Stone was born on 21ˢᵗ July 1967 and has constantly lied about his age since turning thirty. His previous work experiences include four and a half years in the insurance industry where he gained his customer service grounding, but because of a desire to travel and broaden his horizons, plus the need to escape from a jealous girlfriend and irate bank manager he moved into the package holiday industry and has spent the past nine years working in Europe, Africa and Asia.

His love of adventure and gaining new experiences, plus a creative side that was unmasked through the industry training led to some experimental writings, which include a two line novel; a wet poem of apology to an ex-girlfriend and a begging letter to his bank manager. These passages matured, sadly Ceri didn't, and his collective works over the course of a season have now resulted in this first publication, the results of which mean he will never work in travel again.

Notable achievements to date include coming second in a school handwriting competition, until he was disqualified for copying; being dumped by an imaginary girlfriend at the age of fourteen; holding onto a career in insurance, mainly by scoring goals for the company football team, and surviving two military coups, one Luxor massacre and a season in Tunisia without being forced into anal intercourse.

Ceri still lives with his parents in Wales, because his bank manager continually refuses to allow him enough pocket money to buy or rent a place of his own; he has a hectic social life in his own mind.

Ceri still uses the word 'boobies' frequently in conversation.

Foreword

This story can best be described as factional. As the cover says it is the true story of one of my working winters in the delightful tourist resort of Goa. But because it is completely true and everything that happens did actually occur then there is the risk that some people may take offence. If this is the case then I unreservedly apologise, for this was not the intention when I first put pen to paper.

I decided to write this story because I was forever being asked a hundred and one questions by tourists about what it is really like to be a rep. Without fail, most of my customers were fascinated by the workings of our minds, the routine of our day, the make-up of a resort and the sordid goings on of some of our social lives. Then came the TV programmes and the revealing newspaper articles, which never failed to rile the emotions of a hard working rep. So after plenty of badgering from my peers and a desire to explore my creative skills I thought it was time to set the record straight and tell it how it really is. So here it is, warts and all.

Actually most of the warts are mine because I just didn't want to offend anyone, plus this is my story and that of the industry, and not some vengeful mission. But to protect the innocent I have changed the names of every person mentioned except my own, because I am proud of the person I am and the life I have led. I have also changed the names of some of the hotels mentioned, but the obviously better ones still remain in their true form because they deserve a mention. It must also be said that although nothing is inaccurate, some sections are my own thoughts and opinions and I stand by what I think and believe. But because time always keeps ticking on and things change, the names are altered because I do not wish to prejudice anyone else's thoughts or opinions on the basis of events that happened six years ago. After all a week is a long time in tourism.

I do hope that you enjoy reading this and do not take it too seriously because this is not a spite induced tell all (despite some meaty revelations). This book is intended to enlighten every tourist who has asked what it is like to be a rep? It is also for every hard working rep who had to sit through a twelve-hour flight delay and as a result missed their sales target and that hot date with the Scandi rep, only to be laden with even more paperwork and a huge complaint from 'Angry from Tunbridge Wells.'

Please just take this book for what it is. That is the inner workings of a holiday rep's state of mind, an exploration into the real working life overseas and the humour that unfolds as one young man struggles to find a balance in his professional life, living in an awe inspiring country and juggling a hectic social life.

This season is by no means exceptional in that greater events will no doubt occur to every other rep at some stage of their careers. For example, in the past I have lived through a military coup, the Luxor massacre and a couple of very near death experiences, all in the course of my daily routine, but they are for another book. However, this season is still very typical and will provide the insight fifteen million tourists a year are looking for.

After reading I hope you will be inspired enough to visit Goa because in the end I spent nigh on five glorious years there and it has become an integral part of my life. I also hope you will forgive me any inaccuracies if my thinking becomes too cynical or romantic, because as they say: "All biography is fiction: All fiction is biography."

Finally, remember: "Suntans fade; memories last forever."

Enjoy.

GOA – WINTER SEASON

WEDNESDAY – 23RD SEPTEMBER

Yet again my beloved company, like all other tour operators, have proved that when it comes to looking after their resort staff, they don't know their arses from their elbows.

To me it would appear that sending a small team of representatives to a resort and putting them up in a hotel for the first few days would be rather straightforward. i.e. they book and pay for flights and hotel rooms, we go where we are told and everything passes by smoothly. Not so! In the seven years I have been in the industry, the first four of which were with a mainstream operator, and having worked thirteen different contracts in ten different destinations I can only recall two occasions when it has all gone according to plan going out to a resort, but never once returning.

So here I am sitting in Bahrain international airport waiting for a connecting flight to Bombay with another hour to kill and I'm surrounded by a group of Indians who have just opened their suitcases to get some stale sandwiches out. Although it has temporarily stopped their incessant loud gabbling about the state of the government and the national cricket team, it has only served to annoy me more, because I can now hear every morsel being crunched on top of their misguided statements.

The man on my left has huge chunks of cheese in between his teeth and he still won't pause for breath, while the guy on my right is English and presumably believes he's emitting the right kind of karma to mingle with locals when he arrives in Bombay by not washing for five days and wearing a cheap, ill-fitting, cotton thread outfit which must have cost no more than £1 from Oxfam. It's a bit overbearing but there is no way that I'm going to move because I had to wait twenty minutes to get the seat and push past two dithering people to get here.

I could look at the duty free tapes for the sixth time, but that would mean walking past the booze for the sixth time and 'uhmming' and 'ahhing' over the five litres of Australian red wine for the sixth time, which does seem to be a bargain at £7.

To get this far I left Heathrow early this morning after yet another argument over excess luggage and approximately eight days behind the original schedule and four days ahead of the last one.

When I arrived back from a seven month working stint in The Maldives in mid August I was summoned to Head Office for a ten-minute meeting to find out the destination and dates of my next contract. This involved a round trip of twelve hours travelling by bus from my home in South Wales and costing the company over £50 in expenses just to be told that I would be coming to Goa on 15th September. A two-minute phone call would have been much easier.

A couple of days later I received a letter saying that I'd been promoted to Head Rep and that I would now be departing four days later on the 19th.

By Monday 14th September I still hadn't heard from the company, so I rang up Stelios George who is my senior product controller. This is basically the person who contracts the flight seats, hotels and arranges the contract with our local agency in resort, plus because we are a small company he also oversees our resort recruitment and looks in on all day to day running matters of the resort, therefore a big cheese – who said:

"Ahh yes, ahh, Ceri I was just about to call you?" which loosely translated means – *Damn, I'd forgotten all about you!*

"Still good that you've rung, because we're looking at sending you out on about the 27th instead" - *It's too late to book seats for the 19th now.*

"So we'll see you next week. Bye"

Despite not being able to get a word in, I left it at that, confident that I wouldn't be going anywhere for a fortnight.

Then on Monday, 21st September at approximately 17:24pm I received the message of, "Aah Ceri. Good to have caught you. You're leaving on Wednesday at 10:00am from Heathrow." Which I said was good because it gave me a day to pack for eight months of living and to generally get myself organised.

"Oh. We need you in the office tomorrow morning to collect some things. Bye"

Not only did he annoy me with his short lingering sentences, as he always has done, but he also exacerbated matters by giving me six minutes to get to an agent five miles away to book a coach seat for the following morning.

Whilst my mother made the necessary phone call and begged and pleaded for them to stay open, I dashed into town and eight minutes after they should have closed I bought a coach ticket from Swansea to Heathrow (which still meant I had to get a lift for the 50 miles from home to Swansea in the early hours of the morning) and spent the rest of the night frantically packing and drying wet laundry with a hairdryer to get myself ready.

When I arrived at the office, via Heathrow, I was given my flight ticket and seven large packages of information books, information boards and headed paper and was promised that the excess baggage was sorted out with Gulf Air. I still can't believe that they've booked me seats on Gulf Air, but it's only because Aeroflot were fully booked!

This morning I arrived at the check-in desk nice and early with one suitcase, 1 rucksack, 1 holdall and 7 heavy packets to be told my luggage allowance was 20kgs. The powers that be had forgotten to request the excess baggage yet again.

Thankfully the lady from Gulf Air was unbelievably helpful, she called her supervisor who said the flight wasn't full and she would see what she could do. As it turned out the packages weighed 47kg and my luggage 36kg (the sum total of my life in 36kg). So she very kindly let me off my own allowance and promised to bill my head office for the rest of the excess baggage. If only the charter airlines could be this helpful! I remember one occasion when I was working for my previous company when I was charged £67 excess baggage, yet I was travelling with the airline I worked for! I claimed this on expenses, which was reclaimed from our resort office and was then collected in turn from our local agent, then from Head Office, through to the airline and eventually back from the flight-handling agent. The whole process took nigh on three months and cost more than double what I was charged in admin fees alone.

Still you live and they don't learn and they've just called my flight; five minutes to boarding.

Excellent, just enough time to get the wine.

THURSDAY – 24TH SEPTEMBER

14:30 local time. I eventually made it to Dabolim International Airport in Goa, to be met by Ravi, who is the manager of our local agency, and one of the office boys Prasad. Janet who happens to be our manager in The Maldives, has also come here for ten days on her way back to the UK to help set the resort up for the beginning of the season.

I must have looked a state coming through. In the end I only had half an hour's kip in Bombay, due to my childish delight at surfing the hotels satellite TV channels. So with saggy eyes and the same clothes I'd worn for twenty-four hours hanging off me, plus the effort of pushing seven large packets and three cases on one small, creaking trolley through a crowd of porters who were all trying to get their hands on each of my bags, even my panda (who always travels in my small rucksack for luck) was trying to disown me.

The guys were pleased to see me and were even more amazed that the packets had made it through in one piece and they duly took me to the Taj Holiday Village, where I'll stay for my first two nights until my permanent room in town is ready.

FRIDAY – 25TH SEPTEMBER

The purpose for coming out to a resort two weeks before it actually opens is to get it, what is commonly known as, 'Set-Up'. This is one of the most exciting, tedious, frustrating and above all important jobs of the whole season because the work we do in the next fortnight lays the foundations for the following eight months.

It's exciting because of the obvious factors of having just arrived in a strange and interesting place where you know there are many disappointments and adventures that lie ahead. Many new friends will be made; some traumatic experiences will no doubt occur somewhere along the line; plenty of exotic food and drink will be consumed at plenty of great nights out and parties, and we will see some amazing sights and learn more about a life altering culture which has enchanted visitors for centuries.

This is a wonderful time thinking about everything that is to come, but it is tedious because we are doing the boring and monotonous paperwork which is not part of the glamorous image of a rep, and in this period it is unlikely there will be any parties or fun.

Although this tedium is absolutely necessary it is frustrating because we just want to actually get out there, greet the guests and get the whole thing underway, yet we are being bogged down by drudgery and in this particular case mounds upon mounds of Indian bureaucracy. However, it will be worth it all in the end because everything we do now will have an effect on the rest of the season in some way or another.

So for the next two weeks we're going to have to run round the hotels checking the reservations, doing the Health and Safety checks, making sure the hotels are up and running and checking on any building work and brochure errors. Then there is the office to sort out, setting up procedures so that we can accurately log and deal with reservations, complaints, financial paperwork, individual hotel files, Federation of Tour Operators (FTO) agendas, Health and Safety logs, insurance files and more, depending on the individual requirements of the resort.

We have to do the information books and boards which will take a few days to compile, type and add all the relevant pictures and postcards; then we have to arrange and sample each of the excursions we will be selling, prepare the airport procedures, transfer speeches and welcome meetings. Finally we need to learn all about the separate resorts, because if we don't know anything about them how could we reasonably hope to inform the forthcoming tourists. To cap it all we have to deal with any hiccups that will inevitably crop up and our main worries at the moment are whether or not we will have any staff, apart from myself, because no one else has been confirmed to join us as yet.

So to start this great big adventure off we - we being one big happy family of Ravi (connected), Janet (whingeing) and myself (excited) –visited six hotels in the South of Goa. The first three were all four star and above, and had been running continuously throughout the 'Off Season' so are therefore ready to take our guests straight away. Then after lunch we went to the Leela Palace.

The Leela Palace has spent the last fifteen months being revamped and it looks absolutely fantastic. The lobby is the most impressive I have ever seen, with huge comfortable chairs, ornate stone elephants at the entrance and rich detail in all of the brickwork depicting stories of the kings and queens from Rajasthan. The rooms are luxurious and it is without doubt the highest standard of hotel I have ever seen in the package industry.

The problem is that the previous management were always a bunch of shifty devils who frequently overbooked our guests, made changes to reservations at the last minute and constantly carried out building work without informing anyone. As a result I am still sceptical about working with them especially seeing as some of the old guard are still here.

Nonetheless one of the front office boys gave us a good and

informative guided tour in some little golf buggies and we then settled in for the obligatory coffee in the lobby and a friendly chat. Ravi was in awe of the surroundings gasping at every little nuance he kept spotting and Janet was happily complaining to anyone who would listen. In this instance it was a young bellhop who didn't know quite what had hit him as he learnt all about her mosquito bites and her need to frequently go to the toilet because of all the teas and coffees we'd been given. I cautiously decided to test the water and inconspicuously asked what the unfinished grey building was at the far end of the Villas.

"That's the new block we are being building," the front office boy replied "but it is not being part of this building!"

"When will it be finished?"

"Soon! In a few weeks I am believing, but there is no disturbance!"

And then right on cue the inevitable sound of drilling pierced our eardrums, which seemed to shake the lobby area causing Janet to spill her tea. I took a deep breath, Ravi smiled wryly and the front office guy didn't bat an eyelid but continued to talk about sales forecasts as if nothing was happening. I'm not too concerned about this hotel though, because we don't have any guests arriving in here until November so they have plenty of time to ensure that everything is ready and I'm confident that all will be okay.

However the following two hotels are names that I will be hearing more about over the coming months. Both the Dona Santa Maria and the SJM were building sites and not in the manner of a small bit of rubble lying around waiting to be tidied up. Both hotels have unfinished buildings with construction work taking place and they were littered with cement bags, sand and hundreds of slim yet muscular Indians in vests carrying tools and bricks back and forth, but seemingly going nowhere in particular.

This is unbelievable, yet typical. They have had since May to get all of this work done, yet they don't bother to start until a month before the season gets underway and now they have a mad two-week dash to get everything ready in time. It doesn't look as if either hotel will be at this present stage, but I suppose it is remotely possible considering they have three hundred people working on shifts around the clock, and we are obliged to give them the benefit of the doubt.

The people we spoke to at the hotels were adamant that the work would be completed, yet not surprisingly the hotel managers were very scarce, even though we had made appointments to see them. This was a big nuisance because we needed to discuss the matters at hand and get a lot more sensible and realistic information out of them, but on the bright side we didn't have to drink any more tea or coffee. Sadly though we couldn't go to the toilet either.

Janet and I wrote our relevant reports, which I am quite sure are not going to be the last, and faxed them through to Head Office on Ravi's machine when we arrived back in Panjim. It had to be on his machine because we do not have one as yet

These are matters that will have to be monitored quite closely but at the moment I don't know where we're going to get the time?

SATURDAY – 26TH SEPTEMBER

There are many days in this industry where no matter how hard you try to get things done all you end up achieving is having pushed a couple of pieces of paper from one side of the desk to another, twiddled your thumbs a lot and rearranged your top five famous bottoms into alphabetical order. This is usually because the height of international bureaucracy is encountered, something which is especially prevalent over here, or because you have to rely on other people to fulfil a task or deliver some goods before you can get on with your own particular agenda.

These days are highly frustrating and although it sounds like an easy life being able to say that you did bugger all, it only serves to increase your workload for the following day. You also have no sense of achievement, and therefore no real sense of self worth, and have to motivate yourself to be ready for the following day's travails.

Today was one of those days, which is even more annoying at present when every moment counts in this current mad dash against time to ensure that everything is ready and in place for the 11th of October, when the season begins for real.

The plan was that Ravi would pick Janet and myself up at 09:30 and move me down to my new home. He would then get us into the office where we could spend the day working on the information books and boards and planning the next fourteen days while (in the meantime) he would also ensure that the company car would be delivered.

At 09:30 we received a call from Ravi to say that he would be a little bit late, but to hold on for a while. But after another marathon tea drinking session he eventually rang again at midday to say that he wouldn't be able to pick us up because he was in a meeting with his boss.

After having wasted three hours hanging around, and having relieved our bladders for what felt like the twentieth time Janet and I hopped cross legged into a taxi and headed for Panjim, the capital, where our office is based. I dumped my bags into the El Pablo, which is to be my home for the rest of the season, before managing to reach the office by 13:30 only to find that the office closes at 14:00 on a Saturday and that I haven't had a key cut for me yet. To add to the fun there was no power in the whole of the city, but that wouldn't have mattered anyway because it transpires that we have no P.C., no direct phone line for local or international calls, no fax (which we knew about yesterday), and no photocopier. All that we could feasibly do was wait for the car and have lunch afterwards.

By 14:15 the car still hadn't arrived and the girls in the office desperately wanted to pack up and go home for the weekend. You can hardly blame them really seeing as they earn something in the region of £30:00 per month and have no vested interest in the resort being ready, or not as the case may be at present

With this in mind we had to make some rapid phone calls before we could get hold of the car supplier only to be told that it will not be ready until Tuesday because it is being serviced, even though he's known for the past three months that we will want the car on this date. I was livid. But it serves no purpose in getting angry and letting it show because it will only make the guy even more petulant and inefficient and would put us back even further. I did however, ask that when he said Tuesday, did he mean Tuesday of this week to which he put the phone down on me.

This meant that with no car and no available office there was no choice but to have lunch and then go home and unpack, which I believe Janet was secretly pleased about. The unpacking went very swiftly though and it gave me a good chance to settle into the El Pablo, which is a very basic hotel even by Indian standards.

The rooms are small and cramped, with two single beds pushed together and very little space between them and the walls. The walls are painted a grim shade of beige and are probably the bright spark of the room because the floor is covered with those really old tiles that were once a sort of off white with grey flecks but now look as if dirt and dust have made the floor their permanent home. They are actually very clean, but it doesn't give that impression and this isn't aided by having an old, dark brown rickety wardrobe, which will hold enough clothes for one week, but no way will it hold enough for a full season's worth of gear. To round off the complement of furniture for the room there is a small glass table in the only available space, which I covered with a cloth and put my mini CD player and collection of CD's onto.

If I thought the bedroom was small then the bathroom takes the biscuit. It is so cramped, with the shower, sink and toilet so close it's possible to shit, shower and shave all at the same time.

I suppose I'll have to get used to it and can see that there are some positives in that there will be around eight other reps from various other tour operators living here, so I'll have some good company on hand; it's clean and it's convenient for the office. This is home for the next eight months. Actually home for the next eight months with rules!

- No playing of electrical equipment. Radios, Stereos etc.
- No coming in later than 23:00 hours.
- Use hot water sparingly.
- No Washing in the sink. (I think they mean clothing).
- No Laundry. (maybe they don't mean clothing above).
- No people to ever come into your room.

Great. If in the slightest chance I manage to get a deaf, dumb, blind hunchback drunk enough to come back to my place she's not going to be allowed in! It looks like I have three options:

- Go to her place and hope she doesn't have the same rules to abide by.
- Get friendly with reception and pay out a fortune in bribes.
- Spend eight months playing helicopters in the shower.

SUNDAY – 27TH SEPTEMBER

In this period of manic preparation before a season is due to start I tend to suffer from a few little nervous problems, which are definitely not good for my health. The reason for these is the anxieties of actually trying to get everything ready and the feeling of being completely out of place. No matter how many times I go through this, it is always the same and I have just learned to accept it and continue blundering along, trying to put the discomfort to the back of my mind.

Every time I have been in this situation before we have always managed to get everything ready so I should be fairly calm these days, now that I am older and a little wiser, but I can't help but worry about getting the work done. I wonder if the hotels will be ready? Will we get the reservations through on time? Will they be confirmed? What problems will we have to deal with? Will we get the books and boards done? Will we get some other reps and what will they be like? Will I like them? Will I respect them? Will they like or respect me? Will I fancy any of them? Will we get the office equipment that is needed before the season starts? Will I ever meet a decent woman? If so, could she please be Scandinavian? And so on.

Not only do I feel out of my depth but I also feel out of place. The thing is we are in a tourist resort and are supposed to be here doing a specific job and it is when we are doing that job that people take notice of you and afford you more respect. But now I am not doing my job, I am not a tourist and I am not a local so I feel as if I am in limbo, hanging around waiting for someone to decide who I am, where I should be and what I should be doing! I know it's all irrational but I, and every other person I know in the industry, always feels the same way and until those first guests arrive we have to work to the best of our abilities and deal with them in our own individual ways. Me, I do the work, but at some stage I will lose my appetite and thus lose too much weight way too rapidly, but that is the good stage because I know I am almost there then. Preceding this will be the sudden bout of excruciating diarrhoea, which never fails to catch me short, and the current problem of not being able to sleep and, on finally dozing off, waking at 05:00am as I did this morning. Once this is over and the season is underway there are only the occasional bad dreams, sporadic bouts of the 'two bob bits' and sexual frustration to deal with.

But having woken so early I had to wait over four hours for Ravi to turn up. This did give me an opportunity to run a few ideas through my head and put some of them down on paper, which in turn helped assuage some of my tension before we embarked on what was quite a productive and enjoyable day.

Because there is not a lot we can do on a Sunday at present, we allocated today for visiting each of the hotels in the Northern coastal resorts of Candolim, Calangute and Baga, where we have the bulk of our programme in a lot of basic two star hotels and a couple of five stars for good measure.

We picked up an excursion supplier en route called Sandip and because the hotels are generally very basic, simple and within a short journey of each other we were able to see them all and make the acquaintance of the managers and/or owners in just under four hours. There were no major problems and it was hard to gauge how prepared most of the hotels are because we are still at the tail end of the rainy season and huge bucket loads of water are still intermittently being dumped upon us throughout the day. This meant that all of the rooms and interior work were ready, but the exterior of most of the hotels was very drab and mouldy due to five months of no attention. This is normal because the hotels are painted, or rather whitewashed, before the beginning of every season and they only need a couple of dry days to do this, which fingers crossed we should get.

Again I found myself hoping everything will be ready in time and cannot envisage too many problems here. There were no additional worries and, because Janet was taking a day off, there were no unnecessary complaints about the humidity or copious amounts of tea that was consumed. We were therefore still in good spirits and ready for a spot of lunch.

With Ravi and Sandip on hand there was no need to gamble on an unknown restaurant and we opted for one of Ravi's favourite haunts back in Panjim. We feasted on a seemingly never ending stream of Masala Papads, Aloo Chats, Chicken Tikka's, Naan breads, Salads, Pakora's, Stuffed Chilli's and glycerine filled Kingfisher beer and before we knew it, it was 16:30 and the waiters were asking us to leave so that they could have a siesta and prepare for their evening shift. Being suitably squiffy, we trundled off to Ravi's house to watch some videos and have a few more beers served by his boy.

We were watching 'Ghost' on video, frequently rewinding the pottery scene and gradually becoming more and more inebriated when all of a sudden Sandip drunkenly jumps to his feet, waits for the head rush to subside and shouts – "SHIT! I've forgotten it's my cousin's birthday party!" Ravi and I forced ourselves up, Sandip ushered us into Ravi's car and we dashed into town with a less than steady Ravi behind the wheel. Apparently there are drink-driving laws over here which are strict, severe and largely ignored because they are all pretty useless drivers at the best of times and the police generally don't know the rules of the road. We buy the first Barbie Doll we can find and go to this six-year-old girl's party.

The house is on the outskirts of the town and thankfully Ravi's driving improves when he's had a few because he makes an effort to watch out for other cars and pedestrians. He then safely delivered us to a surreal situation where an hour or so later I was even more squiffy, standing against a wall with the sound of kids playing upstairs echoing above me; men were sitting down, drinking cheap beer and brandy, and discussing the latest politics while the ladies were running back and forth with trays of wonderful home made Samosa's, sandwiches and Bhajia's etc and refusing to let me take less than two of each.

What's amazing is that I haven't got the faintest idea who anyone is, yet they not only welcome me into their homes with open arms, but also treat me like a royal guest. I know I'm a bit of a curiosity and I suppose it's a bit of a status symbol to have European friends, but this would almost certainly never happen back home. However, this is one of the delightful things about this job, in that you never cease to be amazed and humbled by the people you meet.

Even though I'd had a few drinks, I was able to take in the surroundings and I always marvel at the homes people live in. This house was quite quaint because it was very spacious yet very basic inside with just a lino-covered floor and plain, beige painted walls. The furniture was formal with no thought given to comfort and was situated in one corner of the living room leaving the rest of the building very sparse indeed. However, covering all of one wall in the dining area was a glorious Teak cabinet and inside was a display of pristine porcelain, which was perfectly symmetrical and must have been worth thousands. I counted over 200 pieces on one shelf alone and there were six different display areas.

Some of the younger ladies were also very stunning and unfortunately spoken for and with my respect for individual countries and their traditions my mum would be glad to know that I was on my best behaviour, for the time being at least. Ravi, if anything, was feeling even more uncomfortable than I and eventually dragged Sandip away and took us to a bar called 'Pete's' on the Western edge of town. This happened to be my kind of joint;

dingy, simple and full of men drinking beer and farting.

We dutifully consumed another half a dozen pints of the local brew into the early hours and resumed our discussion on the respective merits of Demi Moore's boobs before and after she had them done.

THURSDAY – 24ᵀᴴ SEPTEMBER

Again I woke up dead early, this time at 06:00, and again I ran through a few ideas in my head, as well as listing my current top five dream women in numerical order before Ravi and Janet appeared at 09:00 to take me to the office. This was a frustrating waste of three hours and it set the tone for the rest of the day.

The morning wasn't too bad because we managed to steal the best bits from the previous year's information book, compile some more interesting details and generally set the format for the whole of the book. This was a bit of a speedy result, because this process has been known to take days and involve many a sleepless night sitting at a bedside lamp, scribbling down notes and checking facts from guide books and local journals. However, we were drastically hindered by the lack of equipment and facilities that were available to us in the office.

We wanted to put what we have for the information book onto Ravi's computer (which until we get our own is supposed to be for our shared use), but Ravi was out on a long business lunch and had locked the door to his cabin. Just as Janet and I were seething with the utmost of rage and criticizing everything Indian, Ravi turned up at about 16:30. It then transpired that we do not have the full use of the computer because Ravi, and his desperate need to assist, insists on doing everything himself, so I had to dictate to Ravi what we required, then the three of us would discuss fonts and layout.

All the while the phone would keep ringing, so Ravi would stop what he was doing, Janet and I would shuffle out of his cabin to give him some privacy, he would answer the phone, chat away for five minutes and then call us in as soon as he was free again. Eventually we developed quite a good routine of type one paragraph, phone ring, shuffle out, chat, shuffle in, type one paragraph, phone ring and so forth.

It took five hours to do a 45-minute job, wasting three people's time, efforts and patience, which is in effect a full productive day's work down the drain. But this is the way in India, because everywhere you go it seems that there are three people doing one job, especially in the service industries, and this results in 100% employment, 50% efficiency and 0% crime.

By the time we had finished Janet and I were red faced from the constant irritation of the routine, yet Ravi was happily sitting there, plodding away with his two fingers on the keyboard and a huge grin on his face because he was pleased that he could help.

We did have one break in the midst of all this Indian efficiency, when Stelios George rang to speak to Janet to see how things were going. They went through all the preliminaries of how the hotels were (Stelios completely ignoring the building work reports we had sent a few days earlier), how Janet was feeling and errands we should run for him when he casually dropped a minor bombshell on us. We are only having two more reps this year, both of whom will be brand new, completely inexperienced and will require complete training when they arrive in the resort, but we do not know when that will be yet because they can't get any flight seats for them.

In a resort which has seventeen hotels spread the length of the state, with over five hundred guests arriving every week, and in previous quieter years has struggled to get by with four experienced reps in what can be a demanding programme, he now decides that we increase the size of the programme and decrease the number of reps. His only suggestion to assist us throughout, is that instead of giving us a couple more reps I should rep full time as well as fulfil my management responsibilities, and so should our resort manager. By the way, we should now be getting a resort manager by the name of Kate, but we are still not 100% sure if she will be coming yet.

That was actually a piece of good news because Kate is someone I know quite well and although she is quite young she is a hard worker who is organised and efficient and is very good fun to be around.

However, I am annoyed because it was always understood that I, as the Head Rep, would cover one or two hotels and then help out in the office and the continued training of the reps. The manager would then run the office and look after the hoteliers and any other suppliers. Now, according to Stelios, we will both have to rep full time as well as continue with the rest of our duties, thus giving us two full time jobs for a measly £150 extra per month. As a result we'll be disorganised in resort, which means the service we provide will suffer as will our level of excursion sales and therefore our commission levels will be low. This in turn will increase the size of the snowball by virtue of being even more demoralising. Because of this, Stelios and the other UK departments will get on our backs and tell us we're not doing well enough, insist upon improvements without giving us the resources to do so, and when improvements are not forthcoming threaten us with our positions, which of course will demotivate us further and thus increase the size of the snowball even further. It could all be prevented at the very start of the hill by Stelios actually doing his job properly and giving us a fair crack at the whip from the offset.

I know though, that all I will do is sulk for a day or two, then throw myself into the work way too much and do a good job, as I always have done, for which I will be given no credit and will be expected to do even more often in the future, which is sadly a very common industry scenario at present and will continue until all the good ones leave.

Right now the only problem with this is that with our company having recently being bought by another mainstream tour operator we don't know where our jobs stand and we are aware that we could be dismissed on any one of the next 365 days that we go to work. So what's the point of making the effort and why don't I pack my bags right now?

- Personal pride.
- I enjoy it.
- I haven't met any Scandi Babes yet!

As Janet commented with one of her rare pearls of wisdom, with all companies the overseas staff are treated with no respect They are considered a necessary burden, who are on a paid holiday yet seem to do the hardest job of the lot, which has the greatest effect on both the guests, the hotels and the companies image. But then again we are biased.

It does make me wonder if this may be my last season though.

WEDNESDAY – 30TH SEPTEMBER

Found out this afternoon, in the midst of more delightful paper pushing, that our two brand new reps will not be coming out on Thursday, which we were finally informed of yesterday. This is because our agent forgot to inform their Bombay branch that the girls would be arriving in Bombay and onward tickets to Goa need to be booked. They'll be put on standby for four possible flights which are fully booked at present, but it's highly unlikely that they'll get on any because tomorrow and Friday are public holidays, which means that hundreds of wealthy Bombayites come down to Goa to spend their cash and be rude to waiters. With a bit of luck though they should be here by Friday and at least they'll get a chance to see Bombay, which is one of the excursions we sell.

Eight days to train and induct two brand new reps.

Every other tour operator will have had their reps here for at least two weeks before the season starts and they'll all be experienced, which means that they only have to learn about the resort and make sure the hotels are ready. They won't have to teach any of their staff how to do the job and they won't have next to no time to do so.

Bloody marvellous this company sometimes.

THURSDAY – 1ST OCTOBER

My hands are not in the best of condition they have ever been in because the past two days have been spent putting the majority of the information books together. My finger tips are raw from handling so many pieces of damned paper, I've cut myself umpteen times when I should be trimming the edges off postcards and my fingers are covered in glue from sticking the postcards into their allotted sections.

It's quite amusing to think that having gained one solitary 'A' level in English and an HND in Business and Finance, the only practical thing from the whole of my education that is being used, is sticking pictures onto paper and colouring in.

At present I am bored witless but thankfully know that there is not much more of this. Unfortunately though, I still have to put up with the great Janet and Ravi friendship for a while longer, which is becoming more and more strained as their differing attitudes towards our office requirements and ways of dealing with people are starting to come to the fore.

Ravi is a slow worker; he has his own office space with his own computer, phone and fax and desperately wants to feel important and be involved with everything remotely related with the company. This means that whenever we want to do anything which has the most tenuous of links to the office, we have to go through him, which in turn is very time consuming as the Monday night typing session proved. He also has very different ideas as to the standards of professionalism required and is occasionally content to cut corners. E.G. He can't see why we want the office to be clean or why we want to have our own P.C., fax, International direct dial phone or photocopier (although to his credit he has promised us a phone/fax line for next Monday). He tries to help and means well, but because he's seen the resort run sufficiently well enough in the past he doesn't have our sense of urgency.

Janet on the other hand is very forthright, has a low tolerance level of anything remotely different to her and her ways and is not prepared to adapt to alternative situations or circumstances. She cannot, and will not, try to understand the local way of thinking or a lot of the local working idiosyncrasies, so as a result we have a lot of unnecessary conflict and friction within the office.

I agree with Janet in that a lot of the things she is pushing for and working towards are vitally important, such as the phone etc. However, because of the nature of the place these things will not happen overnight. This is India after all! Plus the company have successfully run operations over here for a decade or so without half of what we are asking for. The guys in the office are trying very hard to accommodate us, and with their limited resources they are doing their best, such as running down the road to do our photocopying and when it comes to passing on phone messages they are only lazy instead of very lazy.

Janet though, spends most of her day upstairs with me, not actually doing a great deal of physical work, but preferring to sit and continuously harp on about the agency defects and explaining why she wants what she does. Although I am on her side, to a degree, I've heard the same thing over and over and I'm sick to bloody death of it. I'm sick of hearing the same moans in her middle aged, 'I'm so righteous' whine, 'because I lived in Europe for fourteen years and am manager in The Maldives'. Every 30 minutes or so she jumps up, shouts, "That's it!" and the office boys dive for cover. I sigh again and she bulldozes her way into Ravi's office like Lennox Lewis going into a ring with Mike Tyson and demands to know when each of the P.C, phone etc are going to be installed?

Ravi to his credit just sits there and twiddles with his big bushy moustache, lights up a revolting Gold Flake cigarette and smiles in a nonplussed manner that winds Janet up even further. She then storms back up stairs, even redder in the face, her wrinkles show even further and she'll huff and puff for a few minutes before recommencing her diatribe about the same complaints over, and over again. In the meantime Ravi actually makes a few phone calls to try and help us, but is determined not to let her see him doing so and will then call me down stairs to ask me why Janet is like she is?

I'm therefore caught in the crossfire and try to explain that she's right in what she is asking for, but it's just her way to be direct rather than more charming. He can understand what I'm saying and I think he's quite clever in that he is playing a few games with her, but she bites the line he feeds every time and he has a lot of fun reeling her in. I want to tell them both to grow up and get on with their work, but I can't because I have to keep sweet with Ravi, as I'll be working with him for the rest of the season, and also with Janet because for the time being she is still my superior. Plus I just can't be bothered.

I wish she'd try charming the locals a bit more, because it would certainly make things a lot easier. But we may have a bit of temporary respite, because at the tail end of the day Ravi announced that he may be leaving for Kerela on Friday to go and get engaged. He's obviously found his way of getting some peace and I found my own spot of breathing space by disappearing into town for a couple of hours on another unsuccessful material shopping excursion.

This is another of the drawbacks of working for a smaller company. While we could be having fun (not) in the office producing the books and listening to the fun and games of inter office politics, we have to design and make our own uniform, whereas all other tour operators provide it for their staff in the UK before they depart for a resort. It sounds like fun designing a uniform, but it's another thing that eats up unnecessary time and is not as straightforward as you would think. The company colours are orange and blue and we have to find something that will match this, so off I popped for another adventure of frustrating repetition in an effort to do so.

"Hi' I'd like some material please" I would ask.

"You want a saree?" would be the inevitable reply. At this stage I would take a deep breath and avoid the temptation of a witty riposte, which would no doubt go over their heads, and then continue to politely persist.

"No. I would like some material for a uniform with two colours – Blue and Orange." I would state, in the manner of a policeman talking to a lost child.

"Uniform. Yes, I am having nice saree? Come look."

"I do NOT want a saree, I would like some material please."

"But what about uniform? You are not wanting uniform now?"

"Yes I am wanting – damn! I want uniform. The material is for the uniform. In blue and orange."

"Okay, I am understanding you. You want material for uniform. No?"

"Yes"

"Good. I am having some nice saree material for uniform!"

"NO! – I do not want saree and I do not want saree material. I want normal cotton and silk for the uniform."

"Okay. You are wanting material. What colour?"

"ORANGE & BLUE! FOR CHRISSAKES!"

"Okay you are not needing to shout I am understanding you. I have nice red and black here. Come look." at which point my patience would run out every time and I would leave, misguidedly hoping that the next shop would be better.

It's funny when they get an idea in their heads that it will stay there as gospel no matter if it's right or wrong. The Indians are unbelievably intelligent, with most of them speaking at least three languages, but when it comes to common sense they were at the very back of the queue when it was dished out. But it is part of the charm of the place, part of the great experience of travelling and learning to tolerate and work with the different cultures and attitudes, something I am always trying to adjust to, but sadly something Janet does not.

I wonder how she would get on in the shoebox for a hotel that I am living in? Back there in the evening I noticed that I'd run out of toilet paper and that my towel was still the same sandpaper style one from the first day. So at about 23:00, I was in the lobby, parked in front of the communal television with a beer in hand settling down to watch some Champions League football when I asked the receptionist if I could get some new ones.

In the process I learnt three new rules for the hotel:

- 1 towel every five days.

- I pay for toilet rolls.
- I can watch T.V after 23:00, but only with the sound down and lobby lights turned off, because that is when the hotel staff lay down their mattresses and go to sleep for the night.

FRIDAY – 2ND OCTOBER

I picked the car up today; Two new reps arrived; Anniversary of Ghandi's birthday; Nearly killed a man.

At about midday Janet and I were heading towards Dabolim airport, which is close to Vasco Da Gama and about an hours drive from Panjim. We were preceded by one of the agency vehicles on the way to picking up the two new reps who we were praying would arrive.

We were on a flat stretch of road doing about 50 KM per hour, with Prasad in the other car about 30 metres in front, and approaching an inconspicuous junction on the right hand side of the road. The road was almost deserted apart from a group of four guys just off the left-hand side of the tarmac, sitting on motorbikes and sharing cigarettes.

The rains had subsided for a while and the sun had come through to make driving conditions perfect. Janet had thankfully stopped talking for five minutes and all that could be heard was the faint sound of Bruce Springsteen on the car stereo. Things were looking up with the thought of meeting two new members of the team. They would have a lot of hard work ahead, but could at least share some of the workload and, I had convinced myself, must be keen and of course would give me more opportunities to get away from Janet and her moans for a while.

The car had turned up almost on time and was in relatively good working order, although we sensed it may cause more problems down the line. But at least it was roadworthy and the mechanic had bothered to clean the car for us and leave the Springsteen tape in it, albeit in error. Ironic really that I was thinking for the first time that things were starting to improve, when all of a sudden there was a blur in front of me as one of the guys who had been sitting on bikes just drove straight out.

I seem to recall seeing him sitting on his bike and edging it towards the side of the road, but not really paying any attention to him because we were so close and there was no way he could have pulled out. Unfortunately he didn't look and did just that, coming right across us, at a complete right angle so that he ended up parallel to us, from all of about five metres away.

No signal, no looking, he just turned and I instantly slammed on the brakes. But there was no chance and I couldn't avoid hitting him head on, sending him and his bike careering down the road, slightly to my right hand side, a good twenty metres. There was the horrible, penetrating thud of metal on metal, followed by a sickening crack of skull colliding with the tarmac. Needless to say he didn't have a helmet on, because nobody wears helmets over here, and to round off the pretty picture there was a trail of scraped metal and little drops of blood on the tarmac.

I pulled the car over about 10 metres ahead of the guy, while Prasad in front had missed the whole thing and had carried on, oblivious to what had happened. I was a little shaken and a hundred thoughts raced through my head: *Shit! Had I killed him? Could he move? Will I be lynched? Is there a mob already? Should I drive off? Shall we call the police? What would they do? They'd arrest me because I'm white and in their minds rich? They could revoke my visa? I could be kicked out of the country? The season could be over before it's even started! Shit!*

"What the f***ing hell was that?" Janet shouted "Oh, my bloody toe!" She added for good measure and as I started to get out of the car she was muttering something about being okay and hating India. This seemed to wake me up a bit, because I recall thinking how selfish she could be worrying about her toe when there's a guy lying in the middle of the road with a gash the size of a melon on his head.

I ran over to him, where already there was a group of about five men dragging him over to the side of the road. This didn't seem right and I dredged up some memories of my old Medic First Aid and realised they could be doing further damage and he should remain motionless. I made them stop, told the guy I had medical training and that I was going to try and help him and just wanted to check for any injuries.

He looked up and said, "good" which was a positive sign seeing that he was still conscious, although Christ knows how, because he must have scraped his head for eighteen of the twenty metres. I started feeling at the back of his head and the other five guys just grabbed hold of him and dragged him to the far side of the road.

I stood there with this incredulous look on my face, but they paid no attention to me and shouted to a woman to get some ice. I was part scared of what may happen but also intrigued at the uneducated response to a dramatic situation. They have way too many accidents on the roads and anyone who drives around regularly will witness at least one a day, so they have their own pre-programmed responses, which are aimed at getting the guy off the road and trying to get as much money as possible out of who is at fault.

Someone shouted to the lady again to get the ice and we took a closer look at the guy, who miraculously was not that badly hurt. He had a large cut in the side of his head which was starting to swell a little, some scrapes down the side of his left arm and the little toe on his left foot was almost hanging off, which makes sense seeing that if he didn't wear a helmet he didn't wear shoes either. But at this stage he was unaware of the damage to his foot.

I heard someone ask what happened and I instantly went on the defensive and explained that he was at fault because he pulled out in front of me and I had no chance whatsoever to stop.

"Liar!" a voice shouted, "You will be paying for this!"

I tried to reason but couldn't make myself heard above the now growing crowd, which had gathered in curiosity to see what the white man had done to the poor guy on the bike.

The guy was starting to come around and he exclaimed that I had hit him, which I sensed was inciting the crowd a little. I have to admit that at this stage I was beginning to fear a bit of a beating, even though I know the majority of the people from Goa are just not like that, but they do know how to seize an opportunity for money and I was intimidated at being surrounded by a group of what seemed like thirty unfriendly faces.

I suggested I take him to the nearest doctor, which everyone thought was a good idea and four of the guys helped me carry him over to our car. As we got there, a middle aged woman came running over with a huge block of ice, exclaimed that she 'had it!' and proceeded to try and force the ice onto the poor guy's head, but only succeeding in dropping it onto his injured foot.

In the car Janet was shakily smoking a cigarette and wanted to know what in the hell I was doing. She then saw the guy being pushed into the back seat and so she decided to start shouting at him. I appreciate that she may have been in shock, but I was desperately trying to calm the situation down, so that I wouldn't lose any money or get beaten up, but she went off on one and screamed:

"You stupid bloody idiot! What in the hell do you think you were doing? You could have killed us you know!"

The poor bugger was momentarily stunned. To think that he could have been killed, but all that he lives for is to have Janet shouting inane abuse at him.

We drove him into the heart of Vasco Da Gama, to a nearby doctor's surgery, followed by two of his mates on motorbikes. All the way in he kept shouting and half mumbling – "I am Portuguese! I am not going to die! I am strong!" Janet kept telling him to shut up and I was praying to God that I wouldn't be attacked.

The doctors asked us to pay for the consultation fee up front, plus also any necessary medication afterwards, which I initially refused to do. I was adamant that I was not at fault. This merely incensed the two friends who simply demanded that I pay or they would get the police. I could have called their bluff, but knew that if the police were called the injured guy would have half a dozen lying witnesses on his side, whereas I would only have a hysterical Janet on mine. No doubt we would also spend six hours in the police station whilst the officer in charge typed up a report with just one finger and would then demand a bribe from me to make the whole thing go away.

We were at a point of stalemate and I was trying to gather my thoughts, when I realised we were late for picking up the girls and that there was no sign of Prasad who had gone on ahead of us. I had to get away from this and so asked how much the bill would be and then agreed to pay that amount plus a little extra on top to make it all disappear. We also swapped addresses for insurance purposes, although I know he doesn't have any insurance. I then paid the money over from what little cash I had in my pocket. We shook hands, promised each other that we were friends, whilst his friends looked on angrily, and we drove off hoping that we would be in time to meet the girls at the airport.

Unbelievable. I paid 200 Indian rupees, which is under £3.00 to make the whole thing go away.

Unfortunately though, we were about half an hour late to meet the two new girls whose flight, as luck would have it, had come down early. Prasad though had hung around to greet them and he had made sure they were looked after and was just waiting for Janet and I to turn up. I thought this was quite commendable because it meant he was doing a little bit of thinking on his feet, however Janet thought otherwise and shouted at him, although thankfully not in front of the girls. First the guy on the bike and now poor Prasad was on the wrong end of an ear bashing as she asked 'where the bloody hell he was and what the bloody hell did he think he was thinking of?'

Still, the girls seemed pleasant enough. They were very cheerful and upbeat and had enjoyed a day in Bombay, although how anyone can enjoy Bombay is beyond me. We gave them the afternoon to settle in to their temporary rooms and have a wander around the resort to familiarise themselves with the local area and we agreed to meet them for dinner in the evening, where I was in dire need of a beer.

On the drive back, we found the bumper was badly damaged, the new windscreen wipers and horn were not working, nor was the stereo and the steering wheel was way off balance. Needless to say, in my slightly bewildered state I drove at no more than 10 kph all the way back to Panjim, thus turning a one-hour drive into a two and a half-hour journey.

Two and a half hours of no stereo and having to listen to Janet recreating the accident over and over again, blaming Prasad for not returning to us, blaming me for paying off the guys, blaming the guy on the bike for being alive and complaining about her bad toe which she thinks she may have bruised as a result of the impact. The thought of a long cool beer is the only thing that kept me going.

We met the girls who are called Sharon (blond and talks a lot) and Ruth (redhead and odd) for dinner on the beach and it was pleasing to see that they are very enthusiastic and have settled in very easily. It was almost a positive end to a day of mixed fortunes. However, to round it all off, today is a dry day in honour of Ghandi's birthday, which means no alcohol can be had anywhere in India!

Janet's toe still hurts.

MONDAY – 5TH OCTOBER

Not such a good day, which is to be expected with the mad rush to get things ready at this stage of the season, but what is not expected is some of the unprofessional and inadequate responses we get from some of the staff working at our UK end. Also, as I write it's 04:00, I'm knackered and can't get to sleep because I had a thirty minute doze in the car on the way back to the office after checking the building work in the South yesterday and now my sleep patterns are back out of synch again.

I suppose I should be counting my blessings that the two bob bits haven't come yet, but I couldn't have felt much worse in the office this morning because I had a hangover from hell, complete with furry mouth syndrome, pneumatic drills pounding in my head and a severe case of washing machine stomach. India must be one of the worst countries in the world to be suffering the after effects of the night before, what with the constant noise of traffic and people shouting, the heat, and a profusion of odours, from overflowing sewers to curried breakfasts. It's hard enough to keep your stomach down on a normal day.

To compound matters Paul Rodrigues rang us in the afternoon to discuss the building work reports we'd sent in. Janet briefed him about the state of play in both of the hotels we'd visited yesterday and also one other in the North of Goa, which is not quite as desperate. To her credit she clearly outlined what was wrong, explained that they will not be ready until the beginning of November at the earliest, so we would obviously have to do something about the guests who are due to arrive at the weekend.

Unfortunately it sounds as if both of the hotels have contacted Paul as well and they've confirmed that they will be able to take the bookings. In their words, there is only a minor bit of work taking place and in their opinion the guests will not be inconvenienced. This coupled with the fact that Janet has a reputation for being a bit dramatic, although she is spot on this time, and also the factor of Paul's position, has surely had a great influence on his response.

Paul heads our operations department in head office and his role involves him being slightly superior to overseas staff so he can influence the running of a resort. More importantly, he is the one who will have to telephone guests before they depart if there is any change to their holiday. As I understand it, by EC law we're required to inform guests, or at least make every effort to contact them, and tell them of any alterations to their booking or brochure changes/errors etc. However, the one thing we do not want is to lose the booking at such a late stage and as a result have empty seats coming out on the airplane, because this would be a substantial loss, especially with our brochure prices. Therefore Paul's response was, "The work is normal for this time of year, we'll just leave it for now and see how it goes!"

What a crock of shit! It's attitudes like this that wind me up something rotten. We've got a chance to turn a potential problem into a huge advantage and get some free advertising and maintain our excellent name in the industry. All we have to do is provide a good service and act responsibly for the guests, by informing them in advance of the situation and offering them a free upgrade to a superior hotel, which will cost us next to nothing with trade rates, and also increase their board basis and give them a voucher for £50 off their next holiday with us.

It may cost a small amount, but nothing compared to what we'll eventually pay out in compensation and it means that the guests will have a great holiday and will return with us in the future, thus generating further revenue. It sounds idealistic again I know, but the guests will be happy and we'll make money in the long run, which is supposed to be the whole purpose of the industry.

Instead, with our official response, the guests will arrive, hate it and complain en masse. We'll eventually move them at a far greater cost than it would have been originally, but they still won't be happy because now they will have a negative mindset. They'll continue to moan, will have a miserable stay, won't book any excursions, which affects their happiness and our profits, will never use our company again and will provide enough material for a whole series of *Watchdog*. To top it all, we'll be required to pay out a small fortune in compensation. We're nearing the millennium, and in this day and age of professionalism and consumer rights we shouldn't be operating like this.

Needless to say I was glad to get out of the office and take my negative thoughts of the industry with me and away from the girls who we want to remain upbeat. I've decided this will definitely be my last season.

It's raining and I still can't sleep.

TUESDAY – 6TH OCTOBER

The roller coaster ride of emotions continues to swing like a pendulum in a coastal breeze. In complete contrast to yesterday's 'downer', today has been far more productive on most counts and we actually seem to be getting somewhere. In brief we got the girls into the office early and I spent the morning teaching them how to do welcome meetings whilst Janet set about typing up the excursion pages for the information books.

Welcome meetings are such a huge part of our job, because they can set the tone for a guest's holiday and have the biggest influence on the role we play with the guests. I was lucky, depending on how you look at it, to have worked for a large mainstream operator for four years and received an excellent all round training from them

In those days, giving out compensation in resort was unheard of and the service we were expected to provide was not as high as that of most other companies. Basically we had to make sure there were as few hotel changes as possible, which meant getting tourists to stay where they don't want to and selling as many excursions as possible to recoup the losses incurred in selling a holiday so cheap. Therefore a good, strong, informative welcome meeting is required, which sells you, sells the hotel, sells the resort, sells the destination and, importantly, sells our excursions. With that particular company if you didn't do it well, you'd have a lot of problems on your hands, which I found out the hard way on more than a few occasions.

The girls to their credit grasped most of it and hopefully took everything on board as we went through the main stages of a meeting, which are:

- Introduction – *Time to sell yourself.*
- Hotel information – *Sell the hotel, so people will like it and not want to move.*
- Local resort information – *To sell the resort area the guests are in.*
- Destination Information – *Selling the island or country and dripping a few excursions.*
- Excursion Sales – *Selecting a minimum of four trips to give a hard sell on.*
- Close – *Get those bookings and money in.*

Sharon asked an awful lot of questions, which I am pleased about and it shows that she is listening. However she has a tendency to talk over others, which means she may not be taking everything on board but formulating her own opinions. This does not always help other team members who can feel a little intimidated. She does have a strong sales background though and I am confident she will do well.

Ruth joined in but didn't make any notes so I am a little concerned about her. She is intelligent and is confident that she will retain everything, but from experience I know this never happens. I'm also worried about her 'it'll be alright on the night' attitude, because in this industry you have to be 110% prepared, otherwise everything could come crumbling down in front of your eyes. However, they have had a lot to take-in, learning the job as we go along and also cramming in excursions, which we did again in the afternoon.

Janet even managed to come and enjoy herself for a little while, even though we weren't in the best of moods with each other because I have disagreed with her over what course of action we should take regarding the two hotels in the South. I think we should be taking the matters more seriously than the company is at present and therefore pushing Paul Rodrigues to pull his finger out of his bottom, or otherwise go over his head. Janet though is unwilling to do so and because she is above me, albeit for a few days only, we have to go along with what she says and she currently agrees with the '*let's see how it goes*' attitude.

This is one of Janet's problems in that she talks a good game, and spends all day commenting on it to anyone who will listen, but yet rarely gets anything constructive done. I agreed with her completely yesterday, but now she's singing a different tune and is happy to roll over and play it by ear. Maybe the fact that I will be here from Sunday onwards and she will not, therefore meaning she doesn't have to face any of the crap, has a bit of a bearing on her decision, because the easy way out for her is not to make any waves in the UK. Or maybe it's just that I'm afraid of taking the abuse when the guests arrive.

Although she is above me, I find it hard to respect her, because she doesn't take on board my opinions or anyone else's for that matter. This is because she is very inflexible a) to other people's ideas and b) to other customs, traditions and ways of life.

We still have the issue of the P.C., phone, fax and photocopier as an ongoing concern and it doesn't look as if we'll get much joy in the near future. She is absolutely, 100% correct in her way of thinking (as I say she talks a good game) in that we desperately require the above for the company to come into the twentieth century before we depart it. However, she has done nothing but moan, groan, whinge and bitch about being behind the times, which rubs the local staff up the wrong way and means everything gets resolved at an even slower pace than before. The rest of us have just accepted the fact that we are behind the times and are simply trying to get on with the job in hand.

Her toe still hurts.

THURSDAY – 8TH OCTOBER

It's odd that I've only been here for about two weeks and I'm already pondering over my future and whether or not I still want to be doing this job, or even if I want to stay in the industry for much longer. I'm putting this down to the anxieties of trying to get everything ready for the season. Although the office is coming along and the books and boards are nearly ready, there is still a lot of work to do with the girls plus we still need to cram in a few more excursions. This is why we have just sampled three trips, which would usually last a combined total of four days, and crammed them into two days. As the locals say, "What to do?"

The events in question are 'Crocs & Spice', 'Shanti Village' and 'Waterfalls Adventure" and because the places visited on all three are relatively close to each other we have juggled the itineraries around to fit each one in as we go along. The only possible drawback is that we had two separate excursion suppliers who had to work together on this to make sure all were completed.

This is supposed to be a learning part of the job and is also a perk, because we get to do the trips for free and get spoiled rotten to boot. But these past two days, although enjoyable have been a little confusing and a tad demanding.

We got going one and a half hours late, which made the first day's itinerary even more rushed than before, but it did give us the chance to meet the local Somak reps who were doing the itinerary with us.

Off we drove, heading inland, away from the bustle of the city streets and the tourist resorts and into the more tranquil surroundings of the sharp green countryside, sleepy villages and pot holed roads. We followed the itineraries in an order that was just about understandable before arriving at the place known as Shanti, late in the afternoon.

The Shanti village is glorious. Set just below the eastern hills of Goa, it consists of wooden camping huts in the midst of a wooded glaze. Every single thing in the camp is produced naturally, from the bricks, which are dug out of the earth, the wooden beds and coir rope fastenings to the hardened cow dung on the floors, which are supposed to be an excellent method for keeping the rooms cool and a great deterrent for mosquitoes. A stream runs alongside the site and no more than a lap of a cricket field away is a lush, dark green forest of trees working its way up the hillside and reaching into the clouds.

At this time of year, there is a clearly contrasting skyline. Directly above us it is a brilliant blue, yet perfectly adjacent, almost as if someone has drawn a line down the middle with a pencil, is a deep mass of thunderous black rain cloud nestling into the hills and threatening to erupt. I couldn't help but marvel at how beautiful this country can be and temporarily all my worries seemed to ease away.

The first order of the day was to head down to the stream, slip into our swimming togs and in we went for a dip and a refreshing glass of kingfisher. One of those memorable moments in life was then spent with four of the locals, standing waist high in the water, beer in hand, discussing the merits of the Indian cricket team and gazing up, through a clearing in the woods to the glorious mountain scenery. We didn't want the moment to end, but as nightfall came we headed back to camp for a charming home-cooked dinner and some more Kingfisher. The evening was rounded off with entertainment around the camp fire which included a typical Indian sing song. Strangely the songs included 'La Bamba', 'Alice' and 'Words'. Further glasses of complimentary Kingfisher were consumed, before we headed to our respective huts at about 02:00. Sadly, none of the girls crawled into my hut, so I suppose they're right about the cow muck. No bites for me!

We were woken up at 06:00 by the local guide John, and I have no idea how he consistently manages it, because he was the last to bed and he drank more than enough for the lot of us the previous night. But awake he was and he took us off for a nature trail, which was highly enjoyable for the first hour or so. Then for the first time this season, and right on cue seeing that it's only a couple of days before we start, I felt the first shooting pains in my stomach and knew I had very little time to make it back to the camp.

I was lucky that we had just come out by the roadside no more than 400 metres from the camp, so I made some hasty, blurred excuses and set off for the huts faster than Michael Owen running at an Argentine defence.

When I was about three quarters of the way there, I caught a severe shooting pain in the spot between my belly button and my groin and was instantly doubled up in agony. I was holding onto my stomach, trying to breathe deeply and clenching my buttocks so tight they would have cracked coconuts if I'd moved. I prayed to God, Allah, Buddha and every one of the 30 odd Indian gods I know, that I could hold it all in for just a hundred metres more and I also prayed that no-one could see me.

I tried moving, but my insides were more determined to move than me and they were rapidly winning the battle of wills. I looked around frantically, through a sweat soaked face, and couldn't see or hear anyone. I desperately inched to the side of the road, took a deep breath, counted to one and a half, because that was all the time I had, and then in one swift movement I squatted, whipped off my boxers and shorts and released the pressure from my buttocks. I was a fraction of a second too late.

Most of the day's first anal waterfall hit the wayside, but it felt like wave upon wave was flying down and I had no control over the direction, so it was no surprise to see that a small fraction had caught my boxers and splashed onto my left leg. I took a deep breath, tried to gather my senses and take in the surroundings to see if anyone was coming, but all I could feel was another sensation, which would no doubt be upon me in a matter of seconds.

I rapidly pulled up my shorts, sped to the camp, nearly falling over a gate at the entrance and burst into my room. I landed on the toilet seat just in time to see the second gush hit the porcelain, or more accurately the cow-dung enforced, home made loo. The next twenty minutes were spent cleaning both my clothes and myself and continuously praying that, that was the last. I walked back out into daylight just as everyone was returning from the trek, apparently oblivious to my predicament and ready for a hearty breakfast, which I simply couldn't face. I was relieved that no one found out, but the cleaner would have had a shock later in the day when she saw my soiled boxers in the bin.

FRIDAY – 9TH OCTOBER

As I write it's 21:00, Ravi who has just returned from getting engaged in Kerela is coming to pick me up for dinner with the girls. I'm playing seventies summer hits on the CD, wearing my new Levis shirt and Calvin Klein Escape eau de toilette and am on the way to being a little bit squiffy on three glasses of the red wine I bought in Bahrain. I'm so upbeat I might even pull tonight, although that is an unlikely scenario seeing as there isn't much totty about at present, but who knows? We're going to Tito's afterwards, which is one of the most famous bars in Goa, and India, and I've got my lucky aftershave, boxers and buttock combination on.

Nothing like a last minute struggle to put me in a positive frame of mind! For the first time I feel as if I'm doing some work and that we're actually getting somewhere!

The whole day started well when we set off early and returned to the office bang on time at 14:00 after a highly enjoyable yet condensed tour of the more archaic areas and ways of existing.

In the office we finished all the information books and nearly completed the information boards, plus we test drove and delivered the mopeds for Sharon and Ruth and the one that I will eventually be having. We also finished the girls training, prepared their welcome meetings and transfer speeches for the coaches, picked up our uniforms from the tailor who had eventually supplied the material we wanted and temporarily resolved the building work problems at the Dona Santa Maria and the SJM. Janet nearly smiled once as well.

Actually the two problems in the South resolved themselves without much input from us, thanks to both of the hotel managers taking a bit of responsibility and acting professionally.

The Dona Santa Maria manager is actually quite switched on and has promised in writing to have 95% of the work completed by Sunday. We've agreed to send the guests in and he'll spoil them rotten with lobster meals, free trips etc and if they're still unhappy he'll move them to a better hotel out of his own pocket. It's still not ideal but we've really appreciated him making an effort and trying to provide a service and it should make Ruth's life a lot easier.

After a week of chasing him the SJM manager made it into the office and Janet bullied him into agreeing to upgrade all of our arrivals into the Holiday Inn, which is a move from a poor 2* unit to a good 4*. He's going to foot the bill and it is a just penance for being a cowboy and messing us about. It's going to cost him a bomb and it'll teach him to toy with a British tourist's holiday!

Finally, after two weeks, a constructive day and as a reward I'm off to get bladdered.

SATURDAY – 10TH OCTOBER

So that's it. Nothing more can be done and now I just hope and pray that we'll be ready and that there won't be too many problems.

I took the girls to the airport to show them around and run through the procedures for departures and arrivals as well as showing them where they can buy me cups of coffee. Sharon, as always, hung on every word and asked an incessant stream of questions, which for me is encouraging because she has an eye for detail and I think she'll do a good job. Ruth just appears to soak everything up and I hope to God that she's taking it all in. I believe she is, but you can't always tell and the jury is still out on her.

The afternoon was spent tying up the formalities in the office and at the midway point in the afternoon Ravi and I heaved two huge sighs of relief as Janet left for the final time, but not until she'd had a final rant about the office, India in general and her bruised toe.

As Ravi and I both agreed, when we were in a rather more relaxed atmosphere, she certainly knows her stuff, but she has no tolerance for other people, countries and customs and has no ability whatsoever to communicate with people. A lot of it I put down to the fact that she hasn't had a holiday in twelve months and she must obviously be quite stressed. Having said that, she went and proved me wrong when I had dinner with her earlier tonight. We chatted about India and how she's enjoyed it (after all she's said), my future, her forthcoming holiday, the future of the company and the industry as a whole. She was open, charming and very positive towards me, and my future (which didn't go amiss) plus she encouraged me to stick the season out no matter what happens (I wonder what she knows). Ultimately she was quite interesting.

She has had her flight seat confirmed and she is definitely leaving tomorrow, being the only passenger on an empty leg from Goa to Gatwick, which means for at least one week I am in sole charge.

After dinner, I headed back to The Ranch, as the El Pablo has become known, and was ready for bed by 20:00. However, I haven't been able to sleep for the past hour because a million and one different anxieties, fretting about tomorrow's arrival have been running through my tiny Welsh mind. But after two weeks of non-stop work and tension, the books and boards are now done; the girls have been trained to the best of our abilities in the limited space of time available; the hotels are as ready as they can be, with two notable exceptions but they have been resolved temporarily; Janet's seat has been booked; the coaches are booked and are readily cleaned; my new shirt and trousers are pressed and ready; my tie and badge have had the mothballs dusted off them; the mobile has been recharged; my shoes polished; the whole filing system set up; the local guides told what is expected of them; Ravi Chauhan's bribes set in place; my lucky airport underwear is set out; 'Clippy' the board is raring to go and my alarm clock is set. There is nothing more we can do except hope the plane lands on time, the coaches turn up and the girls don't fall to pieces. Tomorrow the season starts!

A NEW SEASON DAWNS

SUNDAY – 11TH OCTOBER

A brass band!!

A bloody brass band was what they had! Just to greet the first charter of the season. Unbelievable, nothing in this country ever surprises me but they always manage to astound.

Whenever any guests came through the throng of people who were crammed outside to meet the first arrival of the season, the band would start up and play Goan folk songs, which happen to be more suited to string instruments. This would continue until the guests had checked in with their respective rep and made their way to their coaches and sat down for a cigarette.

Sadly, to the dismay of the representatives on duty, they didn't play any classics like 'The Saints go Marching In' but fortunately they didn't try their hand at marching up and down the concourse. The place was chaotic enough as it was and it would have caused a mild case of pandemonium.

Because this is the first flight of the season there are no departures, except Janet, so we turned up at the airport at 06:00, as opposed to the earlier time of 04:30, which will be the norm from next week, and we only had to wait an extra thirty minutes on top as the flight had a slight delay. The guests coming off the flight must have thought they'd walked into an ambush, because outside the 'Arrivals' hall was the biggest crowd of people we're likely to see outside a Bombay cricket stadium. The arrival procedure at Dabolim International airport is not exactly the most sophisticated in the world and as a result it can be quite frightening for the first time visitor to India.

The passengers get off the plane, straight into a 90-degree oven, even at 07:00 in the morning, and then have to queue for ages to make their way through the ever-officious passport control and the beloved Indian red tape. By the time they reach the two small, rusty carousels, which can cope with 30 guests at a time but not a full charter flight of 272, they're beginning to steam inside their denims, jumpers and shell suits. This is compounded by the fact that there is usually no air conditioning, only a few slow, rickety old fans.

Once they've retrieved their luggage and barged their way through the mass of tourists who have been competing with them to get closer to the conveyor belts, they then have to go through a very meticulous process of having their luggage checked once again. This time the customs officials keep one eye open for a couple of bottles of good whisky and excess cigarettes. If the tourists make it through here with their nerves intact they will then be greeted by us eager reps, with big toothy 'Welcome to Goa' smiles and our 'Clippy' the boards at the ready. On this first charter six tour operators all have guests coming through for the first month of the season. When you consider that for each company in this first week there are three UK reps, a resort manager and a plethora of Indian transfer reps running round like headless chickens, it equates to over fifty people in bright, lairy uniforms to welcome (or frighten) the guests and show them to their buses.

Added to this are the thirty or so porters, in their ugly brown smocks, grabbing at every available trolley and suitcase to make an extra 20 rupees. Then there are the hotel touts looking for any 'Flight Onlys' coming through, the drinks vendors, the aggressive taxi drivers and finally the generally nosy businessmen from the resorts to see how many fresh white faces come trundling through.

The place was a heaving mass of bodies, all desperately struggling to be heard and seen and we were melting in the oppressive heat in our cotton shirts, trousers, skirts and delightfully bright ties. It was a miracle that we were able to meet any of our guests at all. Somehow, as they forced their way timidly through we kept an eager eye out for their luggage tags, managed to locate our respective customers and then struggled to direct them to their coaches above the din of people shouting and the brass band, which by now was in full swing. It had managed to play 'La Bamba' four times before we left.

In the midst of this we had a few minor problems, namely telling the handful of guests who had booked the SJM that they weren't going there but to the Holiday Inn instead.

This shouldn't have been too bad because they were getting a far superior deal for their money, but it still isn't nice finding out that your holiday has been changed after you've just come off an eleven hour flight and been forced to come through this airport. This is one part of the job that I detest and actually fear. Partially it's because of the abuse you get, especially when the people who are at fault are nowhere to be seen, also because I feel helpless and more importantly because I genuinely feel for the guests. I tend to put myself into their shoes and imagine being told that the holiday I'd booked six months previously and had saved and looked forward to for all that time, has suddenly, on arrival in a strange place, been completely rearranged. I can understand why they would be so upset and angry.

The only way I can make this easier for both the guests and myself is to take full responsibility, which usually tends to defuse the situation a little, but can sometimes lead to a punch on the nose. Because the girls are brand new it also meant that I had to inform all four couples who came through and thankfully the first three were delighted but the fourth were looking for a fight.

"I'm F***ing disgusted!! We've saved up all year for this!" was the guy's initial reaction, before I'd actually had the chance to tell him that he was being upgraded. Still I'd been through this hundreds of times before and all I could do was sympathise and try and diffuse his rage a little.

"I know. I understand. I really do and I'm ever so sorry, but if you'll let me fini…."

"I don't F***ing care how sorry you are, you're going to f***ing pay for this and then I'll show you how sorry can feel!!" this was actually quite good because if he has to lose his rag then it's better to get it over and done with and then a period of rational calm usually follows.

"I understand sir, but if you'll let me explain further"

"I don't want no explanations, I want to know whose fault this is and then there'll be hell to pay!!"

"Actually sir it's my fault" I said whilst silently praying that my bowels remained tight.

"What do you mean yours? I ought to knock your nose through to the other side of your face!!" '*HELP*' I thought, '*think quickly and start talking*'.

"If you can calm down for just a moment sir" *potentially fatal thing to say! Stop talking!*

"Don't you f**ing tell me to calm down, you've just ruined my holiday."

"I know sir and I'm sorry. If you could ju.."

"And stop saying you're sorry you piece of shit!"

"Okay sir, sorry. Aaah excuse me. If I could just explain."

"You keep saying that!"

"I know but I'd like to finish if I may, because it may not be as bad as it initially seems."

"Well get on with it, but you better not be giving me any of that rep bullshit." Thankfully he had calmed down a little, as they eventually do, some sooner than others, but I could still sense that a couple of wrong words would see me blowing my nose from out the back of my head.

"Well, as I said I see it as my fault. You see the change of hotel occurred because the hotel you booked isn't quite ready. I personally checked the hotel last week and it looked as if everything was on schedule, but by Friday afternoon it was apparent that it was not and by then it was too late to get hold of you." A little porky pie, but you have to give them something and remarkably my voice was remaining calm and gentle and I prayed to all of my Gods that he was taking it all in.

"Anyway, because the hotel isn't ready and you booked this hotel with us in good faith, I see it as our fault and because I am standing here now representing my company I see it as my fault and it's my responsibility to make sure that you are looked after and get the holiday you deserve." *Please don't hit me, please don't hit me!*

'Now, I'm sorry that this happened and I know it's the worst thing that could possibly happen, because if it was me I'd be livid. So what we've done is arranged accommodation for you at the Holiday Inn which is in a similar area to the SJM."

"Yeah and what's this place like then. It better be good!"

"Well, as you know we don't put star ratings in our brochures, but if we did the SJM would be a two star and the Holiday Inn would be a good four star, so we've actually upgraded your hotel and hopefully improved your holiday."

"Yeah Right! And what extras do we have to pay?"

"None, because as I said the error is ours and we therefore have to cover the costs, plus this doesn't affect your statutory rights as a consumer which means you can still take this up if you wish, when you return to the UK" *please get on the bus because I'm not enjoying this.*

'Yeah, well, we'll see how it goes, but it better be good or I'll be looking for you!" and as they walked off towards the bus, with a porter grabbing at their cases I heard his wife say, "Derrick that's brilliant that is! That's the 'otel we wanted in the first place but couldn't afford it!" So much for my charm and ability to deal with people.

What it does go to show though, is that if a problem is handled correctly it can be the best form of advertising going.

Once we'd got everyone onboard the buses, we headed off to our respective drop offs and all the transfers went along very smoothly, plus we enjoyed the response as we travelled around Calangute and Baga in the bus, because the locals were shouting "Tourists. New charter. Very Good!" In the two and a half weeks that I've been out here the place has transformed from a ghost town to a busy, bustling resort and the joy on the locals faces at the beginning of a new season and the chance to earn some money was plain to see. It remains to be seen how long they'll feel that way.

After dropping everyone off, the driver dropped me back at The Ranch by midday, I grabbed an hours siesta, a bite to eat and then spent the next couple of hours going over my welcome meeting, fine tuning my sales spiel and recalling key phrases like *'suntans fade, memories last forever'* that have served me well over the years, before arriving 45 minutes early for my first meeting of the season, for all of eight people.

I can't believe that after seven years in the industry and over 1,000 meetings I was still nervous and excited but thankfully for the first time since I arrived I was actually starting to enjoy myself. Now that I'm immersed in the work and finally doing what we'd spent the past two and a half weeks preparing for, I can relax a little, in a strange kind of way. The work is bound to get harder, more stressful days certainly lay ahead and I'll put in as many if not more hours, but for now I feel as if I belong and fit into the scheme of things and I am eventually in my rightful place.

There was only one small hitch. The hotel had arranged for me to do the meeting outside on a patio, with thick black clouds overhead. But I was able to overcome this with a bit of insistence and speaking to seven different department managers who all said something along the lines of, "Excusing me your pardon sir, but this is not my responsibility. You must speak to the restaurant manager if you are wishing to do it in his restaurant."

"But I've spoken to the restaurant manager and he told me to speak to you!"

"Well, then I cannot be helping you sir!"

Thankfully though, this was nipped in the bud by the assistant food and beverage manager who took responsibility, and he prevented me from going round in circles by opening up the restaurant and clearing a space for me.

After the Cidade I left for the Taj Holiday Village, which is 40 minutes away in the North resort of Sinquerim, just as the storm clouds that had been threatening decided to make us aware of their presence and exact some form of personal vengeance on me. It pissed down for every second of the moped journey.

I arrived at the Taj, soaked to the skin, having ruined my brand new, tailor made uniform and also having discovered that my waterproof Mac is not waterproof. The hotel staff just stared nonplussed at the navy blue squelching mass that had walked into reception and only came to their senses when a few water bubbled words emerged from behind the black, motorbike helmet.

I had come to do the welcome meeting for just the one couple who had arrived into this hotel earlier in the day and could only laugh when I was told they'd left a message to say they'd already gone out for dinner. I drove back in the relentless downpour, dreaming of a hot shower and curiously the sounds of a brass band still ringing in my head.

The power was off at The Ranch.

WEDNESDAY – 14TH OCTOBER

Woke up at 06:00 with furry mouth syndrome, carpet tongue, a pneumatic drill pounding away in my head and an unbelievably sharp pain in my groin which was screaming - 'Pee now or you'll be mortally embarrassed!' I managed to oblige and thus temporarily alleviate the pain by bungling my way across the sweat strewn sheets of my bed, which had all crumpled during the night and gathered in a mass by the side of me in a shape that was reminiscent of a large tortoise. I stumbled off and made the one extra step that was needed into the bathroom, bashing my shin in the process and then leant over the toilet, flipped up the lid and relaxed whatever it was that was causing me so much pain down below. As it flowed for what seemed like an eternity I drifted back to sleep with my face pressed against the wall and dribble worked its way down to the cistern.

Why did I drink so much? I didn't think I drank that much! Must have been the curry. Didn't think I'd do an awful lot today.

Midday, I awoke again to hear Joanne screeching across the hall that she had a headache and felt sick. I had a headache, furry mouth syndrome and also felt sick and now the gassy, Bombay sewer smelling, farts had started under the covers. I drifted back to a temporary sleep asking myself why I'd drank so much the night before.

By 13:00 I eventually made it into the office and watched the walls spin around and my paperwork drift in and out of focus. I should have taken my first day off for three weeks, after all, the reps had a day off and the UK get to take their weekends, but I felt compelled to play the martyr for at least half a day, so there I was with the phones ringing around me, the office boys shouting over the top and the sound of traffic getting angry outside. The restaurant next door was preparing its evening meals and the smell of last night's curry came wafting through the walls and set the washing machine in my stomach onto a fast spin cycle. I picked the phone up, pretending to be engrossed in an important conversation and decided that I wouldn't do much.

After five hours of pushing paper from one side of my desk to the other, a dozen fake phone calls and four excruciating visits to the toilet I decided to return to The Ranch. The furry mouth and headache had bid their fond farewells taking with them the nausea and they left a general numbness and inability to concentrate on anything for more than 30 seconds at a time, just for good measure. I then settled in the reception to watch 'Seven' on Star Movies, but after half an hour of not being able to concentrate on the plot, the satellite link failed again. I stumbled back up the stairs to my shoe box room and drifted in and out of sleep for a couple of hours, finally encouraging the last remnants of yesterdays alcohol to leave my system.

Thankfully Joanne and the rest of the girls were doing an overnight trip at Palolem beach, so I was extremely grateful to have a lot of peace and quiet. This meant I could sit in the restaurant later in the evening and have a slow peaceful meal, whilst reading my book and enjoying a hair of the dog that bit me before joyously sitting in the pitch black setting of the reception until two in the morning, to watch England defeat Luxembourg 3 – 0, with the sound turned off and the hotel staff snoring in their sleep beside me.

I really shouldn't have drunk so much last night.

The barman asked if I wanted a beer before they closed completely for the night.

"Why not?" I said, "I've got a lot to do tomorrow."

THURSDAY – 15TH OCTOBER

"What is your good name?"

"Ceri."

"Oh. That is a strange name. How is it spelled?"

"With a 'C'. It's C-E-R-I." I explain, as I show my company badge, which is pinned to my left breast pocket and I therefore lift it upwards creating a small tent with my shirt.

"Oh. With a 'C'. And how are you pronouncing this? Is it Serry? Or Kerry? Or Gerry? Because I am not knowing this name before."

"It's Ceri! It's Welsh!"

"Welsh. That is interesting. And what is Welsh exactly?"

"I am Welsh, because I am from Wales. It's a country!"

"And where is that. Is it near America because I have never heard of it before."

"Not it's not American, Wales is a part of Great Britain."

"Ah England. Very good."

""Noo! Not England, Wales! We're part of Great Britain, but Britain is made up of four different countries, which are Wales, Scotland, Northern Ireland and England."

"Ahh! Very good so you are all from England?"

"No, I am from Wales" I again repeated in a patronising manner as if talking to a child, " Are you from Pakistan?"

"Ha, hah. No I am from India, but yes I am understanding now. Wales, very good. Ceri, Is that a girls name?" At which point I would be on the verge of screaming.

The thing is, I've had this conversation so many times before and today I had it repeated over 14 times in the space of two hours, with each of the different departmental managers in the Cidade De Goa. I was given the grand tour of the hotel, which only our company get because we have a special relationship with them.

The reason I always have this conversation is because it would appear as far as the Indians are concerned, outside of Asia there are only two countries which are England and the United States and as unbelievably intelligent as most of them are, once they get something into their mindset it is almost impossible to change that way of thinking and they then refuse to open themselves up to any new ideas. This always frustrates me, because although I am proud to be British (sometimes) I am Welsh and not English. Although I should take the easy way out of saying that I'm English and that I have a girls name, like the Indians I refuse to alter my mind map, dig my heels in and frustratingly explain the position, which is not an effective use of my energies.

Especially on a day like today when I had to meet the managers and sub managers from Guest Relations, Hospitality (I still don't know what the difference is between the two), Front Office, Reception, Health Club, Sports Centre, Scuba Centre, Restaurant, Food and Beverage, Restaurant Services, Goods Ordering, Security, Accounts, Reservations, Sales and Marketing and Charters Hospitality.

I took in next to nothing and don't suppose that anyone remembered my name or where I was from either. I had eight cups of tea, three cups of coffee, 1 piece of cheesecake, 15 biscuits. I was also given a determined sales presentation by each member telling me how efficient they are, how important their department is and how they have a special relationship with our company, before being whisked off to the next one in a whirlwind voyage where I completely lost my bearings.

I left the hotel late in the afternoon rather shell-shocked and drove up to the Taj Holiday Village to drop off some reservations, where I got soaked yet again in the only downpour of the day, which lasted for a mere 30 minutes. The bike ride had me rueing my luck in having to experience these levels of efficiency and congestion and then ride back to the office whilst soaked through to the skin. I also pondered, yet again, their use of resources. Although it's the same all over Goa and can be extremely frustrating, the fact that they have only 50% efficiency, yet 100% employment and virtually no crime means they are doing something right somewhere along the line.

FRIDAY – 16TH OCTOBER

I'm not having an awful lot of luck on the roads at present what with the accident two weeks ago (which incidentally we appear to have heard nothing more about so it looks like I'll be here for the full duration), being continuously drenched on the moped. Then to compound matters I was stopped by the police today.

It happened in the morning when I was on my way to the Taj Holiday Village and had just stopped at a garage to fill the bike up. I could see the policeman at the exit to the forecourt and he kept giving me funny glances while the attendant was putting the petrol into the bike. I put it down to him not seeing a white guy in a shirt and tie every day of the week and hoped that it was curiosity more than opportunism.

I paid the attendant the 70 Rupees that it cost to fill it up, hopped on and rode casually to the exit, making a point of putting my helmet on beforehand, even though no one else wears them over here. As soon as I stopped to look at the traffic, the policeman walked in front of the bike, blocking my path. He stared at me harshly through a pair of cold and tired looking brown eyes and told me to show him my licence.

Fortunately I had had the foresight to get an international licence before leaving the UK, otherwise I would have been in deep shit right now, and so reached into my briefcase that was in between my feet and duly handed it over. He took ages examining it carefully, which at first looked as if he was being meticulous, but as he seemed to take an absolute age I could tell by the way he was focusing on nothing in particular that he was probably illiterate and was after a fast buck.

"This licence for your country! Show me India licence!" he demanded, in an almost but not quite, threatening tone.

I knew I had to be calm and polite. If I rubbed him up the wrong way he could do pretty much what he wanted to, being the law, and that could cost me a lot more money and inconvenience than necessary, plus I was already late for the Taj visit. I explained that I do not have an Indian licence, because I have an international one which he was holding and I know full well that I do not need an Indian licence because we'd checked this out with the chief of police, who happens to be a good friend of Ravi's. So this licence must therefore be valid.

This wasn't the cleverest of moves, because although I was polite and trying desperately to be humble, I probably came across as cheeky and cocksure, which can be a bit of a problem of mine. I had also inadvertently shown him that he was wrong and I was right, which must have dented his pride and rubbed him up the wrong way a little. It probably explains why he bellowed in a barely coherent voice, "Show me your papers for bike!" Then he thought for a second and said, "quickly!" for good measure.

Now this is where there could have been a potential problem, because we are supposed to have them on us at all times, but for some reason Ravi insists on keeping them locked in his personal safe in his cabin. I tried explaining this but he didn't seem to understand.

"Show me your papers!" he repeated becoming more agitated and possibly thinking he was moving in to close the deal.

"I don't have them, they are in office!" I replied in that pigeon English that Brits always revert to when speaking to foreigners whose English isn't that great.

After telling me I must have them on me at all times he said I would have to pay an on the spot fine, which I had been expecting and I wasn't too surprised when he said 500 Rupees, which is the equivalent of £7:00. Now I know this isn't much money and paying it right away would make life a lot easier and I could merrily go about my work, but well, it's the principle of the thing isn't it?

"Sorry", I told him "I don't have money, but I'll come to station and pay. Give me ticket and number of identification please?"

"You must pay now!"

Again I offered to pay at the station and asked for a ticket, knowing full well that he didn't want to do any paperwork and probably wasn't capable of doing so either. I also started making a note of his identification number, which is on every policeman's shoulder pads.

"Why you want number? Pay now!"

"I need to know that you are real." I replied, "but I will pay at the station".

"You must pay now!"

"Sorry, I don't have any money now." I said a bit too patronisingly.

"But you must have money. You are white and European have money!" he stammered, trotting out that age-old cliché that they think all white people have a bottomless pit of gold.

I wondered briefly if it was worth explaining to him that I've got five thousand pounds worth of debts back home and that he is probably better off than me by not being allowed credit. I thought better of it though, and firmly stated that I didn't have any money, so I couldn't pay him now, but I was more than willing to pay at the station.

He looked at me with a mixture of hatred in his eyes and sorrow on his old and tired looking face because he hadn't been able to get any money out of me and as he told me to go, I almost felt sorry for him, because he probably needs the money more than I do.

Good on Ravi though, who had warned me that this often happens. Corrupt local policemen try to supplement their living by giving tourists on the spot fines, which are enough to make a difference to them and not enough to unduly worry the victim. Ravi had therefore told me to take down their number as a way of getting out of it, which is a little ironic seeing that I had £2,000 of company money in my briefcase.

As a penance, I am sure, I was duly drenched on the bike ride back from the Taj Holiday Village which really pissed me off for a couple of reasons: Firstly I want some prolonged sunshine and I wish the rains would finish and let the real Indian summer begin. Secondly, over the past week I have developed an excruciatingly irritating rash on the back of my right leg, which I have put down to a skin reaction to my new trousers and the friction caused as a result of each time I get soaked.

At the beginning of the week, a day after the first real soaking, there had been a few small patches of itchy redness on the pits behind the knees (what is that area called?) and towards the hamstring area of the leg. This morning I woke up to find it had spread over the majority of my right leg and parts of my left. The right leg has also ballooned to look a bit like a rugby ball and the irritation is unbearable.

Everywhere I go I am rubbing my legs against any available object, getting some curious looks in hotel receptions and the quieter my duties are, the more aware of the irritation I become. I bought some cream from the chemist, which has cooled it down a bit, but the annoyance is still there and has affected my sleep patterns a bit over the past couple of days, because I can't seem to relax long enough to drift off. I've had rashes, mosquito bites, quite a few infections and tropical bouts of diarrhoea over the seasons I've been in this job, but at the moment this beats them all hands down.

SATURDAY – 17TH OCTOBER

I walked into Ravi's cabin in the early afternoon whilst he was busy playing chess on his computer, waiting for 14:00 to arrive so that he could knock off for the day and get an early Kingfisher before getting an even earlier night's sleep.

He looked up and saw me standing there with a pained expression on my face, before I said, "have a look at this" and undid my belt and unfastened the buttons and zip on my trousers.

"Whoa, Ceri. What are you doing?" he exclaimed with a frightened look on his face, not quite sure what I was up to.

"It's alright Ravi, I just want to show you something, and I need your opinion."

"But I don't know if I want to see what you want to show me and close that door before you embarrass the girls."

I closed the door, a bit too suddenly because we could instantly hear the girls giggling outside, but nevertheless I needed someone else's opinion. I ignored their childish delight and Ravi's bewildered eyes, dropped my trousers and turned to face away from him.

"Look." I told him, to which he asked at what and I then had to tell him to take his hands away from his face, because I wasn't doing anything rude and would he have a look at the rash on the back of my legs.

"Oh my goodness!" I love the way Ravi exclaims sometimes, it's almost as if he has learnt his English from the Peter Sellers impression of an Indian, "You want to go and see a doctor right now!"

"What do you think it could be?" I queried, hoping he might have an idea, which was unlikely seeing as he was peeping through his fingertips and suffering from having gone over sixty seconds without a Gold Flake cigarette.

"I don't think it's a stress reaction, because what we're doing now is nothing new and it can't be from the trouser material because I've reverted to wearing an older pair the last two days and the rash and swelling has got worse, so what do you think it could be?"

"I don't know. But if I were you I'd go to the doctors immediately!" This is what I did, although I'm still not sure if Ravi said that because he was genuinely concerned about the state of my legs or because he just wanted me out of his office.

But he made me pull my trousers up quite sharply and arranged for Dilip, one of the office boys and also one of the nicest, funniest men I have ever worked with, to take me to a surgery around the corner.

The doctors was quite an interesting little place, because unless you are from the area you wouldn't know it was a doctors, considering there is no sign outside to indicate the purpose of the office inside. That is apart from a stencilled name on the door, which opened inwards, declaring the name of the incumbent with a few letters dotted afterwards. The flaky green door lead into a small sparse room, which looked as if it was painted a light shade of beige over twenty years ago, but the paint peeling off the walls and the current shade of smoke stained brown belied the lack of attention the place had received in the interim. The floor had those ugly tiles we have in the Ranch, but with neater piles of dust sitting in the corners, and around the outside of three of the walls were uncomfortable, worn wooden benches, the sort we used to get in my old school gym, for patients to sit on. There was no table laden with back issues of 'Horse & Hounds', but there was the obligatory 'Men do you suffer from the following' poster. To complete the picture a bedraggled male receptionist, with no shoes, sweat stained shirt with three buttons missing was sitting at an empty rickety desk and chain smoking a pack of Ravi's beloved Gold Flakes.

After twenty minutes or so, I realised that there isn't an orderly queuing system, just a quickest to the door competition when the last patient leaves. So I had no choice but to join in the game. My first tentative attempts were quite feeble, much to Dilip's delight, because I was shoved aside by a middle aged woman with her arm in plaster on the first go and I was sold an excellent dummy by a young boy, with what looked like measles, on the second. When he feigned to get up, I followed suit, realised there was no-one coming out and while I was sitting down again he jumped up and moved through the door with the grace of a young Gazelle.

Eventually though, I got the hang of it and on my third attempt I shoved aside a middle-aged guy with a limp, a little too eagerly, and neatly side-stepped a young girl with a cough and heaved a sigh of relief as I made it through the door unimpeded to see the doctor.

Going through that door was like stepping into Mr. Ben's wardrobe, because I moved from third world desolation into a spotless, modern, hi-tech, shiny silver things lying neatly on tables, state of the art surgery. I was amazed at how impressive the room was and even more gob smacked when I only had to pay 15 Rupees (25 pence) for the consultancy fee. I was in and out in a matter of minutes and able to have a little fun at the expense of the others in the waiting room by playing my own, made-up game, of 'Whose jumpy now?' I'd open the door a fraction and everyone would jump to attention and start nudging each other out of the way, so then I'd close it and they'd all sit down slightly disconsolate at missing an opportunity, before I'd rather childishly open it, wait a second then close it. I did this four times, before the doctor gave me the strangest of looks and I sheepishly walked out to see Dilip who was in fits of laughter.

For the consultancy I had to drop my trousers and lie face down on the bed while the doctor prodded, poked and rubbed the rash, which irritated it even more. Thank God he wasn't the obligatory 'Doctor Dress Off' which you get in most resorts, where a girl could go in and say I've got a headache and he would say 'If you'd just like to take your clothes off?' The thought of that would be a tad discomforting at this juncture, seeing as I was lying half exposed with a strange man touching my inner thigh.

He sighed and uhhmed and ahhed as if he knew what he was doing and then asked if I had the rash anywhere else, to which I replied in the negative and stated that it was just on the back of my legs. He then told me to roll over onto my back, asked me if I was sure and pulled at the elastic on my boxers, put his head almost against my stomach and peeked in. I immediately tensed up, felt a tiny flash of rage and asked him what he was doing.

"I have to check that it's not a genital infection." He stated ever so matter of factly, whereas I was screaming inside my head 'GET OFF! GET OFF!"

I think he must have sensed my nervous reaction because he pulled away and told me to put my trousers back on. He explained that he thought many Europeans have genital infections because we have sex a lot with many different people, thus confirming that he is another blinkered, ignorant who thinks all westerners are promiscuous beer drinking, philandering tarts. Well I'm not, although it's not through lack of trying.

Finally he diagnosed a reaction to a chair, which left me baffled to say the least, and sent me away with a prescription for antihistamine tablets and Calamine lotion, which I could have thought of myself without having to go through the rigmarole of being touched up.

The antihistamines worked a treat mind. They didn't do much for the itching but they knocked me out completely and I slept from 19:00 through till 04:00 and right through a wedding reception that was being held downstairs.

I avoided chairs for the next two days.

SUNDAY – 18TH OCTOBER

Ravi picked me up at 04:30 to take me to the airport again and because we only have a dozen people leaving on the flight, I didn't need to do a departure transfer for this week. This was down to the girls and it was merely a case of ensuring that their guests got off okay and doing the 'Meet and Greet' for the others that were arriving.

Thankfully everything went very smoothly, without a single hitch and not even a change of hotel to advise this week, because the guests who were supposed to be going to the SJM had already been forewarned and compensated in the UK. This means that they are happy, we have provided a professional service and gained the guests' trust already and the most positive point of all is that we don't have to deal with the crap at this end.

The only time we were a little nervous was when Prasad told us we had two new coach drivers who didn't know where any of the hotels were. Thankfully there weren't many drop offs and the hotels in Goa are easy enough to find, plus all of our transfer reps know all the routes, which they should do seeing as they have been working with our agency for a few years now. I am pleased to say that the airport, which can be one of the more stressful days of the week, went very well with no delays, no problems and three people of importance all arriving with no complications.

The first one through was Kate Adams who is our new manager and it was great to see her again after a couple of years. She will be taking overall charge from tomorrow, which will relinquish a lot of my responsibilities, which I am not sure if I'm pleased or upset about.

I've enjoyed being in charge for the past week, actually for the past four weeks and know that I could easily do the job of Destination Manager, which I should have been promoted to a long while ago. However I knew all along that there would be someone coming in above me so I have been prepared for this eventuality and it is nice to have someone alleviate a lot of the pressure. Plus from tomorrow I hand over the mobile phone, which means no more phone calls from guests asking for pillows at eleven o'clock at night, or Sharon ringing to tell me all about her day until the phone's battery runs out.

The other two important arrivals work for the company in the UK and are out here on an educational visit. The idea is that they gather as much information about the place, including the problems we have in hotels, how good and how bad some places can be and also get an idea of the resorts and what is available for guests when they come out. Then when any guest rings up in the UK, be it for sales advice or a complaint, these guys should be able to assist whoever is dealing with the guest and in so doing increase sales for Goa and lower the level of complaints and compensation payments.

I met all three and introduced them to the reps and the agency staff and we arranged to meet up for dinner that night in Panjim, whilst in the meantime they had time to settle in and I had a chance to get an hour's siesta before doing my first welcome meeting.

At about 16:15 I was having a shower when the mobile went. I cursed Sharon for not giving me a minute's peace and then offered a silent, momentary prayer of gratitude because I would be handing the damned thing over to Kate tomorrow. I stepped out of the shower, soaking wet, slipped into the bedroom and picked it up off the bed, where it was lying next to a pile of welcome meeting notes, which were subsequently soaked from my dripping wet hair as I leant over.

I answered ' Hello' in a resigned voice, wandering what Sharon wanted now and whether I could get her off the line quickly because I had a meeting to get to, when a disgruntled voice asked, "Is that our rep?"

I replied that I wasn't the rep for their hotel, but that they had got through to the medical emergency number and asked if I could help, to which the guest explained that he had just arrived off tour. We sell week-long tours around various parts of India and the guests then come back to Goa for their final week. It's an excellent idea but the only problem is that the guests have a really high standard of hotel whilst on tour, but often book a two or three star hotel for their final week and the difference can be quite a shock. This particular guest was refusing to check-in because he had been given the wrong type of room by the reception staff at his new hotel.

I listened for a minute or so in an effort to calm him down and managed to get the hotel manager on the line and arranged for him to give the guests the room they had booked, and were supposed to have. But when I returned to the gentleman, he was still so wound up and obviously tired from a weeks worth of travelling that he refused to stay in this hotel and was demanding a move. Ordinarily I would encourage them to stay where they are for the night, in the correct room of course, and see how they feel in the morning. By which time the guests will have usually calmed down, settled in a bit and had a good look at the beautiful surroundings and started to quite enjoy themselves. Nine times out of ten they decide to stay where they are and end up having a good holiday.

The problem with this strategy though, is that it takes time to calm someone down. You have to do a lot of listening and empathising, followed by agreeing with them a little bit and dropping in subtle hints about how great the place they are in actually is and showing them the benefits of where they are, before encouraging them to stay just the one night. The other difficulty as well, was that I was on the phone and this is much harder to do when you don't know whom you are dealing with. It is so much easier to be sympathetic when you are face to face with someone and it's a little harder for them to be so adamant when they have to refuse the matter to your face.

Because of time constraints, where I was left with just over ten minutes to get ready for my welcome meeting, I realised that I had to deal with the matter fairly sharply otherwise I would be very late for the first meeting. So, judging that the guests were too worked up to try calming them down, I decided to resolve it by finding them an alternative hotel, and told them that they would have to pay any price difference.

They weren't too happy about this. But as I explained we had brochured the holiday 100% correctly, had not miss-sold it in any way and as a result of my conversation with the hotel manager they were eventually being offered everything that they had booked. Plus it is unfair on the guests in any hotel we send them to, if these guests get a cut-price deal when the others have had to book and pay full brochure price.

I was amazed to find that the Holiday Inn, which is a far superior hotel, was only one pound more expensive per person, for the week, so I offered the guests the change, which they duly accepted.

I booked the room at the Holiday Inn and they moved right away on the basis that they paid for their own taxi, which would have been £10 at the most and that they pay Ruth, our rep in the Holiday Inn, the £2 for the change the next day.

Unfortunately, this wasn't done quickly enough and I arrived ten minutes late for the Cidade De Goa welcome meeting, which was not the best, first impression I have ever created.

Thankfully it didn't matter too much because I only had a dozen arrivals in the hotel for this week and they have all been to Goa at least once before. This meant that on the plus side there were no problems, but on the negative side my excursion sales suffered because they have done most of the trips before and at present there are no new ventures in the offing.

Again I left late (it's so hard to catch up when you are behind in this industry) and had to race through Panjim and the streets leading North, which was pretty hairy because the streets were crowded with the beginnings of the Dilwali Festival celebrations and if there's one thing the Goans know how to do it's enjoy a party.

This particular festival celebrates the Hindi New Year and the Goddess Laxmi, who is the Goddess of Wealth. It is more familiarly known as the festival of lights, because everywhere you go bright, multi-coloured bulbs adorn the streets, houses, cars, hedges and walls. People dance in the street all night long, to music that is blaring out of speakers from houses, cars, side alleys and anywhere that they can be mounted, to the high pitched sounds of traditional folk songs and the obligatory versions of La Bamba and Alice translated into Hindi. In the midst of all the mayhem in the streets, there are statues made out of a mixture of straw and papière maché representing the old man who bit the Hare Krishna and surrounding all of this is a cacophony of sound as car and motorbike horns toot constantly and people shout above the din just to hear a basic party greeting.

Late in the evening, they hold a massive carnival procession through the streets, with everyone in bright coloured costume, which serves to build the wall of sound up even more. Then at four in the morning the overwhelming energy reaches its peak and they burn the effigies of the old man and set off the fireworks, before suddenly sloping off home shortly afterwards, for a quiet whisky with the family. What I find most amazing about the whole thing is that most people in Panjim are devout Catholics, yet they celebrate a Hindu festival with as much gusto as they would one of their own.

What an amazing place Goa is, when you can get all of the main religions together in perfect harmony. However, when you're running late for a welcome meeting that has the potential to make or break somebody's holiday, the road conditions are not so enthralling.

Because of the traffic, which made it impossible to get through town, I arrived at the Fort Aguada twenty minutes late, to meet just the one honeymoon couple that had arrived earlier today and by some stroke of luck for me, turned up five minutes later than I did. Yet again they said they'd been here before, so again there were no problems as we chatted happily at the bar and again no excursion sales were to be gained from this couple.

By the time I managed to leave the Fort Aguada it was after 21:00 which meant that I was late for dinner already and I still had to renegotiate the streets of Panjim again, before changing, picking Kate up and joining the others.

I also managed to survive the journey with only three near misses, one near fatal skid as I avoided a child running out into the street and I got drenched yet again. As I eventually walked into the exquisite restaurant I could hear Sharon moaning that all of her guests were repeat bookers and that she hadn't sold much either.

Kate didn't want the phone.

MONDAY – 19TH OCTOBER

Being the first day of the Indian New Year I believe, possibly misguidedly, that things have now taken a turn for the better and that the majority of the stress, and hard work has been cast aside and from now on the job will be more productive and rewarding.

The first sign of this was the excellent celebrations last night and the good mood that is prevalent around Panjim at present. Secondly Kate arrived yesterday and she is full of positive energy and has taken a load off my shoulders already. Thirdly, for the first time in the four weeks that I have been here, the sun was shining, the skies were clear blue with not a cloud in sight and the sea was velvet smooth.

This conspired to provide an easy morning in the hotels, with few people to chat to and because I'm completely up to date with my paperwork, and all of my reservations are confirmed for the coming Sunday, I had plenty of time to sit on my visits and catch up with my letter writing.

I also rubbed the backs of my legs against chairs, table legs, plant pots and any other inanimate object that was in the vicinity, because although the rash has started to go down, ironically the arrival of sunny skies has caused it to become even more irritating than I had thought possible.

We can't have everything though can we?

WEDNESDAY – 21ST OCTOBER

Some days in Goa can be so frustrating you feel like running half naked down a street, screaming abuse at anyone who so much as looks at you. I've never known somewhere so difficult in having to overcome bureaucracy, local workers' apathy and government indifference to the industry even though we bring in the bulk of the states revenue and worst of all the frequent power cuts that occur at the most inopportune moments. But yet, the place is so beautiful, the way of life is very easy, the beers are stupidly cheap, the people are so genuine and you can't help but be bowled over by their warmth, innocence and generosity on occasions. This is what happened to me today and showed me why I do this job and come to live in these amazing countries.

I'd managed to drag myself out of bed by midday, after having had a rough six hours sleep. My dear friends, furry mouth, thick head and washing machine stomach, had all returned en masse to pay their regards and spend the best part of the day with me on the soft white sands of Colva beach. I was trying to soak up some rays in a vain attempt in transforming my scrawny lily-white body into that of a bronzed Adonis and chilling out after four weeks of overdoing it.

I settled down outside one of the many stylish, home built, wooden shacks, which really add to the tropical feel and generate a Bounty advert kind of ambience. I then ordered two litres of water for the dehydration, a coke for some glucose and a bit of energy, a beer for the hair of the dog and a fried omelette because I was still drunk from the night before and didn't really know what I was doing. Then I lay my towel on the sun bed, positioned in the direct line of the sunlight to improve my chances of finishing the day looking like a walking advert for Malibu, took off my trusty, 'Day Off' Swansea City 1970's replica jersey and lay back to chill out in paradise. I must have dozed off for a while, because I awoke with a bit of a start to find my three drinks by the right hand side of my bed and two, pretty young Indian girls sitting down by the left hand side, each of whom had a big bundle of goods to sell. But they were just blithely gossiping away, possibly about the hunk of a man next to them, but more likely oblivious to my existence.

"Hello," the one nearest to me said, with a big grin on her face which revealed a set of perfect teeth and huge smiling brown eyes that looked as if they'd seen too much already in her young life. I couldn't guess her age, but assumed she was a teenager. However, with her sunburnt skin and matted hair just covering her forehead and dropping well below her shoulders she could easily have passed as a thirty something to boot.

"What is your good name?"

"Ceri" I replied dreading the inevitable conversation about my name that usually ensues and expecting the hard sell for her sarongs and bracelets in any moment.

"That is nice name," commented the other girl who appeared a bit older, but was equally as pretty with another huge smile, this time with a few gaps in her crooked teeth. Her hair was adorned with heavy, silver looking jewellery and trellises hanging all the way to her face and one connecting to her nose, "What is your good country?"

"Wales, near England," I clarified, praying that we weren't going to repeat the whole 'where is Wales' conversation on my day off.

"That is nice. First time in Goa?"

Of course, I forgot the beach sellers all ask the same three questions every time as a means of striking up conversation and eventually getting you to buy their wares. They aren't particularly interested in the answers; it's more a desperate need for you to respond. I tried to explain that I work in Goa, but most of the locals can't understand the concept of a European coming all the way to India to work, when where we come from is supposedly the dream place and land of opportunity where everyone can become rich overnight. The girls thought I was joking with them.

I expected them to follow up with a demand that I buy a sarong or a bed sheet, but instead the younger of the two just said,

"We sit here okay? We are tired from selling and if policeman come you please say we are your friends".

Beach sellers have supposedly been outlawed in Goa because there were far too many at one stage and they were hassling the tourists way too much. Nowadays, there are still the odd one or two, who have to pay off the local police or hide from them to get onto the beach.

It turns out that the younger girl is called Leela and is fourteen years old and the elder is Sonja who is sixteen and is married with two children already. They sat and chatted away and told me about their lives and how they have travelled from the neighbouring state of Karnataka, leaving their families behind in the hope of making some money to support them further and in Leela's case pay for a younger sibling's education. They were lovely girls who were happy to talk and didn't try and sell me anything. When my omelette eventually arrived, I ordered two more cokes and a bowl of fried rice for the girls, which was worth it, simply to see their eyes light up.

While they were eagerly sipping their cokes, Leela noticed the rash on the back of my legs, which was more than likely being harmed by the heat, and said something to her friend in a conspiratorial tone. I thought they may have assumed that I was an over sexed European, but Sonja leant over, prodded it a couple of times and whispered back to Leela who repeated what she had said into English.

"You must work here, because she says you are having much worries. She thinks copper on the skin will help."

And while she was saying this, Sonja reached into her bag of goods and pulled out a copper bracelet and put it onto my right wrist.

"Here, present. You nice man, make you better."

I was bowled over by their generosity and it completely took my mind off my hangover. I don't know if it is true or not about the copper, or merely a housewives tale or even a way of ingratiating themselves with me so that I would spend some money later in the day. But there were plenty of other people on the beach they could have sat next to and so I have decided to wear the bracelet for as long as it holds out, to remind me how decent some people can be in this world.

The girls spent most of the day with me and possibly out of guilt, I asked them what they were selling. They then went about their business with unbelievable gusto, laying out a multi-coloured bed sheet in the sand and displaying on top of it an array of sarongs, shirts, T-shirts, bangles, baubles and beads. I paid 600 Rupees, which is way over the odds, for a double bed sheet with a picture of a half moon and half sun that will go nicely in my shoebox and a matching tablecloth, but I was more than happy to give the money to them. The girls left me about an hour before I met Kate and we headed back to Panjim where we were due to meet Ravi for dinner at 20:00.

We'd been in the car, with Kate driving this time, for about half an hour and had turned off the coastal road and headed inland through a couple of shortcut lanes to join up with the main highway that would take us straight into the heart of Panjim. There had been a few problems with the car because it kept stalling every time we slowed down and I was having an awful lot of mileage joking about women drivers; more seriously the petrol was running down quicker than it should have been.

The engine stalled seven or eight times, and each time it would shudder more violently than the time before, shaking us around like balls in a jar, so we again tried to get into as high a gear as possible; I have no idea why; it's just something someone once said to me before I ran out of petrol on the M4 once. We kept the revs up and prayed desperately that we could get out of the tight winding roads that we were on and reach the main road, where we could open the car up a bit and wouldn't have to slow down until we reached town.

We eventually saw the lights of traffic speeding busily along the main road about 70 metres ahead of us and breathed a sigh of relief, knowing that if we could just negotiate that turn then we would be on a virtual home stretch. But just as we saw the lights, Kate's foot slipped off the accelerator and we lurched forward as the car stopped and then bounced forward, before cutting out completely. We rolled to a stop just at the entrance to the main road. We tried over and over to get it going again but the trash heap refused to even have the decency to respond. We were not quite in the middle of nowhere, but on the suburbs known as the edge of nowhere not far from assistance-ville and we sat in the car and laughed our socks off. Thank Christ I was with Kate and not with one of a load of less cheery people I know. She too tends to be accident prone like myself and she has this uncanny knack of being one of the most positive people I know and being able to see the funny side in pretty much anything.

We must have looked like a pair of destitute travellers, because we both had T-shirt and shorts on, which were creased from being crumpled up by the beach and poolside. My hair was dry from the sun and tangled and both of us had the beginnings of sunburnt glows. It was pitch black by now and some storm clouds were growing overhead.

We could have been more frightened than we were, but thankfully having both lived around here for a while, we knew the people were wonderful and it was only the snakes and the rats we had to be wary of. A bird cried out in the night and the wind picked up enough to start whistling in the trees, which made Kate start for a brief second and reminded us of the 'Blair Witch Project'. We tried starting the car again to no avail, so waited ten minutes then tried yet again, still to no avail. We jumped out and popped open the bonnet to be met by a wall of grease and stared at the engine with blank expressions on our faces. Neither one of us had the first idea what we were looking for. We tweaked a few wires, opened a couple of caps and re-tightened them, then tried starting the car again to even less avail.

While this was taking place, and after Kate had stopped laughing after the third failure, a motorbike drove past us, had a good stare and then carried on. Five minutes later he'd returned with a jerry can and asked if we were okay. We explained that the car had cut out on us, but we didn't think it was the petrol, although it was certainly low right now. He looked at us a little quizzically, tried starting it and then looked under the bonnet as if he hadn't heard a word we'd said, only to be met with the same emphatic dose of mechanical apathy.

"We try the petrol!" he stated and told me to get on the back of the bike. At the time neither Kate nor I thought much about this, but I was leaving her stranded in a strange country, in the middle of nowhere, on her own where anything could happen to her. Something we would never do back in Britain, but as we both discussed later, we didn't give it a second's thought because we knew she would be safe, in fact far safer than back home. Two minutes down the road I filled up the jerry can for a couple of quid and we then returned, siphoned the petrol into the car and on the fourth or possibly fifth attempt it started and then continued to growl uneasily.

We both looked sheepishly at our Samaritan, who was smiling with satisfaction and we offered to give him 200 Rupees for helping us. He refused saying that he hoped we would do the same if the shoe were on the other foot. Waving goodbye and shouting our thanks for the umpteenth time we set off for Panjim again and thirty minutes later we were on the outskirts of the city. In a rural stretch looking over the almost bright lights of activity we were sitting in the car, stranded again and laughing even harder than before.

It obviously wasn't the petrol. But whatever it was, it was ensuring the petrol was going down quicker than a pint of Kingfisher in Tito's. After a few more shudders and rattles the engine had cut out for a final time and we had freewheeled to a standstill on the side of the road. We didn't bother trying to look at the engine or constantly restarting because we were both fed up with the thing, so instead tried to flag down a passing car, with even less luck than we'd had starting this one previously. After ten minutes of trying, I decided to take a wander and only two minutes away came across a taxi driver cleaning his Auto Rickshaw. I love these little three wheelers, because they look like mopeds with a roof on and are so nippy they are like driving a dodgem car at the fair ground. The only downside is that you feel every bump and they can be very uncomfortable for any journey longer than five minutes in duration.

Still, I explained our predicament and he took his bucket and cloth inside, presumably kissed his wife and then took me back to Kate, where we piled in our bags and headed off to our respective digs. The car was left by the wayside to be collected the next day.

When they dropped me off I asked the guy how much and yet again we had the unbelievable good fortune to have someone who said, "Nothing, you were stuck so I help you."

We both gave him another 200 Rupees each, (about £3) which was four times what the fare should have been and his face lit up like a full moon in a clear sky.

The past month has been demanding, both physically and emotionally, and during this time I have been questioning my commitment and motivation to stay in Goa and in this industry. But this week a few things have taken a turn for the better. Today in particular I was bowled over by the warmth and generosity of the two girls on the beach for giving me the bracelet, by the guy who helped us get the petrol and by the taxi driver for willingly dropping us off. They have shown me exactly why I am here in India and why I do this job, because people are what make the difference. We were only one hour late for another freebie dinner with Ravi. Kate was still laughing.

SATURDAY – 24TH OCTOBER

Why is it that whenever I have a long, hard days work ahead of me, I always go out the night before and say I'll have just the one, but always seem to be suffering the after effects of the night before? I never seem to learn and I'm determined that I'll never drink like that again!

The work I had to do today wasn't the most demanding ever. It was more time consuming if anything and we had to get a lot done before Sunday's arrival, which was pretty uneventful. This is why we afforded ourselves a few quiet drinks when we went out for dinner in the evening. We met up at a quaint, ethnic restaurant in the North, which is famous for its local food and its long table, and seeing as it was gone ten o clock already we wasted no time in pouring Kingfishers down our necks. By the time the food arrived we were already on our way to becoming a little squiffy and also a little bloated because of the Kingfisher. We eventually headed in the general direction of Tito's, convinced that we'd only have one more.

Sadly or not so, our arithmetic was way off, because when we arrived there was quite a large crowd of reps from all companies who were out on a bit of a jolly for the first time this season. It would have been churlish not to join in the drunkenness and debauchery, plus it was an ideal opportunity to lay some foundations for any future displays of swordsmanship with people we hadn't yet met.

Tito's closed at two and the whole crowd seemed to move as one to a newly opened nightclub called West End, which was on the way home to Panjim for us anyway. I don't recall an awful lot of the night except that Kate was talking with her breasts, which she does when she gets drunk; I loved everyone and then proved to the world that white men can't dance. I made some awkward and clumsy advances on another rep, who smiled at me, promised we'd meet up for a drink sometime soon and then promptly went home with some bloke from a rival company. We left for home around 05:30am.

Three and a half hours later I was sitting in the Cidade De Goa reception, slightly red eyed, furry mouthed, sweating like a marathon runner and telling guests how wonderful Panjim is and listing the good places to eat. The last thing I wanted to think about was food and drink. The rest of the day was spent in the dark confines of the office, playing with the laptop and in the process reworking the notice boards, sorting out the following day's transfers and airport routines and generally pushing paper from one side of the desk to the other. During the course of the day we had two problems to deal with and received one piece of excellent news.

Sharon was the first on the phone, because she had two 'Billies' (Billy Bunters – punters) who had arrived off tour and checked into a hotel in the north resort of Sinquerim. As I've mentioned before, people coming off tour into a lower standard of hotel than they are used to will often be disappointed and can cause quite a few problems This was the case here because they instantly decided that they weren't going to stay.

They collared Sharon as she was going into her room in her spare time in the afternoon, demanded a move to another hotel and by all accounts were not too polite in how they requested this. We told her to explain that we'd do all we could to help, but that we'd sold the holiday correctly. The brochure states that the hotel is simple and basic and the price in the nightly rate column states that the hotel is only £7 per night, so it is hardly feasible for them to expect a four star, which is what they would have been used to on tour. Essentially we haven't acted incorrectly or mis-sold the holiday, but we are willing to move the guests if they wish to do so. However, they will have to pay any price difference and also any cancellation fee the hotel may charge (usually three nights of accommodation).

Sharon went back to them and they refused to pay and demanded a free move, which we cannot give. It then resulted in two hours of stalemate, where Sharon explained repeatedly that they could move, but they would have to pay and that we were acting extremely fairly. The Billies in turn were adamant that they weren't going to stay and took great pleasure in calling Sharon all manner of names under the sun. Their conversation ended with the guests deciding to stay where they are and they'll then sue us when they return to the UK, even though they don't have a leg to stand on. As a matter of course they will be contacting Esther Rantzen and The Sun and they also have a friend who works for Watchdog, as if we haven't heard that one before.

After Sharon's call, Ruth then rang because she's got a crowd of unhappy people in the Dona Santa Maria, largely due to her own making because she forgot to book fifteen of them on the Waterfalls trip for today. She was in need of some advice on how to calm them down and to try and rectify the matter. Naturally, the guests are upset and have taken it out on her (you learn the hard way in this job) and because she's inexperienced she wasn't able to pacify them at first. This apparently heightened their anger and we have now lost quite a bit of money from this excursion and all the other ones they've asked to cancel because they don't trust her. Whereas Sharon is a bit more thick-skinned, Ruth took the complaints far more personally, something you learn to eventually distance yourself from. Kate had to pick up a tearful young lady and make sure she was ready for work later on that evening.

Just as we thought the day was going to be a complete disaster, we received a fax from Stelios George, confirming we could employ a chap called Lester Fernandez, as a local rep. We immediately got on the phone to him and he started this evening. We know he's hard working, conscientious, very pleasant and polite, which means he's great with the guests and as a result he generates a good level of excursion sales. He'll take over a few of Sharon's hotels which will ease the workload and to show how pleased we were to welcome him on board, we got him helping out straightaway by sending him out for a take-away.

SUNDAY – 25TH OCTOBER

A confusing feature about Dabolim International airport is that it has two departure areas - one for International flights and the other for Domestic ones. The domestic flights tend to check in approximately a hundred travellers at any one time, sometimes even less, and the international flights have anything up to three hundred passengers at a go, yet the international check-in area is only half the size of the domestic check-in area. This is typical Indian logic, which caused absolute chaos in our first major departure of the season.

The lack of space resulted in most of the passengers having to queue outside the main building in the early morning air, even though there were four check-in desks operational this week. To add to this organised sequence of calamities, the airport authorities have, in their wisdom, this season decided to scan every piece of luggage before it is checked in. The machines for the scanning are at the entrance of the International Departures and as well as adding another queue to deal with they take up half the space of the hall and this slows the whole process by another hour.

Because this was the first large exodus of the season, the local airport officials and authorities were unprepared for the onslaught, as they routinely are every season, despite having had over eight years to get used to it. This resulted in hundreds of tired people milling around trying to find which of the three queues they should be in. They were sweating in their warmer aeroplane clothes, because the air conditioning had failed again and they were desperately wanting to get away from this confusion and jump into the welcoming embrace of a cramped charter airplane.

If someone was looking from above, they would have seen a picture that was reminiscent of an ant's nest, with lots of tiny dots moving around in circles and seemingly going nowhere. However there was some form of order amongst the apparent anarchy, because the passengers did eventually seem to find their way from the luggage scanning, to the check-in desk, to the immigration control and into the departure lounge. All this despite the best efforts of the over officious customs and immigration officials, who took a sadistic delight in holding passengers up at random as it took their fancy.

We also had further problems with our coaches. The driver of the coach carrying Lester and Sharon was adamant that the Zuari Bridge, which connects North Goa to the central and Southern areas, was closed and so he took a detour through Ponda in the middle of the state. This resulted in them turning up an hour after everyone else for checking-in and because most of the seats had already gone, some of the guests were not able to sit together on the flight home, which they were not best pleased about.

As it turns out, it was announced in the local press yesterday that the bridge was officially being opened to buses and commercial traffic again, with effect from today, but trying to get this message across to some of the locals, who always know best, is nigh on impossible.

To add to this, Ruth wasn't picked up at her hotel for her transfer at the Dona Santa Maria, which by coincidence is the hotel where she has over thirty guests who are not overly enamoured with her at present. Therefore muggins here had to greet two coaches full of irate passengers as they arrived, all of whom are related to Anne Robinson. I then took them through the whole check-in procedure and it was all because Ruth didn't turn up. I received a few comments that were unwelcome at 05:00, but kept my easy-going calm and continued to smile until they had all gone through. Amongst the, "We'll be taking you to the cleaners," I did receive a few, "You're much more helpful than that other one. I wish we had you as our rep!"

The annoying thing is that Ruth didn't use her common sense. When she realised she wasn't going to be picked up, she could have either got a taxi or taken her moped to the Dona Santa Maria. Judging by the fact that she didn't arrive at the airport until after all the departures had gone through Immigration Control, therefore being spared the deserved burden of taking the flak she had created, it struck me that she didn't want to take responsibility for her actions and was prepared to let a team member deal with her crap. I am very sceptical about her excuses and am quite suspicious about her motives for wanting to do this job. However, Kate is in charge and she has only had to deal with her for a week, so she is giving her the benefit of the doubt at the moment and is rightfully planning on spending a fair bit of time with her over the next few days.

Thankfully, after the mess with seeing everyone off, the arrivals came through on time, with no problems at all and by 10am I was back at The Ranch and tucking into my breakfast, after having already done a full days work. I also had a couple of hours spare for a siesta before heading off for the evenings welcome meetings.

Both of the meetings I did in the evening went very well in that I had no major problems, made a favourable impression on the Billies and also had a very good return on the excursion sales front. However after having done close to, if not more than, a thousand welcome meetings over the seasons, I should have it down to a fine art by now and I believe I genuinely make a difference to quite a few people's holidays.

Every rep has their own way of doing a meeting and although the basics are always the same it is important to stay true to yourself instead of trying to be something you're not. For me, I believe the key is to be knowledgeable and informative and also interesting and trustworthy, plus I like to make the meetings as fun as possible. The way I see it, the Billies are on holiday to relax and enjoy themselves so why not have a bit of fun with them.

It's a hard balance to get, because if you come across as too carefree people may not take you so seriously and will then decide not to trust you when they have a problem. On the other hand if you are too far the other way, they'll see you as boring and won't want to come and spend time with you, which again loses you their confidence. The other thing with the meetings is that you have to tailor them to your crowd and some of the jokes and routines I used to put in when I was repping an 18 – 35 age group in Faliraki would certainly go down like Manchester City from the premiership with the clientele in a 4 star hotel in Goa.

Also in my favour is that I have always had a naturally great enthusiasm for wherever I work This comes across quite well and automatically spreads confidence in the resort the guests are staying in and I've also learnt that guests can see right through any bullshit and so nowadays I try to be brutally honest, wherever possible.

The one part of my meeting that has almost always been the same, since I got it fine tuned, is the introduction, and wherever I've been in the world I've started with something along the lines of:

"Good Morning Ladies and Gentlemen. We'll get your holiday underway right now so, first things first, on behalf of your tour operator I would like to wish you all a very warm welcome to the (Cidade De Goa) hotel and the resort of (Goa).

My name is Ceri and I am your holiday representative. Now I'll explain my name for you to avoid any confusion, because it's spelt the Welsh way with a letter 'C', and YES, despite the name I am a guy and not a girl.

As your representative, my aim is to make sure your holiday is as enjoyable as possible and if there is anything I can do to help make it so, then please do not hesitate to contact me. This means I am available if you have any questions, any queries, or any PROBLEMS whatsoever, so please come and see me so that I can help.

You see, the thing I dislike most about this job is the stage when people are ready to leave at the end of their holiday and as they are getting ready to board the bus for the airport I ask if they've had a great time, and they turn round and say, "Well yes. But."
I can't do anything about your 'Buts' at that stage because the holiday is over, so come and see me as soon as your 'Buts' occur, because this gives me an opportunity to help you out and you can get on with the important issue of enjoying your stay!"

The idea behind this intro is that I am positive about where they are, have made a joke about myself to help make them a little more at ease with me and of course I mention the dreaded word, 'PROBLEM'. This often surprises some people because they have become accustomed to reps skirting around this word, as I was initially taught to do.

From there on in I let them know how and when they can get hold of me and for the time being in Goa I'm using the tried and tested format of welcome meeting. This consists of giving out hotel information, local resort info, showing them how to get around and giving a guided tour of the state, whilst all the time dropping in little jokes, useful hints and of course dripping our excursions. For example, I might say,

"One of the excellent methods of getting around is by local bus which could take you to the glorious white sands of Palolem beach, which is a real bounty advert paradise and superb place to spend a night amongst the stars in romantic bamboo huts.

The buses are an adventure in themselves and although there are no bus stops, you just flag down one that is passing and hope that its destination is not shown on the back window instead of the front. You get to make a lot of great friends, because they have a seating capacity for 45 and standing capacity for 145 and guaranteed they'll cram people in, livestock and all. You'll also find that they run on what is known as GMT, which stands for Goan Maybe Time, so you'll have plenty of opportunity to take in some of the breathtaking countryside."

The idea with a passage like this is that I have made the local buses sound like a great adventure and have subtly put the guests off in the process. I've sold myself with my enthusiasm and humour and given them some useful hints as well, plus I have dripped one of the trips we do to Palolem beach, which with a bit of luck they'll book with me because there is no way they'll want to go by bus now.

The whole meeting is structured like this, positively putting people off things that affect our trips and giving them useful hints so that you gain their trust and come over well.

Finally I pick out three or four trips at the end that I blatantly give a hard sell on. I was originally trained to gradually link into them, but over the years have found that guests know we are going to sell to them, so I would rather be honest about it and tell them what I genuinely think is worth doing. Plus against the advice of one or two of my previous managers, I actually tell guests not to do one or two trips if I don't think they're any good for two reasons. 1) I don't want to deal with complaints when they come back and 2) It is a major way of gaining someone's trust.

And of course the meeting is rounded off with a very hard close of sale, with the emphasis on getting the guests to book all their trips right away, because if they don't the chances are you've lost them to the taxi drivers and cowboy excursion operators. As one of my better managers once said to me, 'If you don't sell to them, someone else will!'

The close of sale is pretty standard in the industry, with five points that need to be brought across, which are:

1. WHY – they should book it **NOW.**

2. WHEN – they should book a trip = **NOW!!**

3. HOW - they can book.

4. WHEN – they can pay.

5. HOW – they can pay.

They don't need to be in that particular order, but all of the points need to be brought across, because if a rep doesn't, the meeting will be spoiled by not getting any sales in and 25 minutes of previous hard work and effort will be down the drain.

Every rep has their own way of delivering this and mine has always worked very well for me as follows:

"Okay, we're drawing to a close now, but before we finish I'd just like to draw your attention to the booking form that I gave to you all earlier and run through it for you. (Wait while everyone gets a booking form out).

I've gone through a few of our fantastic days and nights out in detail for you and have briefly mentioned some of the others, but what I would like to point out, is that with over 3,000 people having arrived in Goa over the past two days all looking to have a good time like yourselves, it means that places on each of these trips can be very limited (1. WHY – a bit of an industry porky pie, but works every time)!!

Therefore, for every one of the trips you are looking to go on I will need your booking forms to be handed in right…..(pause)………… NOW!! (2. WHEN - to book).

Booking is ever so easy, because all you need to do is fill out this form by putting your names and room numbers in the space provided on the top, and alongside each of the ones (always plural) *you want to go on, you simply put down the number of people in your party and which week you want to go. Be it week one or week two of your holiday.* (3. HOW – to book).

As I said I need your forms in right NOW, but I don't want any money off you just yet because I need to guarantee the places are available first (big porky pie), *so what I want you to do is to come back and see me this evening between five and six and you can settle up then and I will give you your tickets if the places are there.* (4. WHEN – to pay).

You can pay by, cash, travellers cheques or your good old flexible friend your credit card (5. HOW – to pay).

So all that leaves me to say is a big thank you for coming to this introduction to the best holiday of your lives. I hope it has been of some use for you. I'm going to remain here for the next hour or so, to answer any questions that you may have and also to collect the booking forms from you.

I would like to take this opportunity of wishing you all a fantastic stay and if you like Goa half as much as I do, then you'll have a fantastic time. Ladies and Gentlemen….(pause for effect)….Thank you very much!"

And if all went to plan, which it almost always does, there would be a big round of applause followed by people coming up and giving me the booking forms and telling me how great I am.

For anyone who thinks that a meeting is haphazardly thrown together, you're very wrong. They have been carefully thought out over the past four decades and every line, if the rep is good, is carefully tailored to get you thinking how we want you to.

If it works, you'll think we're great, will give us a load of your money and will have a fantastic holiday and being realistic who could resist being charmed like that?

(pause for effect....)

Thank you.

WEDNESDAY - 28TH OCTOBER

I'm in a hotel room in a good standard three star, All Inclusive hotel in the south of Goa. The reason we stayed here last night was because they held the best party of the season so far and provided us with two complimentary rooms, even though we don't have any working relationship with them, yet.

I'm about to join up with Sharon and Kate to go to 'Shakeys' tacky American pizza parlour in the deep south of Cavellosim and it should round my day off quite nicely, which was desperately needed, following the week's efforts.

Actually not all of the week was bad, because I didn't have that many problems per se, but it was long and exhausting and then yesterday was absolutely bloody annoying.

Although the season has only been underway for three weeks, we already seem to be settling into a rather uncomfortable pattern where the guys get their work done with as little fuss as necessary, while the girls spend all day long, talking and rewriting because they're not completely with it yet. I appreciate that both Lester and myself are far more experienced than the girls and so should be more organised, plus I remember it took me a couple of months to get the hang of some of the paper work and get myself in order when I first started. But the beauty of the Tuesday afternoon, is that if everyone is organised, Kate and I can get out early and start our day off an hour or two earlier than usual, however, this doesn't look as if it will be the case for the next few months or so.

As usual, my paperwork was all done and dusted by 12:30 and I was feeling rather pleased with myself at hitting our extremely high and pretty much unreasonable target of £40 per head and was ready and misguidedly willing for the others to come in. Lester arrived at about that time, rushing into the office with his hurried, short-strided, walk and permanent grin and within thirty minutes he had handed over all of his paperwork and money and left to spend the afternoon with his girlfriend, before getting ready for his evening visits. He had every reason to smile, because he'd hit £35 per head and had earned himself over £50 of spending money, and when you consider that the average local wage is only something in the region of £40 per month, he was doing very well.

As Lester walked out of the office, Sharon bounced past him on the stairs in her usual whirlwind of blond hair and loud exclamations. Within seconds papers were strewn everywhere as she tried to get herself organised and count her money, whilst simultaneously filling us in on the industry gossip. She hasn't been that bad so far, but this week she was pretty careless and had to rewrite her liquidation three times, because she missed out a couple of tickets the first time and added up her figures wrong the second as she tried to write it out too quickly. Still, she did have a decent return and was in the same region as Lester, so if she continues to bring money in as she has been then we can forgive a few faux pas. At the end of the day, it's profits that the company worries about.

Because Ruth was late again, although forty-five minutes earlier than the past two weeks, this meant we had to listen to Sharon's love life dilemmas for well over two hours. Ruth sadly, is so bloody, irritatingly (even more than my rash which has eventually started to die down) disorganised. She looked a mess when she came in. Her scary red hair was completely dishevelled from a mere taxi ride, her blouse was dirty with a navy blue swimming costume showing prominently underneath and to round it off she had a pair of flip flops on with the rest of her uniform. I prayed that she hadn't been on visits like that, because she gives off the air of someone who is here for the beach and the beach only.

As she sat down at an available desk, she dumped her bag on top of it, pulled out a sandwich and in doing so papers scattered everywhere. This left a disorganised mound of chaos that she did nothing about until she had finished munching on her onion butty, whilst trying to speak some incoherent babble about what a great surfing session she had just had.

"Ruth, you were supposed to be here at one o clock, what happened?" Kate asked her, in an amazingly calm voice, sounding as if they were just two girls having a chat about a couple of guys.

"Yeah, right, liquidation. Well I saw the surfing guy from the Leela and he thought I might like to join him. The surf was good you know." She was beginning to sound like a cross between a hippy and a tramp, with her slow, lazy drawl in a middle England accent.

"Don't you think you should have been here to do your work though, after all, that is what we're all being paid for?"

"Right, but it was only a couple of hours and it hasn't affected how my guests are, so I didn't think it would matter." She lamely commented, showing that she isn't prepared to take any responsibility and doesn't really think of others.

"But because you're two hours late Ruth, that means that Ceri has to stay on an extra two hours, and so does the girl down in accounts and so does Ravi, so it has an effect on other people, plus it doesn't look very professional does it?" Still, Kate was talking as if she was just having a conversation, which really impressed me, although this time it could have been to a six year old.

"Right sorry. Does anyone want an onion and cheese sandwich?"

Kate continued to smile. I was ready to explode but didn't want to tread on any toes, so sat there silently with just a slight hint of rouge smothering my cheeks and Sharon was sitting around the corner trying to stop herself from laughing out loud. Kate, obviously exasperated, but again skilfully not showing it, decided to change tack and asked Ruth how she thought things were going in the South to which Ruth replied.

"Okay I think. I'm enjoying myself, which I think is most important. Yes I think I'll like it here." At which point Kate put her head in her hands, I shouted "Jesus H Christ" out load and Sharon fell on the floor laughing.

She eventually fumbled her way through her mass of papers, found the sheets she was looking for and then had to rewrite her liquidation twice because of a few stupid and careless errors. She still has to go and see two couples tonight to see if they will fill out their credit card details again, because she filled the slips out incorrectly. For the record Kate told her in no uncertain terms that if she doesn't then she will have to pay the difference herself, because there is no way that the company will cover her losses, especially when they are down to carelessness.

As she was packing her bags to go back to the South, she asked how much her sales per head were, something she should know herself, but I worked it out for her and told her it was £6 per head, only £34 off her target. She seemed completely nonplussed and said, "That's good isn't it for a beginner. I think I'll do well here!" I give her two months at the most.

By the time we'd tidied up after her mess, we were able to leave by about seven, which again involved another rush to get showered, changed and ready for another hour long drive down south, but it was worth it for a night off of drunkenness and debauchery of the highest order. It is nice to be slowly getting into a rhythm of socialising with other reps, something that has taken a fair bit of time to get underway this season. It was also nice to see a couple of fairly attractive ladies I could flirt with, while Kate was talking with her breasts from a very early stage.

After I'd had a couple of beers I decided to switch from the glycerine to whisky and coke, which has a tendency to make me a little boisterous from time to time and I angled in towards Janice the manager of a rival operator to see if I could try and create a semi-decent impression.

I knew Janice briefly a couple of years ago and I had always found her quite attractive. I never did anything about it because a mate of mine had a bit of a thing for her and you never break the guy code, plus I was also seeing a Danish girl at the time. She's about a year older than me, but looks about twenty-six with long blond hair, not peroxide but a natural straw colour. She isn't the brightest apple in the bunch, but has a very cute pair of lips that are crying out to be nibbled and an excellent slim figure and cute bum. She was sitting at the table we were at, which had a dozen or so people on and as the night wore on we seemed to be getting closer to each other as people moved around. For a while there was a conversation between just the two of us, and because of the booze it was laden with innuendos. Also because of the booze I couldn't read any of her body language to see how she was responding to me.

It was then that the eight glasses of double whisky really started to kick in and I gradually became louder and louder, to the extent that Kate was tugging at my arm, telling me to play it cool. I listened for all of thirty seconds and then thought that my party trick of falling over would be just the job right now. I offered to go to the bar, took a couple of orders and casually walked around the table, whilst still talking in a vain attempt to keep everyone's attention. I then headed to the bar and deliberately walked into a chair and came crashing to the ground.

Everyone burst into raucous laughter, I put on my stupid grin for effect and to milk the moment and Kate screamed,

'He always does this when he's drunk and trying to show off!'

I brushed myself down, a waiter came running over to see if I was okay and needed any help, but I was too busy looking at Janice, who sadly had her head in her hands so I couldn't tell if it worked or not. The manager came over and asked us to leave.

SATURDAY – 31ST OCTOBER

Despite having had a relatively straightforward past couple of weeks, we're still finding this period in the first couple of months pretty manic. Strange as it may sound we're still doing a lot of the preparation work, which should have been finished before the season even started. The drawback with a lot of this work is that it takes up a lot of our social and working hours, when what we'd like to be doing is having a couple of weeks of purely concentrating on giving the guests a great service and maybe even enjoying a small bit of spare time.

The work that we're still doing at the moment is the continual updating of the information boards, which weren't really completed to our satisfaction before we started. This was mainly because we didn't have the full use of a decent computer, but with Kate's laptop permanently in the office and a brand new international phone and fax that Ravi has bought us, we've been able to redesign a lot of the posters and information sheets. We're also still in the process of completing the list of Famtours, as the locals call them, that need to be done, which is a case of going on every one of the excursions we sell. Finally we are in the season of the nicey, nicey social functions with our suppliers.

This means we've still got to do three full day and two overnight excursions, so it looks like we'll be doing these trips until halfway into the New Year. On the other hand, the social jollies do not take up guest's time and although some of them are tiring and a little bit tedious at having to be overly polite and enthusiastic when we are shattered, they can also turn into a pretty good party, as was the case last night.

The 'do' in question was at the Dona Santa Maria and again they had invited all of the various tour operators and their respective agencies, which boded well for a spot of drunkenness and debauchery.

Kate and I drove down in her new Suzuki Maruti car, which is marginally better than the one we left stranded outside of Panjim and arrived at the Dona Santa Maria by about 9pm. This was after having dropped in to one of our hotels to say 'hi' to Ruth while she was supposed to be on her visits and checking in at the Santa Jose Maria (SJM) where we had a complimentary room booked. We must have arrived at the Goa Renaissance just before seven, knowing that Ruth was doing her last visit of the night there between 19:00 – 20:00. As we walked into the entrance to the lobby, we walked over to the congregation of notice boards from all of the tour companies that were on display to the left hand side of the entrance. This is a bit of an industry disease in that, after having spent years making sure your books and boards are spotless, you have to go and check everyone else's out when you walk into a hotel, anywhere in the world.

Despite our boards being so easy to maintain, Ruth's was a shambles. The top left sheet was turned round back to front, which is sacrilege in this industry, two other spaces were blank and the bottom right had the weekend's flight departure times, but written in an ugly red scrawl. I know previous managers who would have had heart attacks and would have sent her home for this.

In my first year with my old company I received a verbal warning for filling in the blank sections of a pre-written standard message in neat pencil instead of black, block capitals. This just goes to show how obsessive some people become about the books and boards, because they are a twenty-four hour representation of the company.

Trying to laugh it off, we sat down in the lobby bar and ordered a drink whilst we waited for Ruth. In the meantime we bumped into a couple of other reps, called Gina and Terri, the former Kate knew from Skiathos and was more than a little cute. We also said hello to Ruth's friend Melanie, who had a bit of a shocked expression on her face.

We both know people from the hotel and were quite happy having a social drink, but by quarter past she hadn't turned up and Kate was becoming worried (she always thinks the best of people) and I was becoming annoyed. We saw a couple of our guests hanging around and I actually ended up organising a room change for one couple in Ruth's absence. A full hour passed and she hadn't shown. She'd let the company and the rest of her team down and probably lost us revenue through potential excursion sales. This time Kate had decided that a formal warning was in order, which I wholeheartedly agreed with and it meant that what Ruth had done must have been serious if Kate felt this way.

We were determined not to let this spoil our evening, because we'd had a laugh in the car and were bent on having a good time at the jolly. As we walked into the hotel Ruth was already at the bar and she came bounding over to see us, and with a big, blatantly false, grin on her face said "Hi guys, good to see you. Sorry I missed you earlier but I went to the hotel earlier than I was supposed to and rang all of the guests to see if they were okay and didn't think it was necessary to pop back later. Did you want a drink?"

"We'll get our own thanks Ruth," Kate coolly said "and we'll have a chat tomorrow about earlier. Okay?" This I had to admire because she'd shown she was in control and hadn't let it ruin this evening. Both of us also glanced over Ruth's shoulder to see Melanie who was looking pretty sheepish.

Almost as soon as we had gathered our drinks we were introduced to the hotel owners and sat down for a quiet drink and an awkward fifteen minutes of stiff, polite conversation. Because of our earlier good mood and the confines of the current politically correct conversation about projected arrivals for the season, Kate and I reached a decision. We silently decided, with that knowing sparkle in a naughty child's eye that we each have, that tonight we'd have a raucous night out.

In the midst of the 'we're positive we've a successful season ahead of us' type chat, the Karaoke man switched on the machine and started singing a couple of numbers, one of which was the obligatory La Bamba. He then started walking around the bar trying to get people to sing one or two lines from the song that was playing at the time. By the time he reached us I was trying to eye up the cute rep from earlier, Kate was asking if I'd made contact and the disk was changing to Engelbert Humperdink's 'Please Release Me'. Ever the showman, or rather show off, I excitedly grabbed the mic, Kate sighed and the Karaoke guy looked dumbfounded because he knew he wasn't going to get it back.

Now I would love to brag and say that I have a rather soothing baritone and carry a tune with the best of them. But unfortunately I am tone deaf, my vocal chords are flatter than Kate Moss's stomach and I have a tendency to butcher even the simplest children's nursery rhyme. Therefore I improvised, pretended I was drunk, slurred my words and launched into a loud, strident 'pub singer' version, which had the purists heading for the exit and the party revellers laughing their socks off. Despite repeated attempts to wrestle me to the ground, I refused to hand the mic back until the song had finished, which left the Indians looking on in a state of bemusement and the hotel guests wondering what was going on in the secluded area.

From there on in, with the adrenaline permanently coursing through my veins, I was on a high and I believed the evening to be a great success, with most people joining in the fun and games, and the beers flowing in competition with Niagara Falls. A riotous evening of decadence and degradation ensued and after three songs, a dozen whiskies and two drunken and failed passes at the pretty rep, we headed off to a beach club in Colva. The hotel manager drove us in his jeep, while Kate told all the world she loved them like a sister and then collapsed in the back and had to be driven home by Ruth an hour later. Not the best of examples she could have set and a let off for Ruth who avoided the official warning as a result.

Twenty four hours later though and whisky flavoured sweat is dripping off the end of my nose, my eyes have been red all day long and furry mouth is just about ready to bid its fond farewells, which means I must have looked very professional in front of the 'Billies' today. I am also desperate to discharge a pizza we had for lunch but the toilet is now blocked.

SUNDAY – 1ST NOVEMBER

One of the things that is challenging in Goa is the fact that most Indians don't listen properly. They speak English perfectly well, in fact too perfectly some times and end up devising their own version of English. E.G in our office Prasad came in one day last week and said, "What a terrible journey I have just been having, because of that darned bike I had to stop THRICE!" and on another occasion when I asked him if it was permissible for me to tell an Indian lady that she was attractive he told me, "You have to be careful that she is not being scandalised!"

However, speaking a language is one thing, but understanding it is another and twice today I came a proverbial cropper by people not quite cottoning on to what I was saying.

One of the instances was in the airport, with the aforementioned Prasad who handles our transport there. The departure transfers had run relatively smoothly; the check-in was unbelievably quick and the Immigration Control deliberately slow. For once all of the coaches had turned up at the right places on time and they had also arrived at the airport with plenty of time to spare before the check-in desks opened. Disappointingly we'd only forgotten to pick up four people. Ruth again.

I headed down to the arrivals area and checked the coach numbers with Prasad and then inquired as to what we would do with two passengers who were due to fly to Cochin that morning. Their connecting flight was supposed to depart at 08:30, but because there was an hour's delay on the charter it meant they would miss the connection and so we would have to give them overnight accommodation and they'd fly further south the next morning.

"Prasad." I sleepily muttered.

"Who me?" He always asks this.

"Yes you," I always reply, funnily enough never getting tired of it, "Where do we usually put these guests for the one night?"

"They will go to the Park Plaza." He stated firmly, which was pleasing because it is a good four-star hotel, close to the airport."

"Okay Prasad. And what time will they be picked up tomorrow and what board basis are they booked on?"

"Well, you see" he always says this as well, "they will be picked up at 07:00 but I am not knowing the board basis."

"Can we find out please, so that I can tell them when they come through?"

"Well you see, your company are making the booking so I am not knowing."

"By our company, do you mean our Head Office in England Prasad?"

"I am thinking yes."

"But how can Head Office make the booking if they do not know if the flight is delayed?" which I thought was a logical question.

"Well, you see, I am not making the booking so I am not knowing."

"Prasad" I said taking in a mouthful of air and exhaling slowly, "I understand that you don't make the booking, but I need to know who does and what board basis they have!"

"Well, you see.."

"STOP SAYING 'YOU SEE'" I shouted trying desperately to keep my cool and failing a little seeing as it was six o clock in the morning and I would have much preferred to be in bed, dreaming of Kylie.

"Well, it is your company who make the booking."

"How can they do it if they aren't here?"

"Well, you see…"

"PRASAD!"

"Who me?"

"Yes you!"

"Well, you see, sorry, but you see it is not me making the booking."

"Prasad I know it is not you making the booking." Aargh it's catching, if this conversation had carried on much longer I'd have been be moving my head from side to side in time with Prasad, "It's my company who make the booking, so does that mean I need to do it and we get it billed to you guys, who then get it back from our UK Head Office?"

"Well, you see. Yes I am thinking so."

"Good, so now we need to know if I should book half board" I thought out loud rather than asking Prasad directly.

Well, I am not making the booking!"

"Prasad, I know that, please listen to me. Do you think I need to book half board?"

"Yes, you see I am thinking so."

"Thank you Prasad."

"That's okay. So you know I am not making the booking?"

"PRASAD!" I shouted whilst bursting out with laughter, as Prasad remained almost oblivious to our conversation, seeming to be more intent on getting a cup of tea.

"Who me?"

"Yes you Prasad" I sighed calming down rapidly now and displaying the early signs of schizophrenia which this job seems to induce, "I know you see and I know that you are not making the booking, because I'll do it and I'll book half board as well."

"That is good I am feeling pleased that you understand." And off he sloped to go and grab a cup of tea with the transfer reps, lost in his own world and probably going to have a laugh with the guys about how I don't understand English.

Amazingly the whole of the airport went well this week and before I knew it I was dropping off eighteen guests at the Cidade De Goa. One of the couples had requested room 208, having had that particular room on a couple of previous stays at the hotel, but on checking in they were given room 115. I was called over and before I knew it I was back on my everyday verge of tearing my receding hair out.

"Hi Harris," I said to the receptionist who is quite a good mate of mine," this couple requested room 208 a long while ago and last week Reservations confirmed that it was okay for them to have it. "Is it available please?"

"Well yes, you see," Please not again. Lord give me strength, "but 115 is a better room I think sir."

"That's not really the point Harris. The guests want room 208 because they've had that room before and like its location." I explained patiently, without the slightest trace of hair falling down my forehead and onto the floor yet.

"Okay sir, but 115 has a double bed and 208 only has twin beds."

"But the guests want room 208 Prasad. They are not that bothered about the double bed."

"But 115 is a nice room and has a double bed!" he persisted not really taking in what I had said, because he had this preconceived idea that this couple desperately wanted a double bed.

"Harris," I said, and for the second time before ten in the morning took in a big breath of air, "is room 208 available?"

"But room 208 doesn't have a double bed sir!" he pleaded, with confusion written all over his face.

"Harris, please listen to me," I let out whilst managing to maintain a soothing tone, "is 208 available? Just answer yes or no."

"Well, you see. Yes sir."

"Can the guests have it please?"

"But it doesn't have a double bed!"

"They don't want a double bed! They want 208! Please give them 208!"

"Okay Sir you only had to ask!"

"Thank you Harris" I spluttered and went back to where the guests were sitting to give them the good news.

"Do you think it's possible we could have a double bed this year?" the lady asked.

SATURDAY – 7ᵀᴴ NOVEMBER

After my visit at the Majorda on Tuesday I was already running late. I still had to get back to the Cidade De Goa to drop off some messages and then into the office to collect the girls' liquidation and also have a meeting with Ravi to discuss some possible new excursions. I was really pushed for time and decided to pull back on the throttle even more, not that you get that big a response from a Honda Kinetic, but I needed to take a few chances and started overtaking the slower traffic and squeezing in between cars at any hold-ups.

The larger vehicles certainly do not approve of such impudence and because they have a tendency to overtake on blind corners I found myself being forced off the road twice, narrowly missing pedestrians in one of those instances and leaving some rather deep tyre tracks in the dirt paths by the side of the road.

However, there was one incident, where I had just come over the ridge of a hill and was starting on a downward slope in the first moment of moderately quiet traffic of the day, when a truck, without looking, pulled out of a junction, which was to the right-hand side of me.

I saw him out of the corner of my eye in the distance as I noticed him approaching his T-junction at a pretty hectic speed. I remember thinking that if he doesn't slow down he'll have a head on collision with anyone coming in my opposite direction. I continued to watch my side of the road, paying more attention to the Tata jeep that was blocking my way ahead, when the truck came careering straight through his junction, without slowing down, and it was fortunate that no-one was coming up the hill. He veered right to join my lane and headed straight towards the front end of where my bike was travelling. I caught a brief glimpse of the driver who looked as if he was drunk, with a distinct satanic glaze in eyes, and I had a split second to react before he was going to take me with him into a hedge. I heaved back on the brakes as sharply as I could and heard a deafening squeal from the friction of rubber being scraped along hot tarmac, which was not from me but the truck. The driver was fighting to retain control as he tried to straighten up.

If I'd had time to think I would have prayed that he went into the hedge and severely hurt himself. I've had enough scares with people like him in the past and he'll no doubt kill someone, somewhere along the line, but I was too busy fighting to control my own bike, which was skidding at 60 kilometres per hour and wobbling slightly. I must have gone about 15 metres when I realised that the bike was going to topple and amazingly I had the presence of mind to push myself off the back and landed on my feet, jarring my right heel a little, but for an instant I was upright.

As my bike careered into a deep grassy ditch in front of me, I did a very brief impression of Franz Klammer. I slid along the ground, taking a layer off both of my shoes, before falling backwards and landing on my buttocks, bouncing a couple of times and eventually sliding to a quick stop by the side of the road. Fortunately there were no cars immediately behind me, otherwise I would certainly have been run over, but I was able to get shakily to my feet and watch the truck head off into the distance, oblivious to any of the damage he had caused, and bound, I hoped, for a fatal brush with tarmac himself.

I brushed myself down, still trembling a little, but for some odd reason when it comes to extreme situations I tend to remain very calm; it's usually a day or so later that I get a horrendously frightened reaction. I noticed that there were two big holes in the seat of my trousers, but as always my Marks and Spencer's boxer shorts were perfectly intact.

Luckily enough so was my bike, because all I had to do was spend a couple of minutes taking grass out of it and realign the steering column. It started first time and I was fortunate that my briefcase had been thrown clear and had landed close to the bike perfectly intact, for which I breathed a huge sigh of relief. Once again I had a sizeable amount of company money in there.

I tentatively got on board and nervously rode back towards Panjim at no more than 10 kilometres per hour for the second time this season. Once there I dropped off the reservations at the Cidade De Goa, went home to have a shower and change my trousers and then headed to the office determined to be unrepentant for being late and also wanting to keep this incident quiet because I felt like such a fool.

A fool is what I've been making of myself with Janice recently, because I've been receiving some mixed signals and have therefore been procrastinating as well as Hamlet ever did. We've met at a couple of functions but I haven't grabbed the bull by the horns or seized the day and now I am left in a position of not knowing where I stand and rueing some missed opportunities.

My method of getting it on with women is by using my humour, which being offbeat not everyone understands, but it's a good defence mechanism. It means I can drop in subtle innuendos and test the water comfortably without fear of offending and of course some people get to laugh. Over the years I've become quite realistic about myself and although I'm definitely not ugly, neither am I drop dead, knickers falling, juices flowing, nipples erect gorgeous. I'm about 5'11", medium build, fairly solid with the beginnings of an expanding midriff due to way too many nights on the glycerine and I have been told (not just by my mum) that I have a cute, firm bum. Physically I am nothing remarkable but neither am I offensive to the eye.

Facially, I have a prominent nose, goodish cheekbones, blue eyes when they're not red from the night before, a mop of thinning mousy brown hair, an honest smile and something that is very important to me, good, straight teeth. I would like to think that I am attractive, but judging by the evidence that on only three occasions in my entire life, have I walked into a room and someone has gone, 'Phwooar!' I am not convinced. Especially when you consider that two of those instances were from men.

But this industry does present some wonderful opportunities to be treasured, and this past week I have managed to lay something resembling foundations, which I must build upon. This is why I have just come off the phone from Janice in an effort to do so, because I wasn't too sure where things stood after the past few days and I'm paranoid that because she's such an attractive lady my affections may be usurped.

She was at the function we went to on Tuesday night and because most of us had the following day off we consumed quite a bit of the complimentary booze a little too rapidly. This increased my confidence quite a bit, but I was pleased to see that I was also still relatively compos mentis, so we upped the flirting and introduced some mutual and discreet thigh rubbing and playful, secret knowing winks. But I left that night a deeply frustrated man and very confused, as I'm sure Janice must have been, because I presume I was sending out some odd signals. I was unsure as to whether or not this was going to happen; even less sure about whether or not she took me seriously and I was aching to nibble at her lips and see her naked.

We did spend the following day on the beach, but again there weren't any moments when we could get some peace or privacy, which was mainly my fault, because I was preoccupied with the beach football and body surfing and I think that put a dampener on things. So to rectify matters and renew her interest, as well as feebly test the water, I decided to phone her and pretend to be an Indian ringing up for a date, as some have been known to do.

"Hello," I said whilst wobbling my head and trying desperately to sound like Peter Sellers, but probably becoming even more Welsh, to the amusement of Prasad who was sitting opposite me "is this miss Janice?"

"Yes?" she answered, unsure of who was on the line, but intrigued a little, I felt.

"My name is Ranjit and I was just ringing you to say that I am thinking you are a very beautiful lady, because I am seeing you every day in the street when you walk past my shop and because we were having a nice conversation last night."

"Really." She answered in a completely uninterested tone.

"Yes ma'am. And, I was hoping that you and your friends would like to come to my restaurant one night and be having some food, and drink, and …..Uh, well," and then I paused for what felt like three minutes but was probably just a matter of seconds, before she broke the static and queried very suspiciously, "what was your name again?"

"Ranjit ma'am. And may I say I am thinking you are very beautiful."

"I don't remember speaking to a Ranjit last night, are you sure I know you?"

"Oh yes ma'am. You were talking to me by the exit of the West End nightclub." Which was a bit of a giveaway because she had seen me there when she was in a drunken stupor.

"I'm sorry I don't remember."

"Oh yes ma'am, and I am thinking that we were getting on very well and maybe your friends could be coming with you to my restaurant."

"Who is this?" she demanded quite pointedly in her slight northern brogue.

I couldn't hold the accent any longer, which was degenerating into a Swansea council estate rather than an Indian businessman and burst out laughing down the line.

"Who is this?!?!"

"It's me Jan, Ceri. I'm sorry but I had you there for a minute."

"Yeah, you bastard! But you're the Welshest sounding Indian I've ever heard!" She did know? "So why are you ringing and wasting my time?" getting to the point quicker than I ever will.

I was a little perturbed by her last quite sharp riposte, but thought to hell with it. I decided to take the bull by the horns, throw caution to the wind, spit into the face of my own fear and pee into the wind by testing the water a bit more.

"I just wanted a bit of fun and it was a nice way to get to talk to you and see how you'd react if I asked you out."

"Why don't you just ask me out then, I may just say yes!"

What did she mean by 'May'. Could there be a possibility that she might have said no?

"Well, I just might do that next time!" I asserted trying to be strong.

"Well why don't you?"

"I think I will!"

"Well go on then!"

"Okay I will!"

Yes,yes,yes,yes,yes,yes,yes,yes,yes,yes. This is mother India to ground control. WE HAVE CONTACT!!

'BRRRING.....BRRRRING' – Other bloody line!

"Jan I've got to go, that's the international line. Call you later. Bye."

"Bye."

Stupid! Stupidy! Stupidest!

MONDAY – 9TH NOVEMBER

I'd just mustered up the courage to say hello to an attractive Scandinavian rep, who was sat in the reception area of one of my hotels when I received a phone call from Kate. She asked if I could go to the SJM, which was having its first load of arrivals this week. She also asked if I would assist Ruth with her welcome meeting, because she'd rung Kate earlier and said that there was the possibility of a riot amongst our guests. We both knew she was dramatising the fact that one person had probably complained to her on her way out of there in the morning, but I had to go, to be on the safe side and to make sure she didn't do any further damage.

Her meeting was scheduled for 12:00 but the earliest I could get there was a quarter past. However, I was very disappointed to turn into the road leading to the hotel to find Ruth was only a matter of seconds ahead of me. She had a pair of sandals on instead of regulation blue court shoes, her blouse was dishevelled and hanging out and she wasn't wearing her helmet, which is now company policy. It wasn't the ideal first impression she could have created with some distressed guests, to say the least.

I walked in with her and I told her to get the meeting set up and start it and I'd go and have a chat with the manager to see what was wrong and also see what we could get done ahead of the other tour operators. I also told her that if there was anyone who had a major complaint to send them down to me and I would do what I possibly could for them, but that she had to do the meeting. There was no way that she was going to get out of doing this meeting, and difficult as it may be, this is the best way to learn, plus it really distinguishes the wheat from the chaff in the quality of representatives. Besides, whenever I had bigger problems than this in my first couple of years, I didn't go running for help, I just put up with it, did the best I could, and kept smiling. I would have been lambasted at the very thought of asking for help. I went downstairs and introduced myself to the manager and no sooner had we sat down than Ruth came running into the room, in a state of panic, flapping so hard she was almost on the ceiling, saying the guests were rioting and could I help.

I went upstairs to the meeting room to see the guests and out of twenty-two couples, only two rooms had major complaints, the rest just wanted Ruth to hold a welcome meeting. A few of them were standing up which didn't help their mood, so I arranged for more chairs to be sent up together with some soft drinks, which helped relax things a bit and started dealing with a couple of individual complaints.

I won't deny there are problems in the SJM because the whole complex is not organised and was not ready for over 120 guests to suddenly arrive on the first Sunday of their operation, but Ruth had grossly overstated the severity of it all with her drama queen flapping and had exacerbated the whole situation.

The main problems in the hotel were very long waiting periods for food in the restaurant; food not being covered; incompetent, albeit pleasant, waiters; no organisation at the outdoor buffet when it rained; not enough seating; not enough sun beds; general public areas being dirty; some light building work to the side of the complex was still going on (which they had been informed about beforehand) and a highly incompetent reception. The rooms though were fine, apart from a few insects, which because it had just rained and after all we are in India, is only natural and was nothing a few mosquito coils couldn't solve.

I took all of the information down from the guests, then left Ruth to do the meeting, which is what the guests had asked for, and went downstairs to speak to the manager to see what we could do. After thirty minutes he had promised to operate the buffet inside, cover all the food, provide extra fruit for breakfast, supply extra seating and sun beds, replace the front office staff (who were waiters filling in) within three days, put mosquito coils in the rooms together with a complimentary bottle of wine for the inconvenience. Plus he'd agreed to move everyone free of charge to a sister hotel in the north of Goa or refund their half board allowance if they were still not happy.

I was pleased with the initial response and impressed that with a little calm persuasion the guy was actually taking responsibility, although it still remained to be seen if any of the above would be achieved. But just as we were agreeing this Ruth came back down again in an even bigger state than before and if she'd have been flapping any more she would have been able to make her way back to Britain. I honestly don't know how she did it but within the space of thirty minutes, the guests had gone from looking forward to a welcome meeting and wanting to get on with their holidays, to her doing the sales bit of the meeting and every single one of them wanting to leave. She has an unusual talent for making matters worse and judging by her performance so far, she is a liability and I now don't give her much more than a month.

I eventually left the hotel at 16:00, tired, hungry and sweaty and headed back to Panjim on the bike again, this time having only the two near misses. Once I was in the office I got on the phone to the big cheese in charge of the hotel to try and prevent this happening again. Kate assisted and she spoke to him later on, when he rang back to say that he would cover the cost of a move if any of our guests wanted to move to the Dona Santa Maria, which is a higher standard of hotel. I then had to pass all the responsibility of the SJM to Kate for the evening, although having said that she's the boss and I was just helping her and Ruth out, while I went to the Cidade for my evening visit.

I had time to rush home for a shower and a quick sandwich at 17:00 only to find the water was switched off again and the restaurant was closed.

This just goes to show what a Mickey Mouse piece of crap they give us to live in, and still expect us to keep smiling and pretend that our company is the best in the world. Instead I grabbed my gym bag, remained sweaty and headed to the Cidade an hour early, so that I could grab a sandwich before my duties were due to start.

Not a chance! As I walked into the hotel with plenty of time to spare, I found two guests who just wanted a chat sitting in the lobby waiting for me. I had no option but to join them, despite the growls of protest from my stomach and I sat down and politely answered all of the questions about what it's like to be a rep, that I've answered a thousand times before. I did manage to drop in a question about why they were there in the lobby so early seeing as my visit didn't start until 18:30.

"Oh we know that," they replied, "But we know you like to get here early so we thought we'd come and sit with you." This confirmed my suspicions that they were to be the winners of this season's Mr and Mrs Dreary award.

Everywhere you go in the world, somewhere along the line there will be a Mr and Mrs Dreary, who have no social skills, no outgoing nature, but are intensely nosey and have no understanding of any one else's opinions or beliefs but their own. These people can make a rep's life hell, because they idolise you and because you're the first person to talk to them since their last holiday, you're automatically smothered and labelled as their best friend. As a result they dominate all of your time, they monitor everything you do, talk to every other guest about you as if they happen to be family out on holiday and they turn up at odd places where you least expect them. You get one couple like this every season and you pray that they are not on an extended holiday of three months, which has been known to happen in the SAGA type programs. Fortunately this couple is here for just the fortnight.

I was rescued after an hour and a half by another guest wanting to book and pay for some trips, which was a welcome relief. The rest of the visit went by very quickly as more guests came over to book more trips and I ended up collecting about a thousand pounds in that visit, but all the time I could feel Mr and Mrs Dreary staring at me from across the room.

After my official duties had finished and I saw the dreaded couple head downstairs for dinner I headed into the gym for a quick leg workout. To finish off I hopped onto the treadmill and quickly settled into a nice easy rhythm at 13 kmph when all of a sudden it stopped, only the lights were still glowing on the machine, so it couldn't have fused.

One of the gym instructors had switched it off because there was a call for me from Guest Relations. I begrudgingly made my way to the foyer of the sports centre, muttering sweet expletives under my breath all the way and then panted, "Hello" into the phone only to find that Mr and Mrs Dreary wanted to see me in the lobby, because they had decided they wanted to book an excursion. I should have left the hotel forty-five minutes ago and I'd already spent an hour and a half with them, so why in the hell couldn't they book it earlier and why decide what they want to book at this juncture. I bet it's a hoax.

I entered the lobby, soaking wet with sweat, wearing my 'I'M NOT ENGLISH, I'M WELSH' T-shirt only for them to have forgotten their money, but could we meet up on Tuesday instead.

Bastards.

TUESDAY – 10TH NOVEMBER

One of the constants you find working in travel is that it is all about people. No matter how advanced booking techniques become or how slick the brochures and marketing drives develop, the one key factor that will never be taken away is how people behave when they are on holiday. It is not only the guest's behaviour, but also the performance of the reps and the hotel staff, because people are what make the difference.

Tour operators have looked at cutting their costs in the past, by minimizing the role of reps or even trying to do away with them altogether. But they've found it impossible because the majority of guests need the security of having a rep around, because if we do our job well, we're the friendly face who can make a difference in a strange land.

Also the guests make the job interesting for us and it's an old cliché, but no two days are ever the same, because different guests react in different ways to different situations. This keeps us on our toes and helps our character develop because we are always learning something new. Therefore it is only right that I should demonstrate how contrary people can be and how they respond in various ways by illustrating the two principle situations that occurred to me today.

As soon as I walked into the lobby of the Majorda Beach I was 'collared' by a young couple. Actually collared is the wrong word because the guests in question are actually a very pleasant couple and are a pleasure to see each day, unlike The Mr and Mrs Dreary's of this world. They only arrived two days ago and are on their first holiday for three years. They also have a delightful 17-month-old daughter, who is a bundle of smiling energy and they're enjoying every single moment of their stay in the same way a child savours all of Christmas morning. However, that mood has changed overnight because they received bad news in the early hours of the morning, when the lady was told that her mother had passed away. These are moments where we earn our money, because these people are in a distant shore and need professional assistance and sometimes, more often if they're on their own, emotional strength as well.

I sat down with the young couple and first of all let them explain what had happened, because I find it usually helps them if they can speak to someone other than their family. I then explained to them their options and what we could do.

They obviously want to get home as soon as possible and I explained that there are two ways of getting back to the UK and both methods would involve getting in touch with their insurers. I explained that we would do most of the initial work with their insurance company, but eventually the insurers would want to deal with the guests personally, however, for now we would send off all of the relevant information from our office and do most of the chasing up to boot.

The ways in which they can return home are either on one of the direct charter flights this coming Friday, for which I know there are plenty of seats available. Otherwise they can travel on a schedule flight, which would entail going via Delhi or Bombay, possibly staying overnight en route and embarking on a direct flight a day later to the UK. This means that if they were to leave on the Wednesday they probably wouldn't get home until the Friday morning, whereas if they were to take a charter flight on a Friday morning they would get back the same evening, and into their original airport. It was also possible for them to buy their own flight seats and travel that day, but that would have entailed forking out over £1200 for the three of them and then going through the rigmarole of recovering this from their insurers in the UK.

Because there wasn't a lot they could do in the UK at that very moment and also because they had to consider their daughter, who was entitled to some semblance of a holiday and not an arduous journey home, they asked me to get in touch with their insurers and try to get a flight for the coming Friday.

I took down all their insurance policy details and then again further details of what had happened, including her mother's name, age, address, next of kin, cause of death, treating hospital and GP. I then clarified for them the process over the next few days. We would make up an insurance file in our office, then fax all of the details over to the couple's insurers, who would in turn make up their own file, contact the next of kin to verify the death – it's amazing some of the excuses some people will make to try and get a free flight home a week early – and also contact the treating doctor to verify the cause of the death, to ensure that it wasn't a pre-existing illness, which some insurance companies can be difficult about. Finally the insurers would then check their contacts to book the next available flight seats, which would most likely be on the coming weekend and that as soon as anything was arranged or if they had any further questions they would contact either the guests direct or us in the office.

I didn't expect the insurers to come back that same day so told the family to go out and try and enjoy the rest of the day, for their own sake as much as their daughters. Then as soon as we had heard anything I would be in touch right away. I also gave them our office phone number, the number of the Ranch and my mobile number so they could get hold of me at anytime.

I have to say that difficult though it is, I really enjoy this aspect of the job. This is partially because the adrenaline flows a little and I really get involved with my work but also because I actually feel as if I'm genuinely helping someone and I feel that what I'm doing is something worthwhile. It is so much easier however, when you're dealing with such wonderful people like this lovely family, who actually told me not to go to too much trouble. They shook my hand, thanked me for my help and for listening and I headed back towards Panjim feeling motivated and stronger because of their selflessness and courage.

But what a difference a couple of hours can make.

As I walked into the Cidade De Goa reception, after another painful liquidation session, I was met by a blond haired, moderately attractive, middle aged lady with the reddest face I'd seen in ages. She wanted to complain about the boat trip from which she'd just returned.

The day gives them the opportunity to spot a few Dolphins, before heading to a nearby deserted island where the guests have the option of soaking up the sun and topping up their tans, or doing a spot of fishing or snorkelling. A BBQ lunch is included and the guests are then left alone for an hour or two to snorkel by the shore or enjoy the pleasure of the soft white sands and the peace and quiet of a beach without being bothered by any beach sellers. I sell the trip on the strength of the sun and the fun, but this lady was complaining that the sun was too hot, the boat ride was too long and that there were no umbrellas on the deserted beach.

I gathered from the redness in her cheeks, the slightly slurred words and mildly offensive odour emitting from her mouth that she'd had a Gin or two for Dutch courage, as well as the fact that she repeated these same three points over and again for forty minutes before asking for a full refund. I'd obviously have to see what the response was like from the other dozen or so couples I had on the trip, who she said were on the verge of rioting, but seeing as we'd given her everything I had said we would, I couldn't see us giving her any form of a refund.

I didn't want to tell her this right now though, because due to her aggressive state, I was worried about what she may do and whether or not I would be able to get rid of her and get out for the evening. I opted to avoid any form of confrontation if at all possible, so promised her that I would speak to our supplier who runs the boat trip, would do everything that I could for her and I would get back to her on Thursday.

"Why won't you get back to me tomorrow?" she asked and I truthfully replied that it was my day off and that I would be out of town.

"Well I never!" she stormed, spluttering a bit of gin over my tie and leaving an odd dribble on her chin, "That is quite frankfully disgusting! You should be available for me 24 hours a day!"

I ignored her mispronunciation of frankly and the deadly accurate sprays of used alcohol and decided not to answer that. I then took a couple of not so discreet deep breaths and promised again, in my calmer than calm voice, that I would see her on Thursday and that I would do everything I could for her. Unfortunately my honest eyes remained true and I beseeched upon all of the Hindu gods, that she couldn't see through her haze and decipher the big bold letters that outlined 'STUPID BITCH' in the forefront of my silent mind.

She eventually left threatening to sue the company, lose me my job and she shouted at all the staring people, who had now gathered at a safe distance, to stop gawking at her. If I meet many more people like her it would be no great loss if I lost my job. I couldn't believe that in the same day I had come across one tremendous couple who were so calm and brave in very difficult circumstances and then, one obviously sexually frustrated middle aged woman, who more than overreacted about getting mostly what she had booked and paid £16 for. It's amazing how different some people can be.

After escaping from the irate lady and speaking to a few others who were on the day out, who incidentally thought it was fantastic, I made it back into the office with Kate. We chased the insurance company to find out that they were dealing with the matter and that things were in hand, which I instantly relayed to my nicer insurance couple from the Majorda beach.

We eventually left just after 21:30 and although both of us were cream crackered we were still determined to enjoy ourselves and have a laugh at another function. This time it was at a new nightclub that was opening up called Michelangelo's, which was having a party for all of the reps in the hope that we would send a lot of business their way. Actually I was more determined to make some headway with Janice for a change and I was hoping that an earlier phone call we'd had, combined with my lucky boxers and lucky aftershave, might help change my fortunes for the better.
The phone call was from when I was in the office and before the girls had arrived to torture me with their mess and disorganisation. This time I decided to pretend to be Hugh Grant asking her out in the same manner as when he tells Andie MacDowell that he loves her in 'Four Weddings and a Funeral'.

"Hi. Uh Janice, it's me. Oh Bugger! Ooops sorry, I was just calling, to uhhm say, well that is, I was thinking if it was, maybe, possible, if we could, uhhm bugger, no rather daft of me, but what the hell, maybe we could sort of, we could, would you? I can understand why not if you don't want to, but in the words of George Peppard to Katherine Hepburn in 'Breakfast at Tiffanys' shall we go out some time?

Oh, Well.

Bugger!

Bugger!

Sorry! Silly of me to presume. Stupid to even think of it. Forget I even mentioned it! Sorry. Stupid, stupid, stupid, bugger!

Well, important to have said it don't you think?"

"Bravo" she screamed, "Of course I will!"

"Oh, well never mind then." I said dejectedly, having not really listened to what she'd said because I was still admiring myself at my amazingly believable Hugh Grant, "but I promise I'll try again and keep trying until I break you!"

"I SAID YES!" She insisted.

"Well maybe I'll see you later at Michelangelo's then?"

"Yes, I'll look forward to it!"

"Bye"

"Bye"

At last a modicum of courage from the Welshman and thank you Hugh, works every time.

As people who know me can testify, there are times when I can be supremely confident and if I put my mind to it charming, so this evening I started off in that vein, making a big effort to make Janice feel a little bit special. We had a lot of flirtatious chats combined with some sensual arm rubbing and cheek touching, yet I also, and possibly mistakenly, tried to remain cool and a little aloof by chatting to quite a few of the other girls who were there. I misguidedly wanted to keep my options open if Janice were to reject me, plus I wanted her to chase me a little.

But as the evening, and the complimentary drinks wore on I found the effects of a long and emotionally draining day starting to take effect and I ended up becoming more tired and irritated. As this was happening and I started to lose my composure and confidence, the other reps were all becoming more and more squiffy and they were all starting to pair up, which pushed Janice and me together even more.

This should have been ideal, but because I felt we were being forced together and because the whisky had now decided to introduce me to my old friend paranoia, I suddenly thought that everyone was watching us and seeing if I was going to make a move or not. Again I ran through all the reasons in my mind about why I don't like to make a play for someone in public and instead of encouraging myself, I kept on being reminded that my valued private life may be jeopardised; that I could be rejected in public and thus humiliated beyond a season's repair. Plus I still didn't want to ruin my chances with any of the other girls.

On about three separate occasions throughout the course of the evening I tried to ask her out or to make some positive move, but each time, someone would butt in just as I'd get past the first word or otherwise I would feel a couple of pairs of eyes burning into me. Because I was tired, this made me more and more annoyed and frustrated, and I could sense that there was no way that I was going to do this coolly and could probably see myself blurting out something really loud and stupid, just at a point where the music gets switched off. So I backed off even more and played even dumber, much to Janice's chagrin, which was obvious the following day.

The party finished at 03:00 and as the rest of the reps headed off in search of more parties, Janice and I went our separate ways, with me by now in a foul mood, annoyed at my own record high levels of procrastination and decided to drink myself into depression.

Not only is it amazing how different the guests can be in one day, it's also amazing how different I can be in the space of twenty four hours, ranging from confident and in control in grave circumstances to a nervous, frightened wreck when it comes to asking out a girl I know already likes me.

WEDNESDAY – 11TH NOVEMBER

Ceri Stone Stupid Twat!!

THURSDAY – 12TH NOVEMBER

"I have to say that I'm absolutely disgusted!! You are the worst rep I have ever come across and I'm going to make sure you lose your job for this. AND I'm going to sue your company, and I'm contacting Watchdog and, and, and THE SUN!" stammered sexually frustrated middle-aged lady, all in one exasperating and agitated breath.

This outburst has stemmed from my chat with her on Tuesday, when she complained about the 'Castaway' trip and at the same time asked to cancel one of the other excursions that she had previously booked.

As a result of my promises to her I did actually speak to the guy who runs the boat trip and also Ravi at the same time. This was more by chance than skilled planning, because the supplier had popped into our office earlier on in the day to tell us all what a great success the whole trip had been and how he liked me so much for getting so many people on it.

Anyway, I went through the points that the lady had over-heatedly mentioned and Lyndon explained that the only problem he was aware of was that some of the snorkels were leaking but no one had complained about that and that everything else had gone swimmingly. By chance he also had a bundle of questionnaires from the day out, of which it turned out that there were almost fifty people on board and every form that was handed back in, except for sexually frustrated middle aged woman's, had said that the day was excellent. However, as a goodwill gesture they both agreed that we could offer a complimentary day trip from our programme, so that she wouldn't go round the hotel bad mouthing us and possibly ruining our sales figures.

When I saw her this evening I gave her the refund for the 'Crocs and Spice' that she'd cancelled and then explained that I couldn't give her a refund for the 'Castaway' trip, because she had been given everything that I'd sold her and that everyone else had had a wonderful time. We would however, offer her a complimentary day trip, which as I said it I knew was futile. Her jaw dropped, her face reddened and a tiny bit of gin dribbled out of the side of her mouth as her cheek muscles tightened and she looked as if she was about to lose control.

"That's a disgrace! I didn't enjoy it and I want a full refund and you're lying when you say everyone else enjoyed it because they didn't!!"

Now, generally I'm a very reasonable and tolerant guy, but if there is one thing above all others that will really wind me up, it's being called a liar. I have been known to exaggerate in the past, especially if it's in my best interests with a woman, but ever since I have grown up I have never knowingly told a lie. I have always refused to, often to my own personal detriment and I have no intention of doing so in the future.

"I'm sorry that you feel that way, but I assure you that I will always tell the truth and I have no reason to lie to you! I'm also sorry that you didn't enjoy the trip, because I want everyone to leave Goa loving it as much as I do, but we have given you everything that was promised at the end of the day, plus we are also offering you a free trip of your choice. If you're unhappy with this you can take it up with us in the UK, although I expect them to give you the same response because they will be reading my report after all. Also with regards to paying you this money as some form of compensation I can only say that we as a company do not give out compensation in resort, so I'm afraid I can't really help you any further."

"Well you've got to give me the money back! I'm not happy!"

At this stage I'd much prefer to write down a well considered argument from the lady and also some well thought out and persuading ripostes from myself, whereby we both go away happy and I look great. However, when people are flustered and in moments of confrontation, most forms of logical thought pattern disappear and blubbering idiots take over. I suppose I am the better out of the two of us, which is down to years of practice and preparation, but there is a tendency to patronise or speak almost robotically, plus she was beginning to wind me up, because she wouldn't listen. Ultimately there was no way that either of us was going to be happy with the outcome.

"I'm sorry, but as I just explained it is not company policy to give out compensation in resort. The reason we don't is because our holidays are much more expensive than most of your run of the mill tour operators and with our guests spending an average of more than £1500 per person on a holiday, that would mean an average compensation payment of over £500, which is too high an amount for us to decide upon in resort. Now I know this case is only for an amount of £32, but if we pay a small amount out in resort, then that will gradually increase and we may eventually leave ourselves in a position where complete novices pay out amounts which are detrimental to the company's position. So I'm very sorry but I am simply unable to give you the money back for the trip and I'm sorry you didn't enjoy it when forty eight other people did."

I explained all of this in a soft, calm and yet hopefully assured voice. This is something I have developed over the years and is probably as false as Paul Daniel's hair, but it should mean that the guests will listen to what I am saying and understand my point of view. However, it was never going to be the case with this lady who wanted either her money back or a fight. She tossed a few expletives in my direction, to which I sarcastically commended her command of the English language and she stormed off again promising to lose me my job and call her good friend Anne Robinson, all for £32 she didn't deserve.

The only good point about meeting her in the last couple of days is that she kept Mr and Mrs Dreary away from me. Not surprisingly they had been watching everything with glee from a distance and as soon as she had left they came running over to sit with me with a glass of much needed beer, which I'm not allowed to drink on duty. However I gratefully had a few sips as Mrs Dreary screeched, "Oh what a horrible lady! Don't you worry Ceri, we'll make sure you're okay!"

I wanted to scream that I was thirty-one years old and big enough and ugly enough to look after myself, and sensible enough to realise that I didn't have to worry about this woman, because moments like this are part and parcel of the job. But professionalism kicked in and I spent a boring thirty-five minutes being entertained by the Dreary's.

Funnily enough, although what I explained to my red faced, gin dribbling woman was in fact the truth, I don't actually agree with it. In this heightened age of customer service, we should be paying out compensation in resort up to an agreed level, to which the reps or resort managers can be trusted.

So, not only did I finish my working day pissed off at having to deal with sexually frustrated middle aged woman, I was equally as frustrated as she was at my own company's lack of professionalism and my inability to provide the perfect service. Plus this was on top of the complete apathy of the insurance company dealing with my lovely couple in the Majorda Beach. Now I'd made and received a few calls from the insurers on the beach on my day off, and today Kate and I had spoken to them at least half a dozen times in an effort to try and get the couple a flight booked for Friday, but they appear to have their fingers wedged firmly up their posteriors, because they still haven't bothered to contact the deceased's GP yet to verify the death. This means that there is little or no hope of them getting a flight home on Friday and they'll be walking a fine line in arranging one for the rest of the weekend.

This is obviously distressing for such a lovely couple and also frustrating for me. In the past I have been able to arrange flights back to the UK within 12 hours when I have been dealing with a competent insurer, which to be fair most of them are. But every now and then we come across a bunch of young kids on the phones, who don't treat an emergency situation as such and the effect this can have on some of their policyholders, and our guests, can be catastrophic.

As a result I was unable to give any good news to the couple, who are still being amazingly brave but I feel are now on the verge of breaking down in front of their daughter. Not only do they not know what is happening, but they are also unable to tell their family of their arrangements, which is having a knock-on effect with their family in the UK and adding to their woes. I'd like to do much more for the guests, but short of constantly ringing the insurers there isn't much else we can do, except sit tight and wait. I have questioned myself constantly again, about whether or not I am doing enough for them and did I do everything correctly in the first place, but as Kate assured me over dinner, I couldn't have done more.

If I have many more days like this I don't think I'll be doing any more seasons, because I don't like having to give bad news or even provide, what appears to me, to be a less than professional service. Plus I still haven't had the guts to so much as kiss Janice.

Maybe it wouldn't be too bad after all if sexually frustrated middle-aged woman did lose me my job.

FRIDAY – 13TH NOVEMBER

I HAD SEX!!

Yes, yes, yes, yes,yes,yes. I HAD SEX! And not with myself but a real woman. A real, beautiful, fun and attractive woman. Exactly 50 days after arriving in Goa and on Friday the 13th, I had sex. At Last!

For such a supposedly unlucky day, pretty much everything seemed to go right for me, both work wise and socially. Our Friday morning charter flight is now up and running, but because we only have about fifty seats on the flight, not all of the team need to go to the airport, so this week I had a nice quiet morning covering the office, answering the odd phone call, pushing paper from one side of the desk to the other and playing practical jokes on the office girls. Also it gave me time to chase the insurance company as well and we have some promising news at last.

The insurers have finally completed all of their background checks and confirmed the claim is genuine and have agreed to fly the guests home this weekend. They were initially looking at sending them back via Bombay on one of those hideously long, roundabout journeys, but I told them that there were quite a few seats available on the charter flights this coming weekend. So they went away to make a few phone calls and by 14:00 they had rung me back in the office to confirm that a flight had been booked for

Sunday, on our Monarch charter, and could we issue the tickets. This meant that for once I had some good news to give to our lovely couple who are still amazing me with their bravery and have managed to almost continuously put on a joyful front for their daughter.

I even managed to get a couple of hour's siesta in the afternoon, because thanks to Kate, the office was spotlessly organised and in the Cidade later on I was also spared the attentions of Mr and Mrs Dreary and the abuse of sexually frustrated middle aged woman. I had a session in the gym after work and a glass of the Bahrain wine at The Ranch, which put me in an ebullient mood and because I'd had such a good day I was becoming a little hyperactive and fairly confident in myself. Dinner with Kate and a few beers only served to heighten our sense of euphoria and we headed off to a nightclub called 'Up North' in the mood for a party.

This is another nightclub, which was having another opening party and it is designed in a similar fashion to Tito's, in that it is outdoors, plays great music, has a great mix of tourists, Bombay boys, reps and hippies all having copious amounts of cheap alcohol through to the early hours of the morning.

I had a few more Kingfishers and my Jim Carrey mood, of over-acting and making a complete arse of myself, came into full swing and I proceeded to dance like an epileptic nerd and walked into trees.

All the while I was becoming more and more tactile with Janice, who we had joined up with after dinner, by holding her hand occasionally, slipping my arm around her tender waist whilst we spoke and gently kissing her on the neck.

She had confided to Kate that she didn't know where she stood with me. She can never differentiate between the serious and the stupid and whether or not I was being genuine with her, so I had a few more beers to boost my confidence and had every intention of showing her how serious I was about her.

As the evening wore on we became more and more attached, drifting away from the others into the throng of sweaty bodies on the dance floor. We danced, with me not acting so stupid for a few minutes, and as the music seemed to slow so did we until we moved almost as one and I eventually had my arm around her waist, our hips were locked and my free hand was running through her soft, blond hair.

Our eyes locked and our faces moved closer as my temperature rose and my heart pounded harder and faster by the second. My John Thomas was screaming at me in the nether regions of my lucky boxer shorts to frantically rub up against her, but I stayed cool and resisted. Instead we gently let our cheeks caress before I softly kissed her behind the ear as she blew on the back of my neck, making the hairs stand to attention, almost as much as I was downstairs.

Janice's hair fell lightly over her face and onto mine adding an air of mystery, before we gradually and tenderly kissed. For a few moments we were oblivious to everyone around us, my anxieties had been washed away in a sea of deliriousness and we lost each other in our lips and lightly exploring tongues.

We eventually pulled apart and she cheekily nibbled my top lip as I ran my hands from her waist, up her body, momentarily skirting her breasts and softly over her neck and through her hair and then we locked eyes. We both smiled and already knew what was going to happen tonight, before we kissed again.

I wish I could say that later on, back at Janice's apartment, we made love like movie stars, but unfortunately real life doesn't work like that. After sneaking out of the nightclub, having neglected to tell anyone that we were going, we grabbed a cab off the street and almost immediately found ourselves in her bedroom.

We sat on the edge of her neatly made bed and kissed some more, stroked a lot more and fondled the edges of our erogenous zones, before I had to get up and make my excuses.

"What is it?" she asked "I thought we were getting along really well?"

"We are" I replied hopping from one leg to the other rather nervously, "But I desperately need to go."

"But why? You made such a big effort to get me here and now you want to leave?" She was almost pleading, which was quite sweet, or would have been if it weren't for the burning sensation shooting through my groin.

"I do have to go Janice" I said a bit too forcefully, "But not home. To the bloody loo because I think I drank a bit too much earlier on."

"Ahh, alright then, it's the door on the left." She breathed a huge sigh of relief and as I dashed in, also trying to suppress a fart, I heard her whisper to herself, "but not *too* much to drink. I hope."

Ordinarily I would have thought me too, but I was too engrossed in trying not to fall asleep over the toilet as I was peeing and I also hoped that she didn't hear the fart I let out as I closed the door.

After what seemed to be an age waiting for the smell to die down, I rejoined her in the semi darkness, thankful that the mood hadn't been killed and we stood and resumed the tenderness of feeling our lips against each other's. I raised her blouse to reveal her olive skinned, naked upper half and marvelled at her slim waist and small firm breasts which were standing upright, almost pleading with me to stroke them in the moonlight. Whilst kissing her and teasing her breasts I slipped off her skirt to a delighted little groan and she pulled off my shirt and I stepped out of my jeans and boxer shorts, just about managing not to trip over and then gently eased her onto the bed.

There was a lot more kissing and subtle fondling as our temperatures rose and a warm sensation engulfed my chest and shoulders, with the realisation that I was with somebody potentially special. I moved my hand down past her waist and teased her inner thighs as she prepared to welcome my fingers. I skirted around her triangle before moving my hand into her and stroking her warmth. She was so aroused and we moved in time with each other, like two dancers at the Royal ballet lost in a cloud of mist. Janice was so worked up and almost pleading with me to enter her, she locked her arm around me and tugged me over and I gently rolled onto her and lay in the press up position above her, ready for us to become one.

But as I regretfully mentioned real life doesn't allow us to act like movie stars and down below I was suffering the after effects of three glasses of wine, four whiskies and eight pints of beer. As a result, I'd gone to sleep.

I started screaming inside my head, which was rapidly becoming engulfed with furry mouth syndrome as I started to sober up at the realisation of what was happening and I couldn't help but reflect that if I were in the movies, I would be supremely erect and would be giving Janice the time of her life.

But when you look at it a lot of the things they do in the movies just don't seem possible because they make love in so many ways. Be it running up to Sharon Stone, pressing her against a wall and sliding straight in from behind as was the case in Sliver, which is nigh on impossible unless you work in a circus. Or even the romantic meeting of bodies, which should be happening right now, like Mel Gibson and Michelle Pfeiffer in Tequila Sunrise, when they were able to go at it for twenty-four hours and move with the grace of two ice dancers to the sounds of Ravels Bolero. As I was finding out to my detriment, real life isn't like that and although the alcohol was giving me courage and a great imagination it wasn't giving me any strength.

In the actual world of regular human beings we fumble, are sometimes ungraceful, come too quickly, make fanny and belly farts or, in the current circumstances suffer the after-effects of over-consumption, where no amount of stroking, prodding, kissing or persuading of any form will help.

"I'm sorry Jan" I slurred, suddenly realising how drunk I was "Ish really am shorry. Itsh not yoush, becosh your special, but I don' think Ish can do it."

"Why, what's happening. Don't I attract you?"

"O heavensh yesh. But itsh me. Not you. I'm shorry."

And so ensued a twenty-minute conversation, with two naked people sprawled drunkenly across a bed, each trying to reassure the other.

Janice couldn't understand that it was all my fault and she was still blaming herself for not being attractive enough for me, which was most definitely not the problem. Eventually she deteriorated into being pissed off at the gibbering idiot who was lying next to her continuously muttering, "shorry."

I drifted off, into a guilt-ridden sleep, which was interspersed frequently with dreams of people standing outside her window laughing at me until I awoke at 06:30. This happens every time I am with someone, I always wake up very early and as always I had furry mouth syndrome, bleary eyes and a dodgy stomach, but also to my delight, a beautiful, naked lady who was beside me and smiling at a very prominent statement from between my legs.

For the next hour and a half we copulated like movie stars to erase the anxieties of the previous night, except for the moment when we were cuddling in the midst of a light-headed afterglow and I farted.

"Shorry" I said.

SATURDAY – 14TH NOVEMBER

Sitting in the office it was an uphill struggle to keep my eyes open and concentrate on my work, which was an incessant stream of phone calls from guests with queries on the following morning's flight. I was tired from the night before, my head was pounding and I was fighting a losing battle to concentrate as Kate walked in a couple of hours late. She had a big toothy grin on her over made-up face, which meant that she too was feeling rough but was able to disguise it with make-up. Her long, tight curled hair was bouncing with every step and as she reached the top of the stairs, to walk into a crowded work area, she took one look at me and boomed, "You had sex last night Mr Ceri. Didn't you?"

Cheers Kate, subtle as a brick as always. I duly pretended to be talking on the phone and feebly denied any knowledge of what she was talking about, as Prasad and the rest of the boys giggled and the girls turned their heads away and blushed. It was a bit of a faux pas on Kate's behalf to say something like that in front of them.

She sat down in front of me and asked for all the details and I duly gave her all the information about the following morning's flight for our couple in the Majorda Beach, as a weak attempt at letting her know that I can be discreet on the odd occasion.

"Are you going to tell me anything?" She asked about half an hour before lunch, to which I replied in the negative.

"Okay then, I'll ask Janice for all the juicy details, because I'm having lunch with her in a minute." And she packed up her things after having completed a sturdy forty-five minutes worth of work and disappeared for an extended lunch break.

I tried to get out of the office before she returned to avoid any more questioning, but she passed me at the front door with a huge grin on her face, gave me a big wink and said that a little bird might be falling for me. I mumbled some blasé, couldn't care less type response and headed down to the Majorda beach to give our insurance couple their flight tickets and say goodbye to them.

TUESDAY – 17TH NOVEMBER

The Santa Jose Maria, more familiarly known as the SJM, has been the bane of our working lives in recent weeks and because Ruth has struggled with it, Kate has decided that I'm the man for the job and will have to look after it from Thursday.

I'm not too bothered because it will give me some extra work to do, which will keep me out of the office, plus I should be able to earn myself some extra commission and there's the added bonus of an attractive rep called Gina, who spends most of her working day there. It is a bit of a nuisance that I'm doing Ruth's work for her, but as Kate pointed out the overall performance of the resort is what counts. This morning was therefore spent familiarising myself with the hotel, so that I will know it inside out before I'm asked any questions and at the same time I was asked to check up on our other principal concern of the moment: Ruth.

Kate, to her credit, and the detriment of other team members, has been spending a lot of time with Ruth, trying to help her get organised and explaining the importance of fulfilling her role correctly and professionally, but Ruth who has an answer for everything, merely says what she thinks we want to hear and then as soon as our backs are turned returns to her haphazard ways of chaotic bungling.

I think that Kate has been too soft, which could send out signals to Sharon and Lester that they too could be this lackadaisical, but thankfully they've been excellent. Anyway it's very easy for me to say this when it's not me who has to dish out the disciplinary action.

However, I wanted to present Ruth with a flight ticket home and her P45 when I popped into the Leela Palace to check on her information book at the tail end of the morning. Firstly I was surprised to see her in the hotel itself, and in T-shirt and shorts, when she should have been in uniform and visiting guests in the Holiday Inn. When I asked her what she was doing, she said that she was delivering a message to some guests, even though she'd been in this hotel for an hour earlier on in the morning. She quickly disappeared before I could ask her about her uniform.

Secondly, I was dismayed to find out that she hadn't even bothered to complete an information book for the hotel. When you take into account the ten days or so I had putting up with Janet's moans about India and rubbing my fingers raw from putting in postcards and completing a dozen of them myself it is especially annoying. I find it impossible to believe that she's been so busy that she's not had the time to do two measly books and for me this was the proverbial straw that was breaking the camel's back. I discussed this with Kate, feeling like a 'tell tale', and this only served to confirm Kate's decision that Ruth is to receive a written warning.

A lot now depends on how she responds to this and we're hoping she'll gather herself, get organised and become the good rep she can be. Kate is more optimistic than I am, because I don't think she'll understand the significance of the matter and will continue to float with her head in the clouds and surf the waves when she should be with guests. Funnily enough though, we don't want to lose her because she is a pleasant girl who is well liked by most people, plus it would only add to the workload for the rest of us. However, in this business you can't afford to carry anybody, which is what we're doing at present and is the reason why I will now be taking over the SJM.

There are actually a few problems with this hotel, but not nearly as bad as Ruth would have us believe. The rooms are very basic, but are spacious, the location is secluded and very pretty being right next to a glorious stretch of beach. On the down side the restaurant is a disorganised shambles, with a poor selection of undercooked food and imbecilic waiting staff; the reception staff are still the same group of under trained incompetents and half of the complex is still an unfinished building site, although the guests are told about this before they come out to resort so they should know what to expect.

Also against the site is its general first impression, because it looks like a building which is designated for people to stay in at her majesty's pleasure, but there are some wonderfully warm and friendly staff, two swimming pools and a semi-decent bar. Would I come on holiday to this hotel? Never in a million years, not even at the ridiculous rate of £7 per night for half-board which our guests are currently paying.

I'm still positive though, that I can provide a good service and generate some income for myself, thus showing Ruth how she should do the job and thus set a professional example that she can follow.

WEDNESDAY – 18TH NOVEMBER

Yet again I awoke on my day off just before midday. I had what felt like a carpet on my tongue, a pounding head, the whole of the renowned Pontypridd front row rucking and mauling in my stomach and a dead weight slumped across my shoulders. I cautiously opened my eyes, took in the bright sunlight, which blinded me for a minute or two, rubbed the sleep away from my eyes and saw a slender, bronzed arm holding on tight to my upper body. The scent of warm Brandy breath was making the hairs on the back of my neck stand on end.

The walls and the view outside looked decidedly unfamiliar and it was only when Janice whispered, "Morning handsome" that I realised I'd reluctantly stayed at her place the previous night. I say reluctantly for two reasons; the first is that she lives right next to the beach and I'd have to travel thirty minutes home on the pot holed roads back to The Ranch, to shower and change before returning to the same beach we had just left, thus wasting an hour of precious free time.

The second reason is that although we had a good night out on the traditional Tuesday night rep' piss-up, my commitment phobias have already begun to kick-in. Since the previous Friday when we had finally got it together, I hadn't had a chance to either see or speak to her, partially because we were both quite busy but also because I was playing it a little bit cool. However, there is a danger of the cool attitude working too well. Last night Janice was particularly attentive, even though we have managed to keep things relatively discreet, as we shared a lot of furtive winks, smiles and very discreet arm rubs and neck kisses. But Kate is trying to push things forward with us, so I have already run the course of the whole relationship in my own little mind on more than one of my long car journeys South and I am a tad confused. I have to admit that I do find her very attractive and, notwithstanding last Friday's sleepy reaction, she can really turn me on. However, I haven't actually got to know her, although I have a fair idea of what she is like and I think I know where this is ultimately going.

She is a very nice, lovely lady and is probably too nice and not exciting enough for me, because I like strong women who have a dangerous or exciting edge to them, which helps stimulate me as a person and helps me to grow. I also have a general fear of being stuck with the wrong person and I can see Janice becoming attached to my apathy and possibly falling for me a little bit when I do get around to making some romantic gestures. I'll spot her becoming attached and will become more aloof, which will either result in an amicable, unspoken agreement where we just about remain friends or most likely it will deteriorate into lots of nasty jibes at each other in an effort to find out what the other is thinking and will result in a bad atmosphere amongst our friends. So because I am worried about what our friends will think I've as good as decided that it's finished before it's started and ruined the opportunity for a good, casual relationship with a very attractive lady who is a pleasure to be with to boot. If only we could continue having sex occasionally and if only I had the courage to discuss the whole matter with her openly.

Still we had a bit of a kiss and a cuddle, but because we were both feeling as rough as a badger's posterior, Janice jumped in the shower and got ready to go to the beach. I then managed to persuade her to take me back to The Ranch, which she was less than pleased about. I'm not too sure if this was because she wanted to go straight to the beach or because I looked like shit.

Back at The Ranch I put on some music nice and loud, jumped in the shower myself and for the first time in the day found a smidgeon of energy. It would have been churlish not to take advantage of my newfound zest and a beautiful lady handing me a towel. I threw Janice onto the bed and we made passionate love to the raunchy sounds of 'Lily The Pink'.

MONDAY – 30TH NOVEMBER

Yet again, it was another tedious day of easy work. I saw very few guests in each of the hotels, had few problems to deal with and booked even fewer excursions, which means there won't be much in the way of spending money this week. It's just as well that Kate and I had a complimentary dinner with one of our hoteliers in the North in the evening to discuss some Health and Safety issues.

Because it was so quiet I had plenty of time to reflect on why I'm not particularly happy at the moment and these empty visits are a contributing factor to my dissatisfaction. This is then aggravated further by the long car journeys, which combine a handful of near misses each day with even more time for doleful reflection. Thankfully a few guests came along to just chat at the SJM and I was happy to stay with one couple until just after 1:00 before preparing to head back up to the office. As I reached my car I spotted Gina, who I had been keeping an eye out for half the morning and we stopped for a little chat.

Gina is one of those girls who has an amazingly cheerful character at all times and although I would describe her as very attractive, she isn't stunning in the traditional sense. She does grow on you and is very easy to talk to and I've found myself almost looking forward to coming south in the hope that I may bump into her.

We chatted about work for a while, as reps always do, discussing the respective problems that we've had in the SJM and I spent most of my time empathising with her because she has the highest number of 'Billies' in this hotel. To make matters worse they are all on an All-Inclusive basis, which considering the hotel's poor catering record is a recipe for disaster.

We then got onto the old chestnuts of where we've worked before, whom we both know and then where we hang out in Goa at present. All the while her big brown eyes were glowing and she has this engaging habit of always smiling as she talks and her body emits a shimmering glow of positive energy. We'd thrown in a few flirtatious comments and I'd even flicked her hair from across her face without thinking because I was so comfortable with her. That action wasn't rebuked at all, so I suggested we get together for a meal sometime, which was also greeted quite positively.

This was very good. I was cool, witty, interesting and almost charming and I was receiving plenty of positive feedback from a very attractive lady. I also knew that I had to get back to the office to cover Kate's extended lunch break, so I needed to leave Gina on a positive note so that she would hopefully go away thinking lots of nice things about me.

I could have simply said goodbye, or made a joke about the office calling out my name or even said something along the lines of 'I'll look forward to seeing you soon sometime'. But I have this habit of refusing to engage brain when I am with an attractive lady for more than a couple of minutes, so for some reason, out of the middle of nowhere, I thought I could 'wow' her with:

"And maybe I'll sweep you off your feet sometime?"

How corny can that be? I bet Clark Gable was never scripted a line like that in one of his love scenes? Come to think of it I don't think I've ever heard anything so corny or distasteful in a porn movie and even now, a day later, I am still cringing at the thought of it and dreading the thought of having to look her in the eye again.

To Gina's credit she laughed playfully, which she does all the time with guests, and made some inaudible reply like, 'sure' but in her eyes I could see "OH MY GOD! RUN GIRL! RUN!" burning through.
Stupid! Stupidy! Stupidest!

I slouched into the car, hid behind the wheel, my face became slightly redder, my heart raced like Red Rum in the home straight and my hands were shaking furiously as I tried to steady myself and look cool and blasé in the 95-degree heat. I stalled the car twice as she was still looking on in amusement and eventually got it started on a desperate third attempt only for a 'Steps' song to blare out and further humiliate me, before I sheepishly drove out of the complex. I castigated myself for my social inadequacy all the way back to Panjim, all day long in the office and all night long at the dinner.

My heart was pounding a little quicker than usual.

FRIDAY – 4TH DECEMBER

The past few weeks at the airport have passed by very smoothly indeed and with the exception of Ruth, pretty much everything and everyone has settled into a good working routine.

The reps are looking after the guests very well, the coaches are turning up on time and are clean to boot, the flight handlers have the check-in desks ready on time and the guests' transition is going very smoothly. The Immigration officials have got over their early season pedantry and are checking the correct papers very efficiently and there are no unnecessary queues at their end. The baggage handlers have obviously received the correct amount in backhanders and the luggage is not being held up for as long as it could be, plus the cabin crew's make-up is perfect and the flights have been coming in on time. I don't want to tempt fate, but we haven't had any significant delays yet this year and from experience I know that we'll get at least one, because it's sod's law that you experience at least one major delay to break up the season and keep you on your toes.

As for this weekend though, this morning's airport run drifted by ever so smoothly, as it should do when we are only carrying forty passengers both ways on the flight. Although it was hot and sticky, we were able to leave by about 13:00, which is pretty good timing for our Friday charter. Unfortunately I had to dash to the toilet twice, which serves me right for having a spicy Chicken Cafreal the night before I go to the airport, which meant I had to suffer the indignity of using water to wipe myself again because they'd run out of paper.

The toilets in India are a constant source of amusement, bewilderment or distress, depending upon how you look at them and how desperate you are. Within most of the hotels, which cater for Europeans, they are of a good standard and usually with plenty of paper. However, the ones provided for general public use can be a tad harrowing on occasion.

Throughout my life I've survived two military coups, one Luxor massacre, I nearly drowned whilst scuba diving in the Maldives, have climbed into a pit of twenty crocodiles, had a gun pointed at me whilst at a concert in The Gambia, have been in a house that burnt down in Cheltenham and have been chased out of a town by twenty odd skinheads when I was a teenager. The one thing all of these instances have in common, is that they are on a level footing with having to go to the toilet in Dabolim International airport.

As you walk through the door a rancid smell of stale urine and excrement wafts into your nostrils, the walls are stained and the floor is for some reason immaculate. Each cubicle has an old, white coated wooden door, which is either hanging on its hinges or doesn't have a lock, which means you have to concentrate on holding it up whilst holding your nose. Most of the toilet bowls have water that is constantly running and splashing up onto the seat-less rims, yet never seems to be able to wash down the previous three users' mess. The floors in the cubicle are equally as bad, with a mixture of excrement and water floating around ensuring that you also spend the whole ordeal on tip toes in an effort not to soil your trousers or most of your shoes. As always the piece de résistance, which compounds the agony, is the customary lack of toilet paper. When all I need is to urinate I find them pretty amusing, but on a day like today when I was suffering the after effects of overindulgence on my favourite spice they can be traumatic, but not as traumatic as the rest of the day continued to be.

I put the two difficult movements down to the aforementioned overindulgence but later on in the office, I found myself becoming a little light-headed and had to go again on another three occasions. This started to make my bottom a little tender and sore round the edges from all of the wiping with rough paper and chaffing from the water.

After my evening visits, which were thankfully uneventful I decided to skip my usual workout and went home for some home made chicken soup, dry bread and a couple of bottles of flat coke to provide me with some glucose on the advice of a local doctor. I did have a couple more faint twinges, so had another small bottle of the flat stuff and I felt fine afterwards and thought nothing of it. I also bought two litres from the supermarket round the corner, shook them and then left them to stand with the tops off, just in case they'd be needed throughout the night.

I had every intention of having an early night to aid matters as well, even though it was a Friday, but Jo and Eileen from across the hall banged on my door and insisted on dragging me up North to Tito's because they hadn't seen that much of me recently.

I decided they were right and anyway I felt fine, so I shoved on my jeans, lucky boxers and lucky aftershave and by midnight we were with an already inebriated crowd of reps who were celebrating the birthday of another rep.

I stayed off the beer and religiously poured mineral water down my throat and the evening seemed to drift along rather nicely. Most people were drunk, but instead of feeling left out I was quite enjoying their foolish antics and displays of idiocy instead, realising that it's often me that is the stupid one. This made a pleasant change.

The girls were both on good form and kept us entertained for quite a while. Eventually though, I made my excuses, not that I particularly wanted to leave, but because I'd spotted Janice and felt obliged to go and say hello.

It looks like we've both realised that what we had was purely physical and the relationship as such is going nowhere, so we may as well remain very good friends. The other thing we have in common though, is that we are both pretty reticent about coming forward and clearing the air. We had a bit of an awkward conversation at first, going through the 'Hi', 'How are you?' 'Fine, you?' 'Where've you been? What've you been doing?' routine when she accidentally touched my right arm and I felt a slight tingle through my spine.

I took another look at her and again realised that she is very attractive and I suddenly felt myself becoming aroused and noticed what seemed like butterflies forming in my midriff. I smiled and told her she looked good, to which she said, 'thanks' and absentmindedly asked me why I was sweating so much. My first fear was that I looked like a madman, because I was intently staring at her open blouse, but realisation dawned when a second jolt shot through my midriff and I knew I had two minutes or less to make it to safety.

"Excuse me Jan" I mustered in a throaty whine and pushed my way past her, through a crowd of dowdily dressed tourists. I spilled someone's Gin and Tonic and headed to the far side of Tito's, which is thankfully one of the bars that happens to have not only one toilet, but also half a dozen cubicles. They aren't the normal style loos, but the continental hole in the ground variety and at the entrance to them all is a little old man who hands out toilet paper for 10 Rupees a roll. I burst past him, dropping a fifty-rupee note into his box, which didn't raise the slightest flicker of an eyebrow let alone a smile, and I barged into the nearest available cubicle.

The shooting pains were getting sharper and very frequent, my shirt was soaked right through and I daren't loosen the grip on my tensely clenched bowels. I noticed with dismay that the floor was dirty and that to manage to squat and poo at the same time would entail taking off my denims. With one hand on the door, ensuring no soul would burst in on me, I slipped off my lace-less boots and stood on each of them to keep my feet dry, then with my right hand I gingerly took off my denims and then my boxers, which were not feeling too lucky tonight. I leaned against the door, which freed my left hand so that it could help me slide the boots back on and finally, with my right hand holding the jeans, my left pushing against the door, my feet resting on the tread marks by the side of the hole I tentatively relaxed my cheek muscles, which were suffering from exhaustion.

For a minute a dark brown fluid came shooting continuously from my behind, thankfully spraying the hole only and then just as quickly as it had started gushing, it stopped.

I breathed a sigh of relief, gradually eased myself into an upright position and wiped off the considerable mess, which had implanted itself into my cheeks, whilst my left hand was by now holding both my jeans and the door. I pondered the problem of putting the jeans on without letting the door cave in for all and sundry to witness my delicate situation, when I felt the pain again. I stopped thinking and started squatting, but maybe it was because I hesitated in getting down or because I was caught unawares, but this time the mess was not so controlled and it shot out in all directions, catching my inner thighs for the second time in a season.

This session lasted for another minute and I waited a further five to make sure there were no more repercussions, before dealing with the conundrum of putting my clothes back on. I fortunately managed to do this without too much fuss, because I stood on my boots again, leaned my back against the door and used both hands to dress and then wipe my boots off as well. I walked tenderly into the bar, doing my best John Wayne impression. Tears formed in my eyes as I winced with every step and a line of Niagara proportioned sweat ran down my shirt only to find that Janice had already left for a nightclub, which I suppose was just as well. I made my excuses and jumped in a taxi home, praying that we wouldn't have to stop on the way and as soon as I entered my room I immediately consumed the entire amount of flat coke that I'd bought earlier and popped a couple of Imodium in the desperate hope that it would block me up, because I had a long car journey south in the morning.

I took off my clothes before getting into bed, only to realise that I'd forgotten to put my boxers on and that they must still have been lying on the toilet floor at Tito's.

SATURDAY – 5TH DECEMBER

Surprisingly after last night's rear end movements I felt really good in the morning and relatively upbeat, but this was down to a really deep sleep, albeit for five hours only and also the Imodium and the soda drink which was devoid of any effervescence. To aid my mood I was also looking forward to a day's work for the first time in ages, because Saturdays are generally quite straightforward and in the evening it was the Navy Ball, which is another big local jolly where Kate and I had decided we were going to have some fun even though we had an early airport duty the following morning.

The ball itself is held just outside of Vasco Da Gama and is very close to the airport. It is one of the most prestigious events of the Goan social calendar, with reportedly 5,000 guests attending, including the aforementioned military personnel, state-wide dignitaries, wealthy socialites and of course plenty of social hangers on from the travel industry who are always up for a party. There is a renowned beauty queen competition, live bands, free-flowing alcohol and barbecue style meals served at counters to the side of the seating area.

The only drawback is that I'll have to leave a party in full swing and head off to the airport, plus I'm not sure if I'll be able to drink or not. But on the plus side I know I'll be looking smart in my new suit and hopefully Gina will be coming up, because she's recently made friends with Ruth, which goes to show that the flame-haired one can have some uses.

To have a great night out all I had to do was get through a regular day's work, grab an extended siesta if possible and ensure that there were no repercussions with my posterior again. Unfortunately, good fortune never consistently shines my way and I've always been one of those that if things go right for me in one area of my life then they will be counterbalanced by catastrophes in another. As a result, my working day became anything but regular and although I wouldn't class it as a catastrophe, I would expect some smidgeon of joyous providence to roll my way in the coming weeks.

The day started to change at approximately midmorning, which was the moment I walked into the dreaded SJM. Instead of bumping into Gina, which was what I was hoping for, I was given a rather snotty note from some guests who wanted to complain about their early departure time the following morning, the hotel in general, the fact that one of them had an electric shock in the shower and the mistaken fact that I'm never there in the hotel. It reads as follows:

CERI

GUESTS X 2 and 1 OTHER

We leave on Sunday, 8.30 flight. We are intending to get a taxi there as it seems completely unreasonable for us to have to leave at 4.30 in the morning.

Can you leave the departure cards for us at reception.

We have enjoyed Goa very much. This is my 3rd time here and my sister and brother in law's first time.
Unfortunately we can't say the same for the hotel. I am surprised that your company, a company with a good reputation should use this hotel. My sister was electrocuted by the shower, we have no hot water, the food is terrible and we weren't advised about the building work. Perhaps this is why you are here so little.

Signed Guest

Now their complaints are quite genuine, especially the electric shock, but I'm annoyed at the tone of the letter and that I'm being criticised personally despite spending an hour, and often more, each day, six days a week in the bloody place.

I tried knocking on their door, but they'd already left for the day. I took a stroll around the pool, although I didn't know who to look for, it was more in the faint hope that they may stop me, but still to no avail. All I could do was leave a note apologising that they'd not enjoyed the hotel and asking them to call me at the office later on if they had the time.

The electric shock I am treating very seriously because if it had happened to an elderly person it could have been fatal, which in turn would have cost both the hotel and our company a bucket-load of money in compensation and bad publicity, plus it would have entailed an awful lot of messy, time-consuming work.

I tried explaining this to the hotel's managers and tried to bring across the gravity of the situation, but they've become so jaded already with the incessant stream of complaints, that all they would initially say was, "They won't get any money from us!" However, if we pay out any money to the guests, the hotel can rest assured that we'll claim every penny back from them by deducting the amount from the bills we still have to pay them.

With regards to the other complaints, which I also brought up with the disinterested management, they are probably correct about the food, which is an ongoing complaint and no matter how many times we mention it to the hotel, nothing ever seems to get done. The hot water situation could have been resolved if they'd spoken to me, by either getting a plumber/handyman in or changing their room and the building work they should have been informed about in the UK, but if they hadn't then we'd obviously been negligent and would probably have been obliged to change their hotel to an alternative one of similar standard in our brochure.

After going over each of these points with the management, they decided it was time to inform me that an electrician inspected the hotel last year and found 25% of all rooms to be inadequately wired and supplied, which meant that they were live and that was the reason why electric shocks were occurring. I was appalled to say the least and like the guests I can't believe that a company like ours is using such a useless hotel just for the sake of getting a few bums on seats.

I was promised a list of all rooms that are 'live' and have been promised that none of our guests will go into these rooms, so long as I stay quiet and don't tell the other reps. I agreed to that straightaway and then promptly told all of the other reps from the other tour operators who have guests in the hotel. I am still staggered to know that they are currently putting guests into the live rooms and even worse, that Stelios George knew about this last year and he is still selling the hotel in our brochure. But as one of the hotel's managers said, he and Stelios have a special, mutually beneficial relationship.

He then winked and sneered at me simultaneously. All I can do is what's known as Cover My Ass. As well as sending a note of apology to the guests (if the reception staff send it), and ensuring this will never happen again in this hotel, I have also written a four page stinking report, detailing all of the inadequacies of the hotel and recommending we discontinue its use in our brochure. I know nothing will come of this and I'll probably be accused of being someone who can't take the rough end of the stick, but I don't particularly want to if it's going to be harmful to the guests and could possibly be avoided.

Quite often after I've had a poor visit, or morning's work, I can usually throw myself into more work, by seeing some other guests or even chatting to other reps, but there wasn't a soul around today, so I had a long drive back north, which allowed even more time for negative conjecture. Disappointingly, I had more time to myself in the office, because Kate was on another of her three-hour lunches and I'd been left a phone message to contact some other guests back at the SJM, even after exceeding my visit there yet again.

This proved to be impossible however, because the hotel, with its disorganised array of reservation filing had lost all record of them whatsoever. Although the guests definitely had a room, because its number was left on my message, plus I remember checking them in personally, the hotel hadn't bothered to write their names down, so no one on duty had any idea who they were. For all I knew they were probably sitting in reception as I talked, because that's where the phones are situated for them to call me in the first place.

I spoke to six different members of staff, none of whom could trace them and were equally reluctant to take a message to the room number I'd been given. I tried repeatedly throughout the afternoon and also got Ruth to pop in and see if she could find them, all with no luck so I was left to hope that they'd call me back or otherwise I would go and find them the following day. As is repeatedly demonstrated in this country 100% employment; 50% efficiency; 0% crime.

Both of these instances hadn't done much for my rapidly deteriorating disposition and it was further exacerbated by the car breaking down on the way into the office. I was in the process of overtaking a lorry at the time, half way up a steep hill, which is about 10 kms outside of the city with a queue of traffic immediately behind me. Just as I'd drawn level with him, my vehicle cut out completely and I slowed pretty rapidly seeing as I was on a sharp incline; I faded behind the lorry and banked the steering wheel left, very sharply, in an effort to reach the side of the road. Otherwise the car would have been left stranded in the middle of a busy stretch of highway.

As I turned I managed to get it onto a grassy verge and don't know how I missed the motorbike that was beside me, I can only presume the rider had lightening reflexes. A whole barrage of horns greeted me yet again, but that's just a daily occurrence and more importantly no amount of twiddling, trying to restart, letting it roll back a little and twiddling some more could get it going again, so I was left with no alternative but to get a taxi into the office.

One came along within a matter of minutes of me deciding to walk towards town and I duly flagged him down.

"Panjim, please." I stated and then asked, "How much?"

"What happened?" came the usual response when coming across a white guy with a shirt and tie on, walking in the middle of nowhere.

"My car broke down and I need to get to my office very quickly."

"You work here?" He asked almost incredulously as they always do, as if a non-Indian could actually be allowed into the country, let alone be involved in gainful employment.

"Yes, in travel business, but please I'm in a hurry, so how much?"

"What travel business? Is it with the charters?"

"Yes, but please I'm in a hurry. It's very urgent! So how much?"

"You don't have much good manners when you are busy I am thinking." He commented a little too condescendingly for my liking and then added at a whim, "800 rupees!"

"But the price should only be 200 rupees, I'm not paying that!"

"Okay, you don't pay, but I will be going and you will have no taxi and you are in a hurry." Fair point I thought, but even though I should be able to reclaim this from the company I wasn't going to pay four times the going rate.

"You're right, but I can't pay 800. I'll give 600."

"No thank you it is 800. I think I shall be going."

"No wait." I yelled in desperation, "Hang on" and then fiddled around in my pockets searching for change. "Okay I'll pay 800."

"Very well, then. What is your good name?"

"Ceri."

"Ceri? That is a girl's name. What is your good country?"

MONDAY – 7TH DECEMBER – 11:50 AM

I've mentioned Gina a few times recently and I have become slightly captivated by her as I've slowly started to get to know her. This is because she has great, positive energy and because she is also very pretty. I'd say she's about 5'6" tall, with a Felicity Kendall type figure, being slim, slightly rounded with a small hint of weight in the right places, which gives her bottom a very high 'spankability' rating. Her hair is dark brown, short in a Liza Minelli style and she has big, bright, smiling brown eyes and some cute kissable lips over a set of near perfect teeth.

Over the past couple of weeks I've tried to flirt a little and she hasn't rebuffed any of my subtle advances, which has made me take notice of her more and more, to the extent that I have been casually trying to arrange a time when we might accidentally run into each other and possibly develop our friendship. I'm usually very good at this, because I'm not very good at approaching women or telling them up front how I feel, so I always manage to not so accidentally, accidentally bump into them until I begin to grow on them, a bit like an old wart. However, because our working days and nights clash a little, plus there's the big distance between where we're both based, the chances of saying, "Fancy seeing you here" have been very slim.

But tonight, with a bit of fortune and careful engineering, things may change, because one of my mates is having a birthday meal and Gina is definitely going along. I know this, because I have just double, and triple checked this with her a couple of minutes ago, here in the SJM, just before she left for another hotel visit, elsewhere.

All I have to do is survive the next five minutes of my duty here and get the rest of the days work out of the way.

What a frustrating day's work!

Just after I'd spoken to Gina in the SJM, the lady who had rung the office on Saturday came to see me, only two minutes before I was due to leave, thus scuppering any plans I may have had for a siesta or to catch up on some overdue paperwork.

I apologised for not getting back to them on the Saturday and although I didn't want to blame the SJM for not helping, I tried to explain that I was unable to get through despite ringing every thirty minutes or so for most of the afternoon. I also explained that Ruth had knocked on their door, but had received no response.

They explained that they had gone out after about 15:00 when they realised I wasn't going to call back, but that it was okay. In the lady's face I could see a sense of disbelief, which she was holding in because she wanted to press on with more important matters and it was with that look that I instantly knew that this wasn't going to be a five-minute conversation. The lady is in Goa with her husband and another couple and they are all very unhappy with the complex, which to be frank is very understandable and I'm surprised I've not received that many complaints to date. The reps from the other companies face a barrage most days. Anyway, I spent over half an hour with her, intently listening to her complaints about the restaurant, which is dirty; the service, which is slow; the selection of food, which is poor and the taste even more so; they've been overcharged for drinks; the pool and its surrounding area is dirty, which is a new one on me but hardly surprising; the reception staff are unhelpful and again they weren't advised of the building work before they came out.

All the while I made understanding noises and tried to write everything down, which was quite easy, because with each point she made she would back it up with a dozen or more examples.

For instance, when she told me the food selection was poor, she added, "Yes and on Friday we only had two pieces of dried toast between four of us for breakfast, with only marmalade and no jam and there were lumps in the milk, but the couple next to us had three eggs with their toast, but when we asked the waiter about it he just shrugged and walked away, and then on Saturday it was the same, except the tea was cold and Friday lunchtime my husband…." And so forth.

Now a number of her complaints are very legitimate. But she just kept going on, which didn't give me a chance to really assist her or do anything constructive for her until she'd finished, so all I could do was meekly respond with the standard rep dialogue of nodding my head and repeating the following lines:

"Yes, I understand."

"I'm sorry."

"Let's see what we can do to help" and "I understand, I'm sorry" for good measure.

But she didn't really hear me, because not only did she justify every point, she kept repeating herself over and over and was sounding as if she merely wanted to sound off and didn't want to be helped.

Just as I thought she was beginning to tire and I was able to squeeze a couple of words in, her friend came in looking for her and she then had to have her say and thus started from the beginning, reiterating all of the points that I'd been listening to intently for the past thirty minutes. So for the next half an hour I heard exactly the same news for the third, fourth and what seemed like twentieth time.

Yes I understood, but I was no longer sorry and they weren't letting me help them.

Eventually, after just over an hour of intense ear bashing, I managed to get a word in and tried to agree my actions with them. But I only got as far as saying that I would speak to the owner of the hotel when they both interrupted in unison and said,

"We want to move!"

"Oh right." I said collecting myself, whilst silently thinking '*well why didn't you say that in the first place? All you had to say was we don't like the hotel, the rooms, the restaurant and the pool and we want to move and you would have saved us all an hour in valuable time!*'

After composing myself and trying not to stare at them with this incredulous look on my face, I explained the procedures for changing hotels. I basically told them that I would check what availability we had in our hotels and that they would have to pay any price difference, especially if it meant upgrading the standard of hotel or their board basis. Before they could respond I explained that this is always the case, because the company do not give complimentary changes of accommodation or pay out any form of compensation in resort. It's a company policy with a good grounding. Finally I managed to get in that normally a cancellation fee is payable to the hotel they are leaving, but that I would waive that, because I would simply tell the hotel that it isn't being paid.

I braced myself for the usual riposte of, "We're not paying a penny", which then leads onto an awkward stalemate where I'm unable to stand down and the guests either move or they don't, but either way they end up hating the company, the country and especially myself. However, they are either exceedingly wealthy or I was at the height of my powers of charm because they simply smiled and said that was fine. We agreed that I'd spend the next thirty minutes checking availability while they conferred with their partners as to what type of hotel they wanted and what area they wanted to move to.

They came back with their partners who wanted to go through the whole thing again.

I felt myself shrivelling up, my head was screaming 'NOOOOOO', I must have had a look of abject terror on my face and I was desperately trying to think of something to say very quickly, before I was put through the whole ordeal again.

I couldn't think of anything clever, so meekly mentioned that I was due in my office thirty minutes previously and could we move along. I showed them the brochure and offered them the choice of three different hotels where we had rooms available at a contract price, one being the Dona Santa Maria All-Inclusive complex a couple of kilometres away, which was a bit of an upgrade and also two B & B's in the north.

They quickly opted for the Dona Santa Maria and paid a total of £700 between the four of them for the upgrade, which had the cancellation fee from the hotel and our admin fee of £50 waived. We then spent another twenty minutes completing the paperwork, whereby the gents took it upon themselves to tell me about the restaurant and pool etc and we left it that they would be seeking to claim this payment back from us in the UK. Despite not being happy at forking out more money they were glad to rescue their holiday, which I thought was a fair point, despite taking two hours and forty-two minutes to resolve.

From there on in, I was behind yet again and rushing to get from one place to the next, which meant that I didn't get time for a siesta or a chance to have a chat with the girls in The Ranch. As soon as I finished my evening visit at the Cidade De Goa, I hurried home, packed my bag and headed off for the South yet again, and more specifically to the hotel Goa Renaissance, where I had a complimentary room booked for the night. Immediately upon arrival and after checking-in, I hurried to my room, showered, changed and was on the point of rushing out when it dawned on me that Gina lives in the Renaissance. I called reception to get her room number and then called her in turn, pretending to be Sandip De Souza, a local carpet merchant who was blindly ringing her up to see if she wanted to go out for a drink. Now I know it's corny, old hat and has been done before already this season, but it worked once before so I saw no reason to tamper with a tried and tested formula and as expected she was suitably pissed off yet laughing at the same time.

I met up with the others at 'Mikes Place' for the dinner and Gina turned up, fashionably late, about thirty minutes afterwards. For his birthday I'd brought down three large Cuban cigars and was thankful that there were only three guys and about a dozen girls, so there were no arguments over who had a cigar and who didn't.

The food was good, service was slow, Mike was as hospitable as ever, the whiskies flowed all too quickly, the birthday boy was becoming suitably inebriated and a wonderful air of bonhomie sailed around the table. Because Gina had turned up late, she and I had ended up at different ends of the table, but that wasn't too bad, because it meant I was able to have a cigar, copious amounts of whisky and some long overdue guy chat. As much as I like Kate and the girls in The Ranch, it's not quite the same talking about football and totty with them and this is something that I have therefore been starved of so far this season.

By about midnight we were all a bit squiffy and Mike was wanting to close for the evening, so we made the decision to head down to a beach club in Colva for more alcohol and a bit of a drunken dance on the beach. Not so accidentally, I angled towards Gina to make sure she was coming too, when heaven of all heavens, for the first time in my life I had some semblance of good fortune when chasing a girl.

Gina had arrived with her friend Terri, who is also very attractive and who had also driven her down to the restaurant and she announced that she was tired and going to bed, so would I mind looking after Gina and giving her a lift on my bike.

Well, I was a little bit squiffy, but yes! Yes! Yes! Yes! Yes! Yes! Yes! I had to refrain from jumping with joy and tried to calm myself down and act cool and considerate. I couldn't stop my heart racing again mind, and neither could I suppress a huge grin, which adorned my cheeks that were glowing from the alcohol. I managed to settle down a little, tried not to appear too keen, because there was no way I could pull off cool and hoped Terri wouldn't change her mind.

"Oh come on Terri." I falsely implored, "Come for just one drink please?" which meant, *Don't you dare, but thank you, thank you, thank you.*

"No, I'm tired and I've got a lot of work in the morning."

"Just for one Terri. It's not that far." *Go now, before you change your mind and ruin my life, go now.*

"No. I'm okay"

"Are you sure?" *You better be. Please go. In the nicest possible sense, please leave me alone with Gina.*

"I'm sure."

"Okay, see you tomorrow then." *Yes. Thank all of my gods for that!*

And then my mate piped up and asked her if she was sure, as if I hadn't tried hard enough.

"For God's sake, she's sure and she wants to go. The girl wants to go, so leave her go and I'll drive Gina!" Now this came out way too forcefully and I feared I was sounding a little too desperate. What I did notice and for what I was also grateful, was that throughout the mini-leaving trauma, Gina hadn't said a word and hadn't made a single attempt to try and persuade Terri to stay.

This could have meant that they'd had an argument and weren't getting along at the moment. But they had seemed pretty affable over dinner, so I only hoped that the look in her eye was stating that she felt the same way about me as I felt about her and I think that deep down we both knew more was going to occur between us from now on.

At the beach club, more whiskies flowed, I did my ritual falling over trick and nerdy dancing, people were starting to pair off and leave and I spent most of my time chatting to the locals and other girls, in fact anyone but Gina, in a misguided effort to appear aloof and popular. However, it didn't matter for one single iota. When we were walking along the beach to the club, I took her hand gently, casually stopped her, turned round so that we were facing each other and thanked the gods above again for letting her have the same gaze of longing in her eyes, that I had in mine. I brought my hand up to her face, pulled her closer and we gently and ever so delicately kissed for the first time.

It was only a short kiss, but I wish it could have gone on forever. We'd both applied the right strength and tenderness, had coyly flicked our tongues just the once and our noses had rubbed with a hint of passion. For the first time in my life I was feeling fireworks and thunderbolts from above, all from one little kiss, which had made the hairs on the back of my neck stand up and my legs turn to jelly. This was just as well because I didn't want to press my aroused state against her and ruin the moment. We were completely in tune with each other's movements and thoughts and I knew that we had something more than a rep romance and would remain together for a while to come. If I don't screw things up.

After our entrance, the rest of the night was a blur and somewhere between 03:00 and 04:00 we stupidly decided to take the bike back to the hotel. We automatically went back to her room without thought or words said between us and proceeded to continue with that magical kiss and chatted even more after. It's quite rare that you meet someone like this, but we instantly clicked and I would have been happy talking nonsense with her all night long. But we both felt that special something and as it turned out we made love all night long.

I still find it hard to believe that after a long day's work and all the drink we had, we still managed to share love all through the night until the sun came up, almost like movie stars. We seemed to roll with each other instinctively and my slender frame aroused Gina, as much as her Felicity Kendall one did mine. Neither of us could do any wrong and it was an effort not to declare my undying devotion to her.

Thankfully I did manage to hold that in, but we did have some very sweet conversations. I admitted to being very stuck on her and frightened at how quickly I was falling for her, because everything seemed too perfect and too good to be true. But I even managed to suppress these initial thoughts of negativity, because I wasn't going to let my emotional inadequacies spoil this moment.

But for this one night everything was going so well that one tiny blot of awkwardness had to infringe on our happiness. It occurred when we were holding our sweaty bodies together after having made love for the second time, and we were stroking each other's arms and kissing occasionally, which is something I could do forever. Gina then wriggled a little, turned to face me, looked me in the eye and said she had something to ask me. Although I had an idea what was coming I let her carry on, hoping that we weren't doomed just as soon as we were starting.

"Ceri. Are you seeing anyone else?"

And that was it. The question I was expecting, which would sound the bells of doom and ruin any chance of happiness I might have.

I started thinking quickly, trying to decide what lie or untruth I could feasibly give that would throw her off the scent so that this moment wouldn't be spoiled. But in my afterglow state of haze, I couldn't think quickly enough and so opted for a stalling tactic.

"No. But I know what you're getting at." This was hedging a bit too close to the truth for my liking.

"Oh." She muttered and I could see she was thinking she'd forgotten to add the word 'shit' after it, which meant that I had to come up with a good story here.

"Look, I slept with Janice, you know, the Northern girl, on about three occasions, the last of which was three weeks back. There was nothing in it, we simply got on quite well but there is nothing going on now, at all!" I couldn't believe it. Where had all that straightforward honesty come from? I didn't find the need to lie, not even a small white one and I had been 100% upfront with her instinctively, without a second's thought. This must be good.

"WHAT! With Janice as well!?"

This I did not expect and what does she mean with Janice as well?

"What do you mean as well?"

"Well, what about Kate? Everyone knows you're with her and that you've got this special relationship with her!" At this I laughed out loud, a bit too stridently, which was much to Gina's chagrin judging by the look on her face and replied,

"Kate and I work together and I love her to bits, but as friends only and no more!"

"You're sure?" which I thought was a bit of a stupid question because I'm pretty sure I would have noticed if anything was going on between me and her.

"Positive." I reassured her, "I know where she's been" which was more for Gina's benefit than any truth about Kate.

"Oh that's a relief." *For you and me both girl!*

Gina still had a minor sulk about the Janice situation, but I thought our position was fantastic, because I was breaking new ground by being completely honest and clearing any possible skeletons out to boot. Still I assuaged her hang-ups with some more tender loving and we subsequently engaged in coquettish chitchat all the way through to the morning.

The thing with Janice though, is that it's quite obvious nothing is going on now, only neither of us have had the nerve to actually explain it outright to the other. But I'm sure that she gets the picture.

I hope that she gets the picture?

I'd better explain it to her before I foul things up here!

TUESDAY – 8TH DECEMBER

After a humdrum day at work I jumped on my moped and headed down south, on a spur of the moment decision. Although I was still tired from the night before I went to see Gina and we stayed up all night again, chatting with no inhibitions, no secrets and lots of jollification.

What are these strange, yet warm, emotions I am feeling?

THURSDAY – 10TH DECEMBER

Our regional contractor, Stelios George happens to be in Goa at present, having arrived on Monday off a very comfortable Emirates flight, compared to the usual crap the reps get, and he is due to stay until Saturday.

His actual title is Operations Manager, which means that as well as doing the contracting in his specified areas he also oversees the running of the resorts to boot. This involves looking after staffing, training and operational standards, which is a bit of a Steffi Graf really because the only qualification he has for fulfilling this vitally important role is the fact that he's originally from The Mediterranean. He has never worked in a resort before, neither in a repping nor an admin capacity and he has never managed a resort, so it's safe to say that he's never spoken to a guest, had to motivate disillusioned reps, sold a trip, dealt with a problem, guided an excursion, given a welcome meeting, coped with a delay or a death, or even had to travel on one of our company buses, because he's never been in a resort for more than a week at a time.

Admittedly his contracting skills are excellent and I am in awe of his ability to get fantastic rates out of suppliers and manage to keep them on his side. He has a superb rapport with every one of our suppliers and he generally contracts fairly decent hotels (the SJM excluded). He has also built up an awful lot of goodwill, which comes in very handy when there are mass over-bookings, and although he does very well financially through some unofficial bonuses, he also makes the company some very good profits as well.

However, when it comes to overseeing the resort operations, he has no idea about the practicality of uniforms; what it's like to ride a moped around India; how to deal with irate guests; the practicality of getting from hotel to hotel; dealing with local staff and even locals such as the taxi drivers who are literally fighting to get business. He just expects staff to implement his ideas without any available resources and he expects us to meet deadlines and unrealistic sales targets, which he has just plucked out of thin air and have no basis or foundation for their existence or how they may be achieved.

On a personal level Stelios is very dynamic, if not very personable, but he is judged on results and not popularity. He is certainly very intelligent and very well informed, but he does not listen to team members, like myself, who have an abundance of resort experience; he is not open to new ideas or opinions and unfortunately he controls my future.

He has promised that while he's here we'll have a chat to discuss my progression within the company, but so far the only contact I've had is a stroppy message sent through Kate. This came earlier on today when I was preparing to head back up to the office, after finishing my morning stint in the South. I wasn't in the best of moods because I'd just spent forty minutes with two separate couples going over the same complaints in the hotel that everyone else has and actually giving them a couple of other pointers to complain about when they return to the UK.

The reason I've done this, which is against all of my principles is because Stelios told Kate a couple of days ago that he won't be taking any action against the SJM and will not even entertain the notion of dropping it, because they've not been receiving any complaints coming through to the UK. This is ironically brilliant, because I was sent into the hotel to cut down on the number of complaints and because I've done a fairly decent job and improved the hotel's customer feedback, they've decided the unit must be okay after all. It's typical of this industry and it goes to show that you can do too good a job.

Anyway, after I'd finished with the aforementioned guests I answered the phone, when I could have ignored it, to have Kate telling me to get down to the Goa Renaissance immediately. Stelios was disgusted with the standard of Ruth's information book and board and I've got to re-do them completely in the afternoon.

He does have a point, because this is one of the issues we've been labouring over all season and despite her written warning not so long ago and the constant encouragement, pushing and asking, she simply hasn't done anything she's required to. This hasn't gone unnoticed and she is probably seeing the last of her days in the industry, which although it is cruel to say, will be a blessing for the rest of the team on a professional level. However, this meant that I had to spend three hours doing someone else's work and receiving an ear bashing for it in the process.

My disposition hasn't been its usual sunny self for quite a while now, except for my moments with Gina, which are all that are sustaining me at present. The goings on today on top of my diminishing Head Rep responsibilities, lack of career direction and lack of direction from Kate with regards to my role in the team are beginning to wear me down. I decided that it's time Kate and I had a little chat.

This had been building up for a while and I needed to clear the air before I held everything in way too long and ended up exploding with unnecessary Mount Etna proportions. I went into the office a cross between jaded and worked up, feeling a little schizophrenic and almost certainly expecting a fight. I'd prepared what I needed to say and knew what sort of message I needed to be receiving, but I wasn't realistically expecting any positive responses.

As always I was disappointed that I didn't get the fight or opportunity to let off steam, much like guests are when we can help them when all they want to do is complain, and it turned out that Kate had noticed I wasn't too happy. She appeared genuinely concerned about my welfare and was determined to pick me up and get the best out of me, which to be completely honest she isn't at the moment, but for which I take full responsibility.

We discussed the role of a Head Rep and I expressed my dissatisfaction at running around the country and not being able to help the girls as much as I'd like to. Kate agreed and said that she'd try and give me less repping duties and more managerial and admin responsibilities, plus she pointed out that she'd like to be getting her hands much more dirty and start helping out with the reps' welcome meetings, transfers and to start seeing them on their visits more. I left a little bit happier, hopeful that things may eventually improve, but still a little sceptical as to how matters can improve and will actually pan out.

Later that evening, when I was on duty in the Cidade De Goa hotel, Kate called and asked if I'd cover her airport duties the following morning. I found out the following day that she'd gone out on a drinking binge which she'd planned five minutes after I'd left the office and she wanted a lie-in. This goes to show that she hadn't heard a word I'd said and I'm going to have to make it through the rest of the season, motivating myself to succeed, despite the hindrances of the likes of Kate and Stelios George. So much for mucking in with the rest of us.

FRIDAY – 11TH DECEMBER

I returned from a relatively easy airport duty and headed straight to the office only to bump into Stelios George.

"Hi Stelios. How are you?" I asked trying to sound positive and upbeat.

"Hi. uhhm Ceri. Good. You're looking fit these days."

"Thanks." I knew that this was about as far as Stelios could stretch with preliminaries and social niceties, so hopefully we would get onto some more hard hitting conversation, but I was determined that it wasn't going to be me who makes all the running.

"So." A good start by Stelios and I was still determined not to feel obliged to make more polite chitchat and let him avoid a couple of issues I needed to go over.

"So." What wit. What humour. What repartee.

"So." Equally brilliant Stelios and original to boot.

But as always I lose at these games, or rather Stelios always wins and always gets the conversation on his terms, so I caved and thought to hell with it, I haven't got the time to waste waiting for him to tell me what I want to hear.

"Stelios can we talk about the SJM and also your future plans for me please," I blustered a bit like a bull being let out of a gate.

"Sure. You know I was in the hotel yesterday? Well they've promised me that they'll put up a screen to cover the building work so things should be okay from now on." He tried to assure me, hoping that the matter would now be resolved and I'd go away and sell loads of excursions, thus making him a wealthy man.

But all I could think, beneath my astounded exterior, is what planet is he on? Has he not read any of the reports I've written, which clearly and simply explain all of the problems we have within the hotel. It was clear that I had to seize this brief opportunity to try and set him straight and see if we could penetrate his single-minded determination to brush the subject aside.

"Okay, but it's apparent that we're still not advising the guests of the work before they come out, despite earlier assurances from yourself that this would be the case, and every single one of the other operators in the complex is doing so! Plus the service in the hotel is atrocious, the restaurant is a big problem area, our guests haven't had their half board vouchers explained to them before they come out, so they are always, without fail, disappointed with what they get and that's not even touching on the electric shocks in the showers."

"I see, but with the screen up, things should improve from now on." At which I wanted to smash my head furiously into the floor, because not only does he not read, he doesn't listen either and this guy is our leader.

"Stelios," I tried to start explaining it all again, but he didn't want to listen, made a feeble excuse and promptly left.

SUNDAY – 13TH DECEMBER

Because of the amount of time that I seem to be spending either on the moped or in the car I have grown accustomed to the daily ritual of witnessing the after effects of a gruesome accident. Every day I will see something untoward like a bike being nudged off the road or a scratching of paintwork and I'd say that once every three days I witness something pretty severe, which would be along the lines of a car lying upside down in a ditch or a body, covered in blood and sprawled across the road. This morning though, I just missed the worst incident that I've seen in a long while, as did the rest of the team.

I was taking some guests on their transfer to the airport, when about 4 kilometres outside of our destination we saw a Suzuki Maruti van parked almost diagonally in the middle of the road, but with the misfortune of lying on its side. We had to slow down to get past it and therefore had too good a view of the state it was in.

Its windows were smashed in, leaving bits of broken glass lying all across the road. The front end was crumpled up like a concertina and the seats were lying haphazardly in the remains of the interior. It was quite obvious that the driver couldn't have survived and we only hoped that there was no one in the rear. Also, on the edge of the road was a truck, which had taken a massive bang on the front right-hand side, which judging by the white paint scratched onto it, we presumed was from the taxi. Some of my guests were quite shocked by this and even I, with my blasé attitude to Indian driving, felt a little churning in my stomach, and we all silently wished that no one was badly hurt.

As it turned out, there were two of our guests in the taxi who were making their own way to the airport, in the hope of getting there early to get better seats together. As they were going along the quiet stretch of road, at 04:00 in the morning, their driver, and his friend who was in the front with him, had both fallen asleep. The young man in the couple had noticed his nodding head and so leant over and tapped the driver on the shoulder. The driver apparently woke up in a start and in a reflex action turned the steering wheel sharply to his right, which was unfortunately straight into the oncoming truck.

They don't remember too much about the collision, except for being thrown around in the back and realising that the vehicle wasn't moving any more. They managed to climb out of the rear windows, which were obviously smashed to pieces, without cutting themselves too much and Lester, who was only a few minutes behind them on his transfer, picked them up and brought them to the airport before heading back for the driver and his mate. The guests were miraculously unhurt and were only suffering the effects of severe shock. The driver had died instantly and his friend was in a critical condition and was taken to a nearby military hospital.

The drawback for the guests, aside from the trauma of being in a near fatal accident, was that they'd have to give interviews to the police and be checked over by a doctor to confirm that they were fit to fly and this would take the best part of a couple of days. This would mean that on top of their ordeal, they would miss their flight and would spend the following few days dealing with their insurance company to find them accommodation and a flight home. Obviously we would assist greatly, but they just wanted to get to the loving arms of their families.

Alternatively, they could keep quiet, not inform anyone of the incident and simply board the aircraft as if nothing had happened, thus avoiding all of the necessary hassle.

They opted for the latter of the two choices and went straight onto the flight, which put us, and more importantly Lester and Kate who were dealing with them, in a bit of an awkward position. We are obliged to inform the local flight handling agent for the airline of the situation, as well as the local police and the flight crew, who would be able to assist if there were any problems on the flight. If we did this however, the police wouldn't let them on without a lengthy days questioning and the airline wouldn't allow them onto the flight without a 'fitness to fly' certificate, which there is no way they would have got.

We were in a bit of a dilemma, because we have to look after the best interests of the company and ensure we act in accordance with all local, airport and airline guidelines, but part of this entails looking after the best interests of our customers. After a lot of deliberation, they asked us to remain quiet and we respected their wishes and let them go through.

If I were in their shoes I would have done exactly the same thing, but although our decision to remain ignorant on their behalf was what I would call ethical and something we could all quite easily live with, it was certainly not correct. Imagine if the guy had a seizure on the aircraft and the pilot was forced into an emergency landing in Abu Dhabi, then we'd be in some trouble.

MONDAY – 14TH DECEMBER

I had to hang on an extra twenty minutes after my morning visits because Kate had called earlier in the day saying she was coming down for a chat, which sounded a bit ominous, but that she needed to speak to Ruth first. I had a fair idea what she wanted to talk about, but I was a little taken aback by her negative tone.

When she arrived, we sloped off to one of the restaurants in the SJM, which was empty and where we were hidden from view. Without any pleasantries she started accusing me of not pulling my weight. Apparently I've been lazy, unhelpful and taking liberties with both the work and my friendship with Kate, which I see as a complete sack of shit. I'm the first to admit that I've not been doing the job to the best of my ability, but most of that is down to the fact that I've not been motivated, I've had no back-up, my manager is having an easy time of it and isn't true to her word, plus I've been messed around and am having to spend over three hours of my working day on the road.

I thought she'd taken these points on board the other day when I came to see her and tried to discuss my problems with a view to improving the whole situation for myself first and ultimately the whole team. But Kate has decided to pick up on three principle things that have shown a 'definite deterioration in my service'.

1. I've passed on the collecting of the liquidation to her.
2. I've not done a training session with the local reps.
3. I've not been taking on managerial responsibilities.

As for point number one, I was forced to let her start collecting the liquidation money, because by the time I get to the office on a Tuesday after leaving the South, Lester and Sharon have been and gone, so that is unjustified. Also the fact that I'm hardly in the office nowadays, because I spend all of my time on the road, means I don't have the time to do the training, plus when we did arrange a provisional one, only one person was free to come. Finally, she's absolutely right again in that I've not been taking on managerial responsibilities, because she keeps taking them away from me.

What has made this criticism harder to take, and is the real reason why I'm so angry, is that it's come from someone who has all day Wednesday off, doesn't come into the office until midday on a Thursday and after thirty minutes work, goes off for an extended lunch break. She has also got into the habit of working a half day Saturday and after we finish at the airport on a Sunday and the rest of us go on to do transfers and welcome meetings until 20:00, she spends the day topping up her tan on the Cidade De Goa beach.

I couldn't believe that she'd come all the way down South to tell me this. There must have been an ulterior motive for her putting me on the back foot? As it turned out I was right and my initial suspicions were founded in that as of Wednesday she wants me to move into the SJM and rep every hotel in the South, while Ruth will go to the Cidade De Goa and do one hour's work each day over the Christmas period.

This means that I will lose all managerial responsibilities, I will become a full time rep and will have to move to the hotel I hate the most in the world. So in a couple of days I'll have to pack, move and leave friends behind and to top it all it brings me much closer to Gina, which will probably complicate matters a little.

Things have been going along very nicely with Gina recently. We both adore each other and get along very well and with us being based so far apart we have only been able to see each other about four times in the past week, which has suited me down to the ground, because it means I have a chance to gradually get used to the idea of being in a committed relationship.

However, Gina has proven to be a lot keener than I expected and she is already starting to rush things, which has thrown up a few warning signals for me and I would like to keep the whole thing at arms length for the time being. So with me having to come down South, it may make this a case of make or break with her.

Gina was delighted.

WEDNESDAY – 16TH DECEMBEER

I often refer to how precious our day off can be and that every single moment should be cherished, but the only highlight I had today, was the fact that Gina had got past the night porter last night and was able to spend her precious time with me.

After waking up with hangovers at midday, I franticly packed everything I have, the sum total of my life into the two suitcases I own. This took a couple of hours and made me even more irritable than my hangover had. We did manage to squeeze a couple of hours on the beach, but by 17:00 we were leaving The Ranch in Kate's car, which is on loan to me for the Christmas period and which was also packed to the hilt with my belongings.

It was after dark by the time we arrived at the SJM. We were still sandy after our time on the beach, tired and looking forward to a shower and something to eat, only to spend the next hour in reception with guests constantly bothering us with stupid little questions, because the reception staff couldn't find the key to my new room.

As it transpired, Ruth had taken the key up north with her and they didn't have a spare, so I was put into a temporary room for the night, which had no power or hot water. I dumped my bags in there, without the help of a porter, and took my work stuff around to Gina's for the night so that I would be able to have a shower in the morning.

If I was pissed off before, I was livid this evening. I'm supposed to be motivated to do a demanding job to the best of my abilities, yet I'm stuck in an ugly, problematic hotel, surrounded by whingeing guests, in a room which doesn't function and with my clothes in a suitcase and my paperwork lying in a heap in a Bahrain duty free carrier bag.

Things bode well for the manic period.

THURSDAY – 17TH DECEMBER

Changing over the hotels you cover midway through the season almost always leads to a demanding few days work and today was no exception to the rule. As well as dealing with all of the guests, of which there were many, and any problems that the previous rep may have left behind, of which there were many multiplied by many squared, I also had to re-familiarise myself with each of the hotels and introduce myself to the management and staff. Most of the work, although time consuming, was run of the mill, booking excursions, changing a few rooms where possible, arranging for rooms to be cleaned, toilets to be mended, cockroaches to be killed, reports to be written about the poor quality of food etc.

However, one lady did amuse and exasperate me at the same time. She is staying in the Dona Santa Maria, which has rooms on two stories all away from the crux of the complex so that they have peace and quiet and no noise from the pool and bar, and she arrived last Sunday. She came over to me and asked if she could have a room with a pool view, to which I replied that the complex doesn't have any pool view rooms.

"But they've facking gotta!" she replied in a broad cockney accent, which was showing the signs of wear and tear after 40 years of smoking sixty a day. "That last giwl 'Roof', promised they 'ad 'em!"

"But I can assure you that there aren't any. All of the rooms are away from the focus of the complex in order to give guests an element of tranquillity."

"Don' you go tawkin' that posh English or nuffin wiv me san," she remonstrated, at which I had to stop myself from laughing and also copying her, which was nigh on impossible.

"Sorry. But there aren't any pool view rooms."

"Well what's that over there then," she asked, pointing across the pool to the entertainments room and poolside grill. I pointed this out to her and she looked at me with distrust in her eyes and then told me that "Roof" had told her that they were rooms and would be available when the Finnish guests leave on Friday. I couldn't believe what I was hearing, but then on second thoughts Ruth probably did say something like that just to make her go away with a smile on her face.

"Look, I'm sorry but those aren't rooms. Do you want to come over with me and have a look?"

"Nah dan't bovver. That giwl 'Roof' was far better than you."

I had to laugh; otherwise I would have been swimming around the pool, fully clothed declaring that I was the second coming. I actually had a little soft spot for my pool view woman as well, because she said what she thought, was deadpan honest and was quite sweet to boot.

In spite of the day being busy, it was also rewarding, because I settled in quite quickly and I even managed to persuade the SJM to let me change rooms in the afternoon. This meant I was able to unpack, but I was still unable to have a shower, which meant another evening around at Gina's.

As I turned up she jumped for joy and exclaimed that she was pleased to see me, yet on my behalf it was one of those nights when I would rather have been home by myself. I was tired and needed to prepare my work stuff for the following day and being brutal, I was only round at Gina's out of necessity. We ordered room service, because she lives in a five star hotel compared to my two star Colditz camp, and we settled into bed to watch a film.

I was drifting off to sleep, with her cuddled in my arms, when she whispered into my ear that she wanted to spend the rest of her life with me.

I could have screamed, which I was doing inside, but my body froze and tensed up as rigid as a mountain face. She was oblivious to my fear and carried on chatting about our future, but I was thinking that we've only been together less than two weeks and we're just starting to get to know each other. I've been hurt before and have no intention of going down that road in a hurry, or even leading another innocent down there on false pretences. Also I'm going through a difficult period career wise and we're approaching the busiest period of the season, which needs my full attention, so I didn't need this. I wanted to jump out of bed and run back to the Dona Santa Maria pool, screaming that I was Hitler's long lost brother as opposed to the second coming.

It was disappointing to see something that had been building so nicely and sweetly, was now possibly at the beginning of being slowly eroded. I wanted to talk to her, but I knew that whatever I said would come out wrong and she looked so happy, which I didn't want to spoil tonight. I rolled over and for the first time in our brief relationship, I slept with my back to her.

SATURDAY 19TH DECEMBER

I walked into the SJM for my final visit of the morning and the manager called me over and said he had a major problem. For the following mornings arrivals they had accepted bookings from tour operators for one hundred and sixty rooms, when they only had one hundred rooms in total. They were panicking and asking every tour operator what they could do to help, however there wasn't that much any of us could do, because rooms are at a premium at this time of year and there was nowhere to put them.

I told him there was no way he was going to refuse any of my rooms for the following morning, I only have twenty rooms coming in, and that I was sorry but I just couldn't help. I took a kind of sick joy in telling him no, and for the first time in ages I was quite happy with myself, which I presume was the small rush of power. In the meantime Kate gave me even more power, although I'm not too sure that it was wanted. She rang to say that she was leaving for a week on the following day's flight because her grandmother had just died.

I felt desperately sorry for Kate, despite what had passed between us a week or so previously and I asked her if there was anything I could do. She of course told me that I was to cover the office and look after the resort, as well as do the job of two reps in the south, which rained on my parade, but I was still quite happy to help out. I sat down with a coffee and started thinking about how nothing ever runs smoothly or professionally in this industry and that it was about time someone did something about it.

Then it dawned on me that I could do something to help a few guests, gain some big browny points with the SJM and ease a few of our worries in the South. I got on the phone to the Dona Santa Maria, who had eight rooms to spare but they needed them to be confirmed within the hour because our parent company wanted them as well, so I told them to hold onto the rooms and I would call back as soon as possible. I ran into the manager's office and asked if he still wanted help with his overbookings and if so was he prepared to pay for upgrades to the Dona Santa Maria, to which he gleefully said yes. I rang the Dona Santa Maria and confirmed the rooms and promised to fax over the names of the guests within a couple of hours, which actually got extended because of a well timed power cut and then I ran round the rooms of any guests who had already complained about the SJM offering them a free upgrade. They were all delighted and said yes straightaway.

By the end of the afternoon I'd moved eight rooms and had sixteen happy guests and two very happy hoteliers, both declaring that they owed me one. I also guaranteed that none of my rooms would be overbooked the following day. The only possible drawback is that Gina may get a lot of the overbookings, but I have to do my job first. It does go to prove, that although I was lucky on this occasion, a problem handled well is the best form of advertising available.

Gina was pissed off.

SUNDAY – 20TH DECEMBER

A lecturer of mine at college, who once took a lesson on assertiveness, very wisely told us to always remember that we should never be rude to someone in a service industry, because what they can do to you is far worse than anything you may say to them. Like so much of the work we did in college, no matter how interesting the lecture, we usually forgot these pearls of wisdom. That is until we learnt the hard way and something would register in the back of our minds and we'd say, "Hey. Peter Leyland was right after all! Well what do you know?"

I'm fairly sure that through the years, I've had waiters spit in my tea, shopkeepers have given me lesser items which are identical to the ones I think I've bought and barmen have given me pints of 'slops'. But now that the shoe is firmly on the other foot I have most definitely learned my lesson, because I wouldn't want what I've done in the past, to happen to me.

The worst thing I ever witnessed was to a guest, who shall obviously remain nameless to protect my colleague, who was on holiday in Fuerteventura. This gentleman was of an Arabic origin and was without doubt the rudest man that any rep has ever come across. From day one he complained about everything ranging from the thickness of his mattress, to the size of the chips in the restaurant to the colour of the receptionist's blouse. Without fail, he would be in the reception every morning and every evening of his holiday, not only complaining about situations, but also insulting staff and reducing many of the ladies to tears. He was after whatever he could get and took a sadistic delight in mentally injuring anyone he could. What compounded matters was that he was on holiday in the busiest time of the year, so there were many other complaints to be received and compensation to be paid out. Because he saw other guests receiving compensation, he too wanted a piece of the action. So on top of his torrent of daily abuse he worked on any possible ruse to get money out of the tour operator, which the rep had by now decided wasn't going to happen.

Half way through his holiday he determined that he wanted to hire a car for a few days, but he hadn't brought his licence with him. The rep volunteered to help and said that if he faxed DVLA and gave his name, address, date of birth and credit card details, they would fax out a copy for a nominal fee, which they would take off the credit card. Instead of saying thanks for the help, he unnecessarily bellowed, "you do it!" and made the rep take down his full details including the credit card. The rep duly faxed DVLA and a day later they had efficiently sent a faxed copy of the guest's driving licence, only for him to go and hire a car with someone other than the rep. Unbeknown to the guest, the rep had kept his original fax and had stored it away for future use.

By the end of his holiday three reception ladies were refusing to come to work, as were two waiters and three others had to be restrained from thumping the guest in the midst of a crowded restaurant. The rep however still managed to keep his cool and despite the incessant stream of abuse and insults, he remained polite and calm at all times, until two days before the guy was due to leave and he'd asked him why he hadn't received any compensation yet. The rep replied that it was because nothing was wrong and that the company had acted correctly throughout, which was true, and the guest asked him in turn if it was because he wasn't white.

"Not at all," he replied, keeping his calm on a topic which he found particularly riling.

"I think it is. I think it's because we're not white and you're a racist!"

"I assure you it's not, because that is the last thing in the world you could accuse me of."

"Oh no, I see the picture now. You're a f***ing racist. You're a f***ing Nazi Racist."

"I think you'd better calm down now sir."

"You Nazi racist C***! Give me money as compensation for being a racist."

Well that happened to be the proverbial straw that broke the camel's back and the rep looked him square in the eye, with a stare that would have covered the Sahara with ice and said.

"I am not a racist. My girlfriend happens to be black, my best mate is Indian and if you ever talk to me in that manner again I'll ensure that you spend the rest of your life blowing your nose out of the back of your head. Now I suggest you leave and come nowhere near me in the future."

Of course, the guest ignored him and continued to insult whoever he could for the final two days of his stay.

Some months later, the rep in question was at home on a two-month break before heading off to his next resort, when he found a copy of the guest's fax that was sent to the DVLA. The following Sunday he bought everyone of the weekend papers and although it cost a mini fortune in postage he replied to every advert he could think of on the guest's behalf. In the following six weeks the guest would have received pornography, double glazing, pizzas, duvets, magazines, videos, ducks to go on the walls, that Thora Hird stair lift thing, walk in baths, cement, a Gazebo, potted plants, lots of signed photo's and photo frames, bed linen, carpets, lighting, a three piece suite, baby clothes and finally a huge credit card bill, which could only be reduced by going through the whole inconvenience of sending the whole lot back.

Thankfully, I have never had to resort to such extremes, but today I did wreak a smidgeon of my own personal vengeance. The early morning flight was due to land about two hours late and because we all knew in advance we decided to inform guests on the coaches, on the way to the airport.

When we get a delay it is important that all of the guests are informed at roughly the same time and that they are given the exact same information. Otherwise all hell can break lose, with Chinese whispers playing havoc and before you know it the delay has stretched to five hours, the airport is being closed down and we'll all starve of oxygen as extra terrestrials invade the planet, when in fact it could arrive only an hour late, because of tail winds or head winds or some such aeronautical term. But today we'd all been briefed fully that the flight was coming in two hours late because of air traffic control reasons, so we were able to get the information across and avoid any confusion. Everyone seemed to take it very well, except for one guest from the Dona Santa Maria, who decided to make it his personal mission to ruin my day. As soon as we got off the coach he started calling me all the names under the sun. He insulted our company, the airline and Goa, but his favourites were reserved for me.

I can picture the guy now, with his bald head, beer belly and a resplendent pink vest which helped display his array of henna tattoos. Plus he had skinny legs; a crooked nose and his breath stank to high heaven of whisky. I don't need to elaborate too much, because this is a situation we get regularly throughout a season and we're trained to deal with it, but I gather a slight picture has been painted. However, I was still pissed off about being moved down south and annoyed at having to look after the office over Christmas as well. Combine this with the fear of the busiest week of the year looming and the fact that I didn't even have the refuge of a comfortable room to go home to and I was ready to unleash some of my pent up fury. I decided to get my own back a little.

I had a quiet word with the flight-handling agent, whom I had bought a big box of chocolates for Christmas a week earlier, and when the guest approached the counter we stuck on a luggage tag for Finland instead of Gatwick. This meant that it would be a week until he saw his luggage, at the very least, and I managed to improve my disposition tenfold by getting my own back, in a tiny little way.

By about midday I arrived at the SJM with forty odd guests all waiting to check-in. After we had given them all their allocated rooms and sent them off with porters, two couples had already returned and complained about the state of the complex and asked to move, which I thought was a bit unfair, after all of the efforts I'd made the day before to secure their rooms in the first place. I showed them the brochure, asked where they wanted to go and then showed them the price difference, not knowing if rooms were available. The gamble paid off because they balked at the gulf in price between the hotels, the SJM is only £7 per night per person, and walked off in a huff.

I thought that was the worst part of the day over and done with and desperately needed to grab a sandwich, a shower and get an hour's kip before starting all over again, but yet again the receptionist couldn't find my key. This time it wasn't because the key was lost, it was because they had given my room to some guests and they'd thrown all of my belongings into some boxes and put them all into a store room. I took ten deep breaths while I waited to speak to the manager, tried all of my calming techniques and then went ballistic.

I was on the verge of losing all semblance of control at the busiest period of the year; a time when we especially need to be on our guard, perform at the peak of our powers and must be ready to deal with anything. I couldn't believe that they'd thrown my stuff out of a room and were prepared to leave me on the street. They assumed that I'd get a room in another hotel, but no rooms were available anywhere in Goa, because if there are any rooms empty after the Europeans have come in, the hotels sell them to people from Bombay at exorbitant rates. I spent thirty minutes in the manager's office refusing to let anyone else come in, not even Gina who had a mountain of problems herself, until he agreed to give me a room. Ten minutes later I was shoved into the only available shoebox, which happened to be overlooking the main swimming pool so every guest would know where I lived. Again I had no shower, but was presented instead with a leaking toilet, dirty floors, a broken bed and wires hanging out everywhere. I got out the clothes that I needed, rearranged my paperwork, grabbed a sandwich and then spent the next five hours in the same clothes I'd had on since 03:30 that morning. I did four welcome meetings, where the turnouts were poor, but for once my sales were good.

I was again forced to stay at Gina's, which is not the way I was hoping our relationship would develop, by being forced into a closeted relationship, rather than choosing to spend happy moments together. We'd both had shit days and were despondent about our futures in the industry, which is normal during these stressful and highly emotional periods and is something we simply have to work our way through. I was determined to make the SJM pay for treating a fellow in the service industry so badly and rather foolishly took it out on Gina.

We slept with our backs to each other once again.

THURSDAY – 24TH DECEMBER

Christmas Eve is upon us and I hadn't even seen it coming. I think the same can be said for most of the reps, because this has been a busy period and we've been more concerned about ensuring our bookings are confirmed; that the flights are on time and dealing with the unrelenting spate of problems that the SJM is inflicting upon us, which are all down to the incompetence of the hotel management.

We've not noticed the gaudy decorations that have slowly been going up in the villages, the more tasteful ones in the finer hotels, which are resplendent with subtle, flashing white lights and models of Jesus lying in a straw filled manger and sleeping in a fairy liquid crib. The SJM have not been so imaginative, mind, and have festooned the place with glaring red and blue light bulbs, lashings of bright red crepe paper in all of the buildings and a rather ironic snow scene in the window of one of the guest's rooms, which is at the entrance to the complex.

But for some reason, everybody suddenly seemed to be aware that the festive season is hovering directly above us, and amongst the reps we were forced into making last minute arrangements for our parties. The guests were wanting details of their compulsory gala dinners, which we're obliged to go to and stuff our faces with real turkey and stuffing from a tin, and automatically everyone had become overly friendly with each other, except for the guests in the SJM and my pool view woman at the Dona Santa Maria.

Just after lunch I had to move rooms yet again, or rather the SJM had done it for me and unpacked everything in my new room as well. I haven't had a chance to see if anything has gone missing and I can't find anything either, because my socks are mixed up with my toiletries in the bathroom, my shirts are lying in a heap in one of the drawers, while my collection of old fashioned football shirts have taken pride of place on the hangers and everything else is either on or under the bed.

I had to sort out my paper work yet again, re-iron my work shirts and trousers and find my bearings in the complex, because I keep walking towards the wrong room and without fail end up being collared by someone who wants to complain about their egg sandwich, the lack of chips in India, or a group of nine guests of mine, who have been nicknamed the 'Battersby's' because their kids keep pissing up against peoples walls.

Mrs Pool View is still convinced that the entertainments room is a guest room. Even though she refuses to go over and look at it, she is now propagating a theory around the pool, that there is a conspiracy amongst the reps and the hotel, that we've got spies in the room who have nothing better to do than watch the guests sunbathing all day long. Now I've got nothing against watching some nubile totty for a few hours, especially if we can get a game of volleyball going, but sitting and staring at a bunch of overweight Brits and Germans in luminous, lycra swimsuits, smoking fags and drinking pints of cheap ale, is not my idea of fun. Bless her cotton socks.

After I'd managed to half convince the woman that there were no pool view rooms, that there isn't a conspiracy, that I'm not a German in disguise and that the hotel management aren't Nazi war criminals, I then had the delights of switching rooms before dashing to the office. Once there I spent three hours on the phone and sending faxes to our UK offices in an effort to find out what our seat availability situation is for the coming weekend, because I have a guest who wants to go home early.

What I hadn't taken into account before I left, was that it was Christmas Eve. The staff in the UK stopped working properly a couple of days previously and although they were all up for an office party and extended lunch on this particular day, they had no intention of doing any work before they break off for almost a full week's holiday. This is again frustrating, because the guests don't stop being on holiday and we have to work anti-social hours everyday over Christmas without getting paid any extra for it. This meant that, after three fruitless hours on the phone lines, I couldn't get a response and so had to tell a guest that we had no flight seats available and that they would have to stay for an extra week, whilst no doubt, the likes of Stelios George would be getting drunk on champagne.

I only just made it back into resort in time for my evening visits, which thankfully passed uneventfully and for once in the SJM I had some hot water, albeit for thirty seconds. This meant I could get some semblance of a wash before heading over to Gina's and joining up with the rest of the reps for the Goa Renaissance, five star gala dinner.

I was on best behaviour with Gina, not making any sarcastic comments and I have to say she looked stunning in a purplish coloured, Chinese style dress, which hugged her figure in a way that made her look even more demure and attractive than ever. We joined the others briefly for a party at 'Mikes Place', but sneaked off at about 02:00 because we wanted some alone time to give each other our presents and also because Gina had to go to the airport at 04:00.

We entered her door and Gina slipped out of her dress to reveal matching silk underwear, which aroused me instantly and instead of unwrapping our gifts, she gave me the best Christmas present I could have hoped for. In return, I put all of my anxieties to the back of my mind and gave her my love. It was only then, at half past stupid in the morning, that I realised Christmas was upon us.

Nobody watched Mrs Pool View fall into the swimming pool in a drunken stupor.

FRIDAY – 25TH DECEMBER

Every rep has a catalogue of horror stories or amusing tales to tell and when you get a group of three or more of us around a dinner table, with a couple of beers to boot, the anecdotes will usually start flowing with the ease of water trundling over Victoria falls. After all, we are from different parts of the country, with different backgrounds, varying qualifications and entirely contrasting upbringings and the job is the one big leveller and the one binding matter that we have in common.

The stories will often include accounts relating to troublesome guests, problematic situations, overbookings, delays, deaths in resort, military coups, who we've known and what they've done, who we've slept with and what nationalities they were, big blunders we've made, how we've got our own back on people, good and bad managers and of course the number one topic of all, where we've worked before. No matter how dramatic or exciting the story and no matter how interesting the lives we lead, the one thing every rep will concur with, is that we don't get paid enough for the job we do. For example any other person who has to work Christmas day, will usually be paid an overtime rate and unless they are in something like the health service, which is another poorly looked after trade, they will probably only have to work eight hours in the day and that will most probably be from nine to five.

For me though, on my measly salary, I was meeting a coach at 06:30 and after checking its cleanliness and suitability, as well as confirming each of the pick-ups with the driver, we were picking up our first guests at 07:00. This was after a mere two hours sleep, although that part was self-inflicted. Thankfully the guests were all in the same state as I was.

There weren't many arrivals coming through on this flight, because who in their right mind would book a flight which meant seeing in Christmas over Middle Eastern air space, so the whole procedure went very well and we also had the luxury of a thirty minute delay. This gave Sharon, Ruth and myself time to exchange presents on one of our coaches, whilst the drivers were fast asleep on another.

I managed to get back into resort by about 15:00, dashed round to Gina's, dragged her out of bed and we squeezed in a couple of hours on the beach, sipping cocktails, soaking up the sun and having chicken curry and rice for our Christmas dinner. We weren't too bothered by this non-traditional lunch though, because we were meeting up with a few of the other reps in the evening, this time for the Dona Santa Maria gala dinner.

The night was actually very well run, because they had taken an area away from the centre of the complex, but still to the side of the pool where the two tennis courts usually are. The hard court area was surrounded by bright lights, a huge stage was erected at one end, the centre being a cleverly marked out dance area and at the other end was another comprehensive buffet display, with yet more Turkey and still no bacon. Surrounding the courts was plenty of space on the grassy verge, where tables and chairs were laid out, with helium balloons protruding from the centre of each table, wishing everyone a Happy Christmas.

The food was very tasty and abundant in its supply and the drinks had started to flow, although I was taking it a little easy because I was strangely conscious of the driving laws. The band were playing their full repertoire of Christmas songs and popular numbers, which included the inevitable La Bamba, and the dance floor was crowded with three hundred people having a fantastic party. At one stage I leant over to Toni, the rep for our parent company for this hotel, and pointed out an elderly couple who were jiving completely in tune with each other. I remarked upon how nice it is that some couples remain so close for all of their lives and that I'd like to find that some day. She just laughed and said the drink was making me sentimental.

Before I had a chance to refute the remark about the drink, the compere suddenly came onto the microphone and asked if there was a doctor in the vicinity, because a guest was having a cardiac arrest. An audible hush reverberated around the area, together with whispers of "Oh my God!" and "Not on Christmas Day!" and on the other side of the dance floor from us, we could see a frantic moving of chairs, and people hurriedly standing up, yet looking down to a central figure on the ground.

Toni and I looked at each other and almost in unison exclaimed, "Christ. I hope it's not one of mine!"

Despite our initial response however, we both stood up, moved our chairs out of the way and dashed over to where the gentleman was lying prone on the floor. We had followed in the wake of a doctor, who was even more alert and were relieved to see a solitary lady, who happened to be one of my guests, attempting CPR. The doctor got down and I followed suit to lend a helping hand, whilst the hotel manager had hurtled to the reception area to call for an ambulance, or at least some form of transport to take him to the nearest hospital.

The doctor took one look, checked his pulse quickly and said there wasn't a lot of hope, but we should get him to a hospital as soon as was humanly possible. I picked him up from behind slipping my arms under his armpits and clenching them together around his chest, whilst two other guys grabbed him by the waist and supported the lower part of his body. I felt something wet on my left sleeve and assumed it was sweat, because it was racing off my forehead. We moved as quickly as we could through the crowd of bewildered onlookers, past the pool, through the reception, and out to the foyer entrance where a car was waiting, because there were no ambulances available.

As it had later transpired, there are three emergency ambulances available within a fifteen kilometre radius, but one was on a break for the night, the second was available but the crew were all drunk and the third had a fit and healthy crew, but the ambulance had broken down and needed a new battery, which they wouldn't get until after Christmas.

After we loaded him into the car, his wife hopped in, as did the lady who had been attempting CPR to comfort his wife, and in the meantime someone had told me he was out on holiday with our sister company. As the car sped off, I got on the phone to the manager to inform her of the situation and to also find out where I could get hold of her rep for the south. She was at another gala dinner, with some of her guests at a hotel nearby and within five minutes I had picked her up and we were heading towards the hospital in Margao. We got there in record time, to find what we had already suspected. Dead on arrival.

He died as soon as he'd hit the floor, which in a way was a blessing. As his wife kept bravely saying, he'd died in the middle of a dream holiday, somewhere they'd planned to visit for the past ten years or so and it meant that he would have passed away at one of his happiest moments in life. He was automatically put into cold storage and because they were originally due to travel home in two days time, a post mortem was arranged for the following morning at 09:00.

We went back to the hotel and I shared a drink with my guest who had been involved, hoping to comfort her having been through many similar situations myself in the past. The rep I'd collected spent a couple of hours with the gentleman's wife, who was unbelievably brave, and they went through all of the insurance details getting some of the heartless, yet necessary, paperwork out of the way.

We were there until about 03:00 dealing with the formalities, but even when we'd initially returned, the nosy sick bastards, who like a bit of juicy gossip around the pool in the mornings and love to stir things up, had already started a few malicious rumours. In the first five minutes of sitting in the lobby I heard:

"The hotel was too slow to react!"

"It was food poisoning!"

"He was drinking heavily!"

"He was an alcoholic!"

"He choked on the food!"

"The reps should have saved his life!"

"Why isn't there a doctor on site?"

And these were just a sample. To propagate a heartfelt opinion, these people are stupid, ignorant, interfering, meddlesome bastards, with nothing better to do with their time than create malicious and scandalous stories, not one of which is true, or has any bearing in the circumstances. They only serve to display their own insensitivity at a difficult time for a marvellous lady, who showed more dignity in her little finger nail than the average, malignant idiot who wanted their big shot opinion to be heard.

The only thing that can be said to these people is that: You're in India, a third world country whose Medicare is not up to the same standards that we are fortunate enough to have in the UK. This isn't an episode of 'Casualty'. Sometimes, for reasons only the gods above us can explain, people die.

By the time I got back to the SJM it was 03:30, with Gina having long since departed for her hotel. She'd asked me to come back, but I wasn't in the mood for company and thought solitude was the best answer to deal with my haywire emotions. To compound my luck I'd locked myself out and was forced to sit at the entrance steps to the lobby, while the night porter went to find either a spare or a master key. As I was sat there, with my head in my hands trying to make sense of what had just happened and asking myself if I could have done more to help, two of the guests who had wanted to leave the moment they arrived in the hotel, came walking by.

"Ahh, it's the rep." I heard the guy slightly slur and I looked up, with fatigue burning my eyes, to see him approaching me.

"Hi." I muttered. "Happy Christmas to you. Have you had a good dinner?"

"Bollocks to that you f***er. I've had a good Christmas because my wife is with me, but you and this f***ing shit hole for a hotel that we're staying in can go to hell!"

"Okay," I again murmured, trying to ignore him, "Happy Christmas to you too."

"This hotel is shit. You've done nothing to help us. You're useless, you're company is a pile of shit and I'm going to be suing you personally young man!"

"Peace and goodwill to all men"

"And don't think that because it's Christmas I'm not going to complain, because I'm prepared to make your life a living hell until you get me out of here."

"A time for rejoicing and celebrating the birth of Christ. Cast away your worries and your materialistic gains for now is the time of the righteous man," I again said, but under my breath rather than out loud, because although he probably couldn't hear me seeing that he was a little too drunk to do so, I still didn't want any trouble; I genuinely feared what I may do to him as opposed to what he may inflict on me.

In the meantime his wife had walked on ahead, obviously tired of her husband's drunken ramblings and I hoped that he would follow her and soon. His drunken bravado was not what I needed at this juncture and I was on the point of losing all control, which was why I'd been taking deep breaths, repeating nice Christian virtues and trying to ignore him. The sadness of the earlier situation and the anger that he was instilling into me were building, like a fireball in the pit of my stomach and rapidly working their way through the whole of my body, coursing violence through my veins and urging me to lash out, so that they could free themselves and unleash their full fury on this complete and utter Tosser.

I repeated my made up mantras under my breath and took a few more deep breaths. His wife called him over and realising he wasn't going to get a response from me, he sidled over to her muttering something about what a Wanker I was and how he would get me in the morning.

I was thankfully left in peace for the next ten minutes, before the night porter returned to let me into my room. I closed the door behind me, thought about how £450 a month is not enough for what we do for a living and again gulped down some strained deep breaths. As I did this, I smelled for the first time the vomit that the dying man had dribbled onto my left arm and it all came rushing through like a tidal wave.

I sat on my bed and wept.

SUNDAY – 27TH DECEMBER

Yesterday morning I was told by the SJM that they weren't able to accept three of our rooms because they simply had no rooms available. I was about to try and argue the point and try and charm their way back in by playing on the fact that I saved them eight rooms the week before and they've messed me around a lot in the past week. But the hotel explained that they had been forced to do the same with almost seventy other rooms with the various other operators, so I promised to deal with our three rooms on the understanding that they wouldn't touch my own room. Ordinarily I would be over the moon at the SJM turning away our bookings, because that would mean three less complaints to deal with. But in the week in between Christmas and New Year, it is 200%, absolutely, completely and totally impossible to find an available room anywhere in the state.

I spent five hours ringing every one of our hotels and then I rang every hotel and guesthouse in Goa that was listed in the phone directories, all to no avail, because every one of them was full and had a healthy waiting list to boot. I was rewarded with a stroke of luck in the early evening though, when one of our hotels in the North rang me back and said that they had received some cancellations from Bombay and they could take the three rooms, but only the three rooms, which I was delighted with. Although it still meant having to tell the guests when they arrive.

As it turned out, all of the couples were quite reasonable about the situation. One couple had already heard negative comments about the SJM so they were not that disappointed, a point which they thankfully iterated to the other couples. Although upset and disappointed at being told at the airport they still took the news quite well and were sold on going to the busier Northern resorts. This was the first stroke of luck I'd received all Christmas and it's a shame it didn't last for long.

The evening was one of those nights which just go from bad to worse, where it seems that you start off with a small problem, but with every corner you turn you walk into a bigger problem, which snowballs. This in turn leads you to another corner, where the snowball increasingly grows so large that you expect it to eventually come crashing down on top of you at any second.

I left my room after getting time for a shower and headed to the SJM reception for my 16:00 Welcome Meeting, map in hand, cheesy grin permanently attached and doing a good job of shaking off the effects of having been up since 02:30. Only two couples were due to come to the meeting, which should be a doddle and I'd be able to get away by 17:00 to go onto the next of my four meetings scheduled for that night.

I was drawing to a close of what I thought had been a positive chat and was just leaning down to fold up my map, when the younger of the couples stated they weren't happy with the hotel and demanded a move.

"I'm sorry you're not happy with the hotel and to be frank I do understand your situation. Now it's my policy, as I've just said in this little meeting, that if I can do anything to make your stay more enjoyable, then I will, because at the end of the day you're happy and it makes my job a lot easier, because I don't want a lot of unhappy people in hotels making my life a misery. But unfortunately there are no rooms available anywhere. This is the single busiest period of the year in Goa and there are just no rooms available until Saturday the second of January, which unfortunately is the day before you go home."

I tried to be polite, calm and charming and I desperately hoped they'd understand what I was saying and more importantly accept it, so that I could head off to my next meeting.

"We don't believe you and we want to move now!"

Oh great. Someone demanding to move and I can do nothing at all for them. I hate this part of the job, because it's in my nature to want to help people and I don't enjoy being hated, especially when it's not my fault.

"I'm sorry. But I spent over five hours on the phone yesterday trying to find rooms, which are just not available. There are no rooms to be had in Goa at the moment. I really wish I could help but I just don't see how. I'm ever so sorry."

"But there's got to be a way. I don't think you're trying hard enough."

As I've mentioned before, being accused of lying or having my integrity questioned is something that really winds me up, so again a few more deep breaths, which I seem to be doing a lot of recently. I stood up, took the phone book off the reception counter, handed it to them and said,

"If you can find a room where I can't, then be my guest and if you do find a hotel that has availabilities please let me know, because I have about a dozen other guests in various hotels who would be interested in coming with you."

At which point they stormed off, muttering words about suing me personally and contacting Watchdog, or had I just heard too much of that in recent weeks. Before I could put my pen and clipboard into my briefcase I heard, "Before you go, can we have a quick word" and as all of the reps know, there is no such thing in this hotel.

I then spent from 16:00 until 23:30 in that f***ing hotel, dealing with people requesting to leave, complaining about the gala dinner, the food, the rooms, the maintenance, the service, insects, sewerage, you name it they found something about it to complain about. And most of them demanded a change of hotel on top. Just to aid matters the management of the hotel, who knew that problems were brewing, had disappeared for the day and were nowhere to be seen, so the reps that were in the hotel couldn't get any practical problems resolved.

I desperately felt for most of my guests, because the majority of their complaints were genuine and dealt with issues that I have written endless reports about. But I had to be polite, calm and reiterate the same points over and over, which made me feel useless. I also couldn't get any back up from the company in the UK, because of course there is no one in the offices on the Sunday after Boxing Day and I didn't want to call Kate because she had just come back off a long flight, after a traumatic week and didn't need the burden.

To his credit, Ravi remained in the office most of the day and night, even though he has a young wife he should be spending time with, and he frantically rang round hotels he knows, trying to find rooms and attempting to call in some favours wherever possible, all to little avail. In the meantime, all I could do was muddle along as best I could, churning out the, "there are no rooms," spiel and, "I'm sorry." And hope that something could be resolved the following day.

I had to ring my other hotels to re-arrange their Welcome Meetings, which meant that I couldn't give those guests the full service they deserve and we'd be on the back foot with them for the next two weeks and I'd make no money out of anyone through excursion sales this week.

By the end of the night I'd driven three guests, in my own car, to a half built hotel in the middle of nowhere, for them to view and accept it and also pay for it entirely out of their own pockets at full rack rate. I'd arranged for eight rooms to change hotels as of the Second of January; moved three other rooms out of the hotel temporarily only for them to come back into the hotel for three days over the New Year period and then back to their chosen locations afterwards. I also promised an abundance of room changes in the future and desperately tried to keep my temper in check with Mr. Rude from Xmas night, who only came over looking for an argument.

I'd also had to have a word with the Battersby's to instruct them to keep the noise levels down, and stop pissing at random in the complex, because we'd received so many complaints about them and the hotel was wanting to call the police. That would have been an answer for me though, because it would have released three rooms for the rest of us to play with. But in the end I had to make do with narrowly averting a mass brawl between them and a nosy group from Gina's company who'd had enough, but could only say what they felt with the reassurance of a rep standing in between them and a beating.

I was threatened four times and frequently called useless, lazy, ignorant, unhelpful, a Wanker and a Tosser as well as complimented for keeping my calm and poise in a demanding role. I was bribed, cajoled, bullied and flirted with in an attempt to get people out of the hotel and still no management were in sight. As an indication of how busy we were, Gina and two other reps were all in the hotel at the same time for similar periods and we didn't even get to exchange sympathetic and knowing glances, let alone say something like, "Hi" or "I know".

At 23:30, having missed Liverpool beat Newcastle 4-2, I was tired, hungry and thirsty; I crawled into bed with a strange thought for that time of the night.

Seven years ago guests used to say, "I'd love to do your job!" Now they only state, "I wouldn't do what you do, for all the tea in China!"

MONDAY – 28TH DECEMBER

After a successful Welcome Meeting in the Dona Santa Maria in the morning, where I again topped £50 per head, which almost saved my week, I desperately chased around the rest of my hotels in the afternoon, trying to catch up with the guests I'd missed the night before.

From 17:00 onwards in the SJM it was exactly the same as the night before, except that I finished at 22:30, which is an hour earlier, but still didn't get a chance to say hi to my beloved.

I graciously accepted Kate's offer to come down and help and she did the rest of my visits in the other hotels, so that I could stay in the SJM and give the guests my full attention and take the full amount of their crap. I still couldn't move anyone, still couldn't do any room changes, but the management did turn up. Although they didn't take any responsibility and deflect any of the problems away from us, when it was them who had caused them in the first place, it did mean that we were able to get a few technical things, like leaking toilets and broken windows fixed.

At present, I don't really think all the tea in China is payment enough for doing this job.

TUESDAY – 29TH DECEMBER

I again had a similar day to the past two, which was intensified by a rush up to the office to hand in my liquidation and abundance of reports that have been hastily and savagely written about the SJM and Dona Santa Maria.

It was actually a relief to get away from the South of Goa for a few hours, but the extra workload and tiring journey, meant I had no time for a siesta and went straight back into my swarming mob of people at the SJM, none of whom I was in a position to help. This time I finished just after 22:00, a nervous, frazzled, gibbering wreck and in dire need of a long, cool glass of beer.

Since Christmas Day I've seen nothing of Gina because we've both been as busy and as tired as the other. The effort of changing clothes and driving round to the other's room is too much, when all you want to do is curl up and simultaneously put one day behind you and prepare for the next. It also doesn't help, that at this special time of year, when we are away from our families (who I haven't had time to call yet) that I can't even find the time to spend it with people who I care about, because I have been surrounded by people who have forgotten what season it is and who have all taken a big dislike to me. As Roxy Music profoundly sang once, 'Loneliness is a crowded room' and that is what I've been overwhelmed with in recent days.

However, I don't know if it would have done a lot of good if Gina and I had seen a bit of each other, because we would have both been in miserable spirits and whereas she would have wanted to talk about things, I would have been quite happy to bottle things up and pretend nothing had happened at work. This would have led to a heated conversation about why I'm not opening up to her and then she would have received the pent up fury of my relationship anxieties. This would not only upset her greatly, but is something she doesn't need right now, because she has even bigger problems than I do at the SJM.

So in my slightly offbeat, bizarre way of thinking, I felt it best to keep away from her in an effort to maintain our relationship. Because we have avoided any confrontation, I have avoided hurting her feelings, thus keeping some form of parity in the liaison and I haven't had to confront my feelings at a distressing time. It was therefore, with these reasons in mind that I neglected to call her this evening and headed to the sanctuary of the Pasta Hut in Colva for some banal conversation about cricket with a mate called Popot.

I sat down in front of the T.V. screen and ordered a curry and rice, a big bottle of beer with a whisky chaser and almost immediately lamented my decision to watch the 4th test between England and Australia. I ignored everyone around me, except Popot's ludicrous theories about proposed changes to the LBW rule, and after three or four drinks I finally started to feel myself beginning to unwind.

By 02:00 I staggered along the beach to our favourite club for some more glycerine laden booze and by chance bumped into Gina and her mate Terri, who I am also beginning to fancy a little bit nowadays. I'm not too sure if Gina was pleased to see me or not, especially considering my rapidly deteriorating state of sobriety, but she made polite conversation as I weighed up the pros and cons of asking the two girls for a threesome. Things were obviously not too rosy in the garden, which made me wonder if my thoughts of a ménage a trois were said out loud in error, or whether I had been staring at Terri a bit too lecherously or not. It didn't matter because the girls left shortly afterwards, leaving me to wallow in my drunken night of freedom.

A couple of hours later I decided to follow them and gradually forced my way across the beach, still being just about sober enough to appreciate the stars and the moonlight, until I reached one of the bridges which leads onto the main square in Colva. As I started to cross it, I noticed two guys stumbling in the opposite direction, one of whom was as inebriated as I was and quite obviously looking for a spot of trouble.

I would have to say that apart from the odd game of football where I've lost my temper, I am a very passive person. I'm someone who will always opt for the safer option of talking my way out of a situation, and although I won't run away, I have no intention of getting into a brawl unnecessarily. I have been in a couple of stand off's over the years, but haven't actually been in a fight since I was eleven years of age. However, with the emotions that have been bottled up over the past week and the rage that has been growing, but has been forcibly suppressed, I wasn't in the mood to back down over something petty like a piece of bridge.

As they got closer I saw them mutter something to each other and smile, and as anyone who has ever been under the influence of alcohol will know, paranoia kicks in and I was convinced they were talking about me. This was compounded by their simultaneous laugh and glance in my direction, which made it look as if they had a perfect bullying opportunity. One was decidedly braver than the other and I presume fairly inebriated, because as they got closer I saw from a mile away, that he was preparing to drop his shoulder into me as we passed. For me to notice this in my worse than steady state, must have meant that his move had been telegraphed.

This gave me a second or two to gather myself and as they drew level, I remained true to my path in the middle of the bridge and the braver guy duly did as I expected. As he lowered his shoulder into mine, I stepped back, which left him slightly off balance, and I then applied pressure with my own shoulder, using his weight and my fury to send him spinning backwards. I smiled, stuck my chest out and kept on walking nice and casually until we were about ten metres apart. It was then, that having regained his balance and realising that there were two of them, he very bravely shouted, "F****ing Asshole!" proving to himself that he was a man after all and that his penis must be all of three inches. They turned away and headed along the bridge, content in their own minds that they'd proved themselves as honourable warriors, in the safe knowledge that this drunken fool would be long gone. What they hadn't allowed for, was someone who had taken as much abuse that he could handle without retaliation and this was his ideal opportunity to vent as much of it as possible.

I turned on my heels and went running over to them, screaming, "Who are you f***king calling an asshole, you cowards! You have something to say, you say it to my face!"

I stood only inches away from the bigger guy's face and I could smell the cheap vodka on his breath mixed with stale cigarette smoke and there was no way I was going to back down. The problem was I didn't know what to do next. Because I'm never usually involved in fights, I'm usually the one in the middle with a calm rational voice making the peace but on this occasion I could feel some of the tension draining away and I was unnaturally enjoying myself. So whereas in normal circumstances I would proceed to laugh something like this off, shake hands, offer my apologies and buy the guys a beer, I was actually prepared for a showdown of Ali/Frazier proportions, if only I could think of what to do.

The smaller of the two was plainly more sober and he pulled his mate back for a second, but the big guy resisted because he was in the mood for pounding the living daylights out of me. He drew his hands up and shoved me hard in the chest. After recovering my balance I squared up to him and shoved him equally as hard, although he didn't fall back as far as I had.

His mate was telling us to calm down, but instead of doing so he shouted "Yeah!" to which I rather eloquently replied, "Yeah!" We had reached an impasse where it was time for fight or flight.

We repeatedly asked and answered ourselves with the solitary word, "Yeah?!" and were still shoving each other, albeit a little more gently now. As both of us started to sober up a little, the realisation of what may happen if we were to fight began to dawn on us. We were still at a cock's strutting, chests pushed firmly out, posturing stand off and one of us had to decide to throw the first punch or back down. The latter of which neither of us were prepared to do, but the former was also beginning to look a bit unlikely. The smaller of the guys had obviously picked up on this, because he decided to stop holding his mate back and told him to kick my ass, before shoving me in the chest himself. This riled me again and I defiantly shouted, "Yeah? You want some too?" and again stupidly pushed both of them back.

They glanced at each other with a look that said, we can take this guy without hurting ourselves and advanced a step towards me. I wouldn't move back, but the futility of getting beaten up was now beginning to dawn on me, so I had to decide which one I was going to hit first and then work out how I could avoid being caught by the other. Otherwise I had to depart as quickly as my legs could carry me.

I opted to strike the bigger of the two, in an attempt to intimidate the other one and as we engaged in another bout of "Yeah's!" I heard someone shout something in Konkani behind me. Momentarily I froze, realising that I was outnumbered and that I was going to get a physical beating to go with all of the verbal ones I'd received over the past few days. I braced myself for the first blow and was surprised to see the two guys burst out laughing, instead of raining in with punches. I turned around and saw Dilpak, the head taxi driver from outside the SJM who was standing there with a huge grin all over his face. The guys said something back to him in Konkani, said sorry to me and walked off laughing, heading in the direction of the beach club. I looked at Dilpak and asked him what he had just said and he simply muttered something about bringing back a group of drivers to back me up and also the fact that these guys own a restaurant in Colva, and with me being a rep and him in charge of a group of influential taxi drivers, between the two of us we could ruin their business.

I have to admit that I was grateful that he'd turned up, because who knows what may have happened, aside from a lot more vain posturing, but it transpired that he wasn't there entirely by accident. After dropping Gina and Terri off, they had sent him back to pick me up, because they were worried (rightly) that I might have driven home in a drunken stupor. He took me back to Gina's and along the way he commented that it pays to look after your friends, which I think was borne out of genuine friendship and not a threat. He was right though, because the effort I made to get on with the drivers when I first started in the SJM and the occasional bit of business I have given them, was certainly advantageous to my fortunes this evening.

As he dropped me off, I thanked him yet again; he refused any payment for the journey and told me to talk to Gina and stop acting like a fool and be more like the old Ceri he liked two weeks ago. I knew he had a point, but a defensive barrier went up and my paranoia resurfaced as I convinced myself that Gina had been talking about our relationship to a taxi driver. I knocked on her door, with all of these foolish thoughts running through my head and a little anger still simmering from my run-in with the guys on the bridge. I was nowhere near close to releasing my tensions from the past weeks, but realised that he was right, I should talk to Gina, but I also knew that if I did, she would take it as a sign of true commitment, which is a signal I wasn't prepared to emit.

She sleepily answered the door, said "Oh it's you", didn't smile and then walked back to her bed. I took an unreasonable dislike to her turning her back on me, so took off my clothes, climbed into bed, turned my back on her, so that we were on far sides of the bed from each other and tried to sleep. But I couldn't because I was shaking uncontrollably.

Gina leant over, her mood softening as she sympathised with me a smidgeon and she put her arms around me, squeezed tight and tried to start a conversation. I felt as if I was being suffocated and was desperately confused. I adore this girl, but was still not prepared to let her in, so to compromise I attempted to keep a slight barrier between us. I was also perturbed by my earlier rage, which was so uncharacteristic and that was beginning to frighten me more than the fact that I could have been hurt, because usually I have a warm and giving nature. I was further confused because I was still trying to take in the near hysteria and selfishness of the guests over the past few days, I'd had no time for thoughts for myself, I still hadn't had time to take in what had happened to the gentleman on Christmas Day and I wanted to be with Gina.

She kept hugging and stroking me, and although I thought that this is what I wanted, I kept pushing her away deciding I wanted to be left alone. I was being very selfish and wasn't thinking about how this may affect Gina's feelings or attitude towards me and if anything ever goes wrong between us in the future, this will probably be seen as a defining moment.

She tried to hold me some more and I again shrugged her off, lost in my own selfish abyss of misery. She turned to the middle of the bed and started weeping; presumably at the thought of the man she loves keeping her at arms length. And that was what made me lose all sense of control.

I blurted everything out that had played on my mind over the past seven years. Ranging from the crap I've been taking recently, how I'm not happy in my job, the selfish guilt at the death on Christmas Day, how I've never had anyone to talk to about a military coup in The Gambia or the massacre that happened in Luxor, the fact that I lost a soulmate as a result of the coup and is something I've never truly understood or come to terms with. I cried about other deaths I've had to deal with, friends I'm no longer in touch with, the fact that I don't want to commit just yet, not until I've found my direction in life and I don't know what I'm doing or where I'm going or even where I want to be. Christmas Day was the first time I'd cried in eight years and this was the second, and once I'd opened the floodgates, the whole damn lot wanted to come pouring out.

Poor Gina, she didn't know what had hit her or what to do. This guy she's become attached to, who is always self-assured, joking, laughing, easy going, relaxed, in control of everything and usually so unaffected by the job had just opened up, pretty much on her insistence, and unleashed every anxiety in her direction.

She tried to hug me again, but I didn't want to be held. She tried to comfort me, but I didn't want sympathy and she tried to talk, but I wasn't prepared to listen. She could merely lie there, next to me in bed, while I sobbed and continued to blurt and the more I did, the more helpless and distant she felt. I eventually drifted off into a comfortable sleep. Gina had a restless and tormented night.

THURSDAY – 31ST DECEMBER

I hate New Years Eve. I know exactly why and I've always done so, since I've been old enough to go out and celebrate by getting steaming drunk, snogging any old hag I can see and falling down before going home. For me it's one big anti-climax and it's entirely shallow and false.

Throughout the preceding week people start to get quite worked up, dresses are bought (or hand stitched as the case may be in Goa), parties are prepared, booze is bought, hair is cut and plans are finalised for a riotous night of drunkenness and debauchery. So many people that I have come across, get unbelievably worked up by the whole ticking of a clock, but to me that is all it is, a moment when the long hand and the short hand meet at the highest point of every timepiece, as they do twice a day, every day of the year. It means that when midnight eventually arrives and all the food has been eaten, the booze has been consumed and Auld Lang sang has been sung, nobody really knows what to do, except say, "Happy New Year", which to me, does not an evening make. As a result the whole thing dissipates and people thin out quicker than my receding hairline.

Also, for this particular fiesta, you get all of the mind numbingly, dreary people, who for every other night of the year very rarely make a public appearance after dark, coming out to enjoy the jovial spirit and general bonhomie that should be prevalent. But they end up being legless on two glasses of spritzer and tell the whole world that they love them. Now don't get me wrong, I am all for being a happy drunk and anything that brings people of many different races, backgrounds and communities together is sacred in my book, if it were to be sincere and everlasting. But why should I spend the time of night with persons unknown, who for 364 nights of the year never bother to say hello to me in passing and I never get the opportunity to mumble a faint cheers or a drunken, "I lub yous like a brubber!" to.

To me a friendship is a permanent thing to be cherished and not a fleeting "Happy New Year" at the stroke of a slow ticking clock. Plus this statement of goodwill does not mean that I will forgive a person every ill deed he or she has placed on mankind. I remember so many occasions on this over celebrated night, where people have been friendly, caring, loving and talkative and yet the following week on the bus to work they've completely ignored me and have proceeded to do so for the coming fifty-one weeks of the year. I think the evening is shallow and I find it wholly without joy. I would much rather spend a quiet evening in with a few treasured friends, sipping a fine wine and sharing our hopes for the coming twelve months.

This year started off in the same vein as many others that I can remember, but I did manage to rescue it, albeit with a little personal cost which will no doubt be argued over in the future, and it eventually turned into one of my better one's.

I'd had a long day, with thankfully few problems, but who else could complain? I'd taken note of all of the Dona Santa Maria food complaints, which had been building as the days since Christmas had passed and I'd moved everyone who was unhappy out of the SJM. Also the 'Battersbys' were thankfully leaving in the morning, which would cut out a few more daily moans and groans. One very appreciative couple, who I'd managed to move from the SJM to the Goa Renaissance, which is a leap of three stars, insisted on buying me a cocktail for 'saving their holiday' and by the time I left them, it was gone 21:30. I was supposed to be meeting Gina, and seven other attractive ladies, at the Holiday Inn gala extravaganza at 21:00, which wasn't a great start to the night and I was expecting a bit of earache for that. I dashed home to the SJM to see quite a few red-faced people strolling around outside reception, with angry looks on their faces and a few of them without any tops covering their torsos. I put this down to an early start on the alcohol, until two minutes later when I found myself in exactly the same predicament, as I realised that the whole of the complex was without water. I cursed, fumed, screamed, shouted and threw a couple of chairs around the room and then decided against going back down to the reception to find out what had happened, for fear of being surrounded by unhappy Billies. Instead I took out a couple of bottles of mineral water from the fridge, which I used to wash myself and simultaneously freeze every shrinkable part of my anatomy, before putting on my sharp suit, complete with snazzy black John Travolta shirt and then driving round to the Holiday Inn, faster than Michael Schumacher at Suzuka.

I met Gina and the girls, sat down in the beautiful surroundings and sipped at a glass of wine to take in the whole fantastic scene. They had converted the whole of the gardens into a glorious multi-national garden party, resplendent with silver hats, silver lights and helium filled silver balloons, which were tied to the back of every chair. A band was belting out Neil Diamond hits, whilst some couples were dancing and others were strolling around the glorious international buffets, with freshly prepared food from every corner of the globe. It was absolutely fantastic and I couldn't have wished for more. The girls, especially Gina, looked gorgeous and everyone was laughing and smiling. I didn't want to be there.

I didn't feel good about my current disposition or my actions, but if I'd hung around I would have upset the girls even more with my own particular morose brand of New Year morbidity, so I apologised profusely to Gina, who put a brave face on things and bade my farewells.

Thirty minutes later, after a pit stop at home for a change of clothes and to pick up a bottle of Chivas Regal, I was sitting in one of my mates rooms supping at glasses of whisky, watching Elvis Presley movies on TNT and chuffing away on my last two Cuban cigars. As far as I'm concerned it's the perfect way to see in the New Year, with good company, good whisky and talking about football, music and girls!!

At about 04:00 I crawled round to Gina's where I had my first shag of the New Year, followed by our first argument.

THURSDAY – 7TH JANUARY

"What do you mean you've received no complaints from me about the hotel. Almost every guest who comes in here fills out a complaint form."

I can't believe what I've just heard and I am mortally astounded. Not only does this man have the effrontery to stare me square in the eye and tell me a bare faced lie, he happens to be doing it in front of Stelios George who is passing through Goa for three days to tie up a few loose ends. I've never heard a solitary good word said about Ed De Souza and now that I am meeting him in person for the first time I can see everything that they say is true.

Ed De Souza is the owner of the SJM. He is an exceedingly wealthy man, a successful businessman and he lives a life of luxury in Canada while people like his manager take the crap for his innovations in hotels like the SJM, which happens to be one of a selection of dubious operations he heads. He has a reputation for being rude, arrogant, ruthless, obnoxious, crafty, devious, manipulative, determined, focused and a bastard to work for. All the attributes you would associate with a successful businessman and a lonely social misfit, plus he has everything that will ensure that he and Stelios George are very close friends; he has flown in from Canada especially to meet Stelios.

Stelios didn't tell us he was coming into Goa and he seemed a little bit surprised and even more perturbed when I rolled through the gates of the SJM as he was warmly shaking hands goodbye with Ed; he knew that they would now have to discuss some of the issues that I have constantly been raising in my reports over the past month. Ed didn't look too pleased to see me either which was partially because he knew every rep in this hotel has an axe to grind with him and more importantly because he didn't appreciate having to deal with anyone below senior management level.

After I got out of the car and Stelios had reluctantly introduced me to Ed, a moment where neither one of us offered to shake hands such was our mutual contempt, I boldly asked if all of our problems were about to cease now that Stelios and Ed had finished their confidential meeting. I knew full well that the only matters being discussed were figures. Ed asked me what problems, trying to sound surprised but coming closer to pulling off strained and pissed off.

"Well where shall I start," I intonated in a manner that was way too patronising for Stelios's liking. "How about the lack of selection with the food, the poor quality of food, the abysmal health and safety standards, poor kitchen hygiene, dirty swimming pool, not enough sun beds, dirty rooms, dirty linen, no hot water, erratic electricity supply, unhelpful and untrained staff and guests receiving electric shocks when they take a shower?"

But if I thought I had given a glorious, triumphant performance I was to be disappointed because he wasn't the slightest bit phased. He was bored and didn't want to be having this conversation. He simply implied that he knew nothing about the list I had just reeled off, but that was hardly surprising considering he spends most of his time in Canada.

"I'm not too concerned if you didn't know about these matters Ed,"

I argued, deliberately calling him by his Christian name because I knew he insisted all of his staff referred to him as sir, "but now that you are here I would like to know what you're going to do about the ongoing concerns."

I could see Ramesh, the hotel's manager, smiling to himself in the distance, vainly hoping that he would receive some senior back up for a change.

"Well how can I do something about these things when I know nothing about them?"

"With the greatest of respect, you know about them now and after taking a month of abuse because of the inadequacy of this hotel I would like to know what you will be doing to improve matters?"

"Ceri" Stelios interrupted, "I think we should move indoors and calm down."

I noticed that Ed was glaring at him, almost ordering him to keep his staff under control otherwise he would be in danger of losing his precious contract. However, I didn't care, because I wanted this hotel dropped from our program and at this stage of the season I am not too bothered if I lose my job. We went into the manager's office.

"You have no proof that these problems have occurred because I have not heard a single thing about them!" he stubbornly replied. Ramesh was now with us, seeing as it was his office we were standing in, and I could see the mixed emotions on his face. I felt he quite enjoyed watching someone stand up to his boss, which fuelled my fire even further, but he was also fearful of any fall-out from this conversation and the repercussions it may have on him.

"You should know about them, because we've reported every single complaint."

"No you haven't. I haven't received anything from your company!" and that was where we'd reached the moment where I was on the verge of losing my temper and I shouted my earlier sentence about not being able to believe him. Stelios touched my arm and gave me a look that told me to keep quiet; I looked at Ramesh and I could see him sinking, which upset me a lot, but I had no option but to continue down this path.

"If you'll excuse me a second Ed, I'll just go and get my briefcase from the car" I replied and moved out of the office in an effort to calm down as well as the actual need for 'Briefy The Case'.

"Okay and it is Mr De Souza to you."

"Okay Ed" and I saw Ramesh smile behind his boss's back. I hoped he would forgive me.

"You say you haven't received a single complaint from me," I stated opening the case, "but as you can see I have over forty complaint forms filled out by guests and also three reports I have written on the hotel, all from the past six weeks of operation. The copies I have here are mine; the guests receive a copy, as do our customer services department and the main copy stays with the hotel. I have given a copy of every one of these to Ramesh here and as you can see he has signed them all as proof of receipt."

I gave the forms to Ed for him to see.

"Also we have received a boxful of further complaints, which have been sent into our UK offices all of which have been given to Ramesh and I know he keeps them all in his draw in his desk here. If you don't mind Ramesh, but would you please open the drawer?"

Ed's face was hotting up with rage, Stelios was a little embarrassed that someone would dare speak to his ally like this and Ramesh was almost in tears because he couldn't find any one of our complaints; his drawer was jam packed with complaints from every other tour operator and ours were low on the list of priorities, lying in the middle somewhere.

"You're lying! These aren't complaints they are compliments! Stelios please take this fool, this trouble- maker away!" which is exactly what Stelios did by ushering me outside.

"Ceri you can't speak to him like that. Mr De Souza has to be handled very gently."

"But he's just told me I'm lying, when he has stood there and blatantly tried to pull the wool over our eyes. We've got problems here and he needs to do something about them."

"I know but making him angry will not help us much. You have to calm down and you're not going to get very far in this industry if you think you can solve every problem by confronting it. Some things need to be handled delicately."

"But we're going nowhere with this property Stelios and some things need to be done. I don't see why we keep it on?"

"Because it is a good seller so it is financially good for us and we need to keep hold of it."

"I would rather you stick up for your staff than worry about one crap unit Stelios." But thankfully for me he chose one of his customary moments of not listening to his staff, just as I had accused him of treachery.

"If we are not careful we may lose this contract. Now, I am late so I must be going. You look fit. Bye."

"Bye." I offered in resignation and off he went in his chauffeur driven, air-conditioned car. I could hear Ramesh was on the wrong end of an ear bashing inside the office and I still hoped he'd find it in him to forgive me, because I knew most of the problems in the hotel were nothing to do with him. He is restricted in what he can do by the man who was ironically shouting at him for not doing what he will not let him do.

Ed De Souza came out a few minutes after Stelios had left. His face was beetroot red, his thin Bobby Charlton haircut was completely awry and his shirt was soaked through from the effort of raising his voice in the mid afternoon heat.

"Bye Ed." I said cheerfully as he climbed into his car, knowing full well that there would be no improvements, but at least I'd got some semblance of what I felt off my chest and I had provoked a reaction from the owner. Every little victory counts, I suppose.

"It's Mr De Souza to you!"

"I know Ed."

SATURDAY – 9TH JANUARY

One of the consistent problems I've had in these past weeks is that I've had very little quality time to myself. The work is long and tiring, but that is the same in most resorts so that can't be the soul reason for the black clouds, which have been a permanent fixture above my head. The thing is I've allowed it to get on top of me and I haven't allowed myself to have any fun.

If you ask most reps why they've got into the industry, with the exception of Club 18-30 reps who just want to add to their collection of venereal diseases, they will always say it was for the travel and the way of life. This is most certainly true of myself, someone who never used to waste a spare moment of time in previous seasons. I'd always be out on a moped taking photographs, trying out a new beach or a new golf course, climbing the highest point of an island, going to the Southern most point, visiting the museums to learn more about the history and culture, scuba diving with sharks, going to see an African witch doctor, or doing one of my favourite pastimes of just sitting in an isolated village with the locals, drinking coffee and discussing inane subjects like the back pass rule in football.

So earlier today, I decided to change my bad habits of this season and grabbed Popot from the Pasta Hut and we spent a glorious couple of hours hitting wayward shots around the pitch and putt golf course at the Goa Renaissance. It wasn't a momentous occasion in that we were doing something particularly eventful or significant, but it was in the sense that it helped stop the rot and I finally did something constructive for myself for a change.

I laughed for the first time in daylight hours and I now feel as if a corner has been turned. Up until today I've had nothing but problems at work, problems with a lot of the hoteliers, have wasted my spare time and I have been suffocated by Gina. Now I am starting to enjoy my life again.

TUESDAY – 2nd FEBRUARY

Ruth eventually left today.

The whole deal with Ruth has been dragging on all season, with Kate and I banging our heads against the proverbial brick walls so much we should have lumps the size of rugby balls protruding from our craniums. Ruth's attitude and performance have been deteriorating progressively to the extent that we wanted to dismiss her in early December. But we have been given no back-up from Head Office, more particularly Stelios George, so the situation has been allowed to linger on and she has rapidly tarnished our reputation in the resort and has added plenty of fuel for the gossipmongers fire.

As a summary of her season so far I'd say she started poorly, has not shown the slightest inclination towards improving and by the beginning of December, she was so bad and disorganised she had to go. She was missing duties and when she did bother to turn up she would appear late, looking dishevelled, out of uniform and dirty. She lost over £800 of company money by not taking down someone's correct credit card details, she has been constantly lying to guests, albeit in a very charming way, blaming other people for her mistakes, not turning up for office meetings or for handing in paperwork, not maintaining or properly displaying her information books and boards and, as has since transpired from some departing reps from other companies, she even missed a couple of welcome meetings, which is one of the biggest repping sins of all.

It still took a lot of to'ing and fro'ing with Stelios George, who continually procrastinated and failed to provide the merest hint of back-up, until eventually Kate could take no more. She bravely made the decision to dismiss her and then gained permission from our parent company to recruit Toni, who was due to leave Goa a couple of days back.

In my opinion this is something that was long overdue, but again I don't have to tell the girl that she's losing her job, plus our hands have been tied, very tightly, by Stelios. So last week Kate typed up a three-page letter detailing all of the principle reasons why Ruth was being let go and asked her to meet her in the office. In true fashion Ruth didn't turn up, but she did send a fax handing in her notice. Kate then typed out an acceptance letter detailing the fact that we would provide Ruth with a flight home, on the understanding that she paid back to the company the money that she had lost, and therefore owed, and also that she work two weeks notice.

This notice, although undesirable on our behalf, gave us time to get Toni (our new team member) acquainted with our company methods, and our varying hotels and excursions, and also gave us time to get Sharon back into resort, because she's been back in the UK for a week, recuperating from an illness. Ruth readily agreed.

Two days later, on the Saturday just gone, Ruth rang Kate in the office and ranted, "Kate, I've just had a guest accuse me of stealing money from the company and it's disgusting. I don't know where they've heard this, but I can't work in these conditions so I'm leaving now!" She then put the phone down and that was the last we have seen or heard from her.

This meant that Kate had to cover the Saturday evening visits, which for me was nice to see her eventually getting her hands dirty, although that isn't entirely fair, because she's been excellent and more supportive since she came back from her Grandmother's funeral. She did find that Ruth had again not bothered to turn up to some hotels in the past week, but thankfully Sharon came back the following day, which means she can continue in the North.

Ruth was apparently seen that same Sunday trying to buy a flight ticket for one of the charter flights, but even if she had got one, there is no way that she would have got through immigration control, because her employer and Ravi Chauhan are the only people who could arrange what's known as uplift for her. Uplift basically means getting the permission from the civil aviation authorities for her to leave the country on a charter flight, because she arrived via a schedule flight.

Word has since reached us that she left today, via Bombay, on a schedule flight, which must have cost her something in the region of £400 or more. I don't know which airline she left on, but she could have floated home in the clouds she inhabits for all we care. She still owes the company approximately £1000, part of which we recovered by stopping her salary for January and she'll be receiving a solicitor's letter when she gets home for the rest of the balance.

Our collective attitude though, is one of a sense of relief, because we thank the gods above that she's gone and can no longer cause us any more grief, so that now, for what seems like the first time, we can concentrate on doing our jobs and making the rest of the season successful. Already it would appear that a dark cloud has left the atmosphere and a ray of light is slowly beginning to make its presence felt. She's gone and that's the last we'll hear of her.

FRIDAY – 5TH FEBRUARY

One of the effects of Ruth leaving is that Toni has now come over to her sister company and has today taken over from me in the South. I, in turn, have moved back up to the North of Goa, into my old room at The Ranch and for my first two weeks will be going from one extreme to another. I will be running the resort as temporary manager, much like I did at the beginning of the season, before again reverting to my original role as a repping Head Rep.

This change around has caused a few intense discussions with Gina, because she doesn't want me to leave the South and we both know that we won't be able to see each other every night from now on. However, I see this as a good thing because it will continue to give us some much needed space and we will then cherish the moments that we have together. I feel that we rushed into things too quickly and became suffocated a little as a result, but Gina can't seem to understand this and neither can she comprehend my overzealous glee at having to come back North, which is probably fair enough.

Anyway, after a morning of frantically packing my entire life into two suitcases yet again, I grabbed a taxi at about 09:30 and headed to Panjim to settle in, via a brief stop at the orphanage in Margao, where I dropped off three carrier bags of toiletries, two carrier bags of clothes and also a carrier bag of sweets. The kids of course didn't let me down and I left feeling good about the world, which I thought was a good omen for another new beginning in one short season.

By 13:00 I'd moved, unpacked and was in the office sorting through a lot of Ruth's old rubbish, which needed to be either given away or thrown out. Not surprisingly most of the things she had left behind were only fit for a tramp's dustbin. It is funny though, that with this job you get used to moving at short notice and being able to squeeze your whole life into two small bags. Eventually you tend to lose all track of affection and sentimentality and then stop becoming attached to wherever you may be living at any given moment. As a result everything is kept at arm's length. The friendships we build are all very strong and intense, but we know that although they won't end, we will eventually be apart from people we have been tremendously close with, so that after a few seasons of frequently saying sad goodbyes, we become adept at giving a lot of ourselves, but still manage to keep a little something back, just in case.

Still, I am prone to digress a little and to return to the formalities of my first day back in the North of Goa, I finished sorting through Ruth's junk, hoping that was the last connection I would ever have with her. In the late afternoon Kate and I went along to a very boring Federation of Tour Operators meeting, where further Health and Safety issues were addressed, but no decisions were made.

I was glad to see that nothing seems to have changed and the same could be said about Kate, because afterwards we joined Janice and a couple of others in a pub in town where it would have been churlish not to consume a few beers on empty stomachs.

It's good to get a sense of normality back and it was equally pleasing to visit some old haunts and see some old faces. As much as I loved the South it's also very satisfying to be back up North.

Gina doesn't agree.

TUESDAY – 9ᵀᴴ FEBRUARY

After a relatively straight forward day yesterday, which means two days now without any major problems therefore my leadership skills must be working, I headed down South to do a couple of audits. This also gave me an excuse to stay over with Gina and we had our routine argument before going out for dinner and an enjoyable evening. I then had to get up at the crack of dawn to tidy up the office. This set up the rest of the day nicely though, because it meant we were organised and ready for an afternoon's training session on completing audits and also in a position to be on the wrong end of an important phone call during the course of it.

The call was from Sabina, who looks after our reservations locally in resort, and whenever she calls we know there's a problem. We are due to have eight rooms coming into one of our North based hotels this coming Sunday and every one of the rooms are overbooked.

Immediately after the training session, I went straight back to the office and double, then triple checked with Sabina, but nothing could be done. The rooms were most definitely out of our release period and they are overbooked with a capital 'O'. I then faxed through the full list of names to our UK operations department, together with a list of suggested alternative hotels the guests could go into and waited for a response that wasn't going to come. I wanted to hear that the UK would inform the guests before they arrived in Goa and that they would send bookings for some of the alternative hotels that I'd listed, so that I could confirm that the guests had the rooms. It seemed only fair that the UK did this, because they, or more specifically Paul Rodrigues, made the error in the first instance.

The over-bookings (I even hate the sound of the word) came about because we only received the bookings in our company mailbag this Sunday just gone and Sabina duly faxed them off to the hotel first thing on Monday morning. However, the cut off period we have with this hotel is currently one week and because we are a couple of days inside of this period, the hotel has legitimately released the rooms to other guests. Judging by their booking reference numbers, the guests appear to have booked their holidays seven months ago, yet we only received the bookings six days before they were due to arrive.

I must explain here, that once a booking is made it will not be sent directly to the hotel, especially if the booking is a year in advance of when the guests are due to arrive. This is a popular misconception amongst tourists, but it doesn't happen for a number of reasons.

Firstly every tour operator will have a contract with a hotel for 'x' amount of rooms and with each allocation of rooms there will be an assigned release period. We secure these cut off dates, which are the last date that a certain number of rooms will be held by a hotel on behalf of a tour operator, and if we go beyond that period then the hotel is able to sell the rooms elsewhere. However, if we send the booking before that particular date then the hotel must, by law, give those rooms to us. One of the principle reasons that we operate with this procedure is because if we cancel a booking with a hotel, then the hotel will charge us a cancellation fee. Of course if we send through a lot of bookings to a hotel six months in advance, then the chances are that we'll get one or two cancellations, which will cost us quite a bit of money in the long run with the cancellation fees from the hotels.

This still doesn't disguise the fact though, that we have eight rooms overbooked for this coming weekend and because the UK caused the error, we require them to do something about them. I hadn't received an acknowledgement of my first fax after an hour, so I sent a second, with the words 'URGENT. URGENT. URGENT' emblazoned across the top in bold black print and still didn't get any form of response for another hour. So I sent a third and a fourth fax and then tried calling direct, but couldn't get a reply either because the lines were all tied up. I eventually got through at 20:00 only to be fobbed off by an office junior who was merely manning the phones. I left a curt message for Paul to call me as soon as he could, but left knowing that this would now leave a big cloud hanging over my treasured day off.

I did manage to get home by 21:00 only to receive a phone call from Sharon, who had just spent the previous hour with the manager of the hotel, telling me we have another two rooms overbooked for this coming Friday, because Ruth didn't bother to hand in some reservations when she covered the unit.

We should have foreseen something like this, and it's bloody typical of Ruth that she's still haunting us. I instructed Sharon to double-check every single reservation she has when she returned to work on Thursday. In the meantime I headed back into the office at 22:00 to fax the UK again to advise them of the extra over-bookings, even though we hadn't heard a response from my previous messages. This ruined my night off because I didn't get down to see Gina until just before midnight.

WEDNESDAY – 10TH FEBRUARY

After a sleepy morning, which was thankfully argument free, Gina, Toni and I tried to spend the day relaxing on the beach up at Bogmalo. We duly consumed a large, gluttonous lunch of chicken curry and rice, washed down with a couple of beers and then stretched back on our respective sun beds. We promptly fell asleep for a couple of hours, which is not the best thing you could do in 95 degrees of sunshine and completely against what we advise our guests to do. But they get seven days in a week to sunbathe.

I woke up at 15:30 with work thoughts racing through my head and a cold sweat pouring off my forehead. Apparently I'd been muttering, 'you've got to accept the rooms' in my not so tranquil doze and Gina had decided to wake me up. I'm not sure if she did so because she was concerned or because I was disturbing her sleep. Still I had a swim to clear my head and freshen me up a bit, but no matter how hard I tried I just couldn't switch off or stop thinking about what we were going to do with these rooms that were overbooked. I had no choice really and as well as ruining my day off, I spoiled Gina's too, by packing up and heading back to the office.

There were still no acknowledgements to any of my faxes and Janice had received no phone messages, so I tried calling again, and left a rather blunt message on Paul's voice mail asking to be called back as soon as possible so that we could speak about the over-bookings. It took an hour to get a response and when it came it was from the big cheese himself, Mr. Stelios George.

"Ceri," he succinctly said before giving his obligatory pause where I don't know if I should reply or stay silent?

"Stelios." I thought that would do for the time being.

"How are things?" as if he's interested.

"Okay, apart from these over-bookings." I saw no point in wasting time on small talk on my day off.

"Yes. That's why I'm calling. What's happened?"

"Well, quite simply we haven't received the bookings from you and Sabina only noticed when the confirmations came through in the co-mail this Sunday, which as you know is way past the release date."

"Why haven't you received them?" he stupidly asked.

"Stelios, how can I know why when I'm not sending, I'm receiving. The faxes come to the office and Sabina immediately sends them to the respective hotels. She charts them, gives a copy to the reps, which has to be signed by the hotels and she also files the copies away, which means that when we get a rooming list in resort, Sabina ensures that it is triple and quadruple checked. So all I can say is that we simply haven't received them."

"Well according to our computer they were run off on January 18, so you must have them," he stated.

"I'm sorry Stelios but they haven't come in. What else can I say? And more importantly I'd like to know what we're going to do with the guests?"

I was becoming a little bit annoyed because we weren't getting anywhere and he'd obviously called to make accusations rather than to assist in the matter.

"Ceri," he again said in that condescending tone of his, "you know this costs the company a lot of money and we can't afford for mistakes like this to happen".

"I know that, I've only worked in the industry for the past seven years and come to think of it, do you think I like telling people they're overbooked and then having to deal with their complaints for a fortnight. Sorry Stelios, but it seems to me that you aren't that bothered about the service we give, you seem to be preoccupied with money and covering yourself at your end."

Ooops. I'd gone way too far in emotionally expressing my opinion. It was borne out of frustration, but Stelios expects his staff to be humble and subservient and even though I was probably wrong to speak like that, I was in no mood to play games with these rooms.

"Ceri. I won't help you until I know whose fault it is. I have to get to the bottom of this. Now check again to see if the faxes have been sent and call me back!"

Amazingly for me he hadn't heard a word I'd said, which is probably something that saved my posterior.

Sabina, who had stayed on late, and I checked again and again and I called Stelios back thirty minutes later to find he wasn't in. So I left a message to explain that the faxes had never been received, which meant the bookings had never been received, so whoever is supposed to have sent them is at fault.

Later on in the evening, when I was having dinner with Gina who was in a little sulk, the mobile went and I picked it up to hear the head of reservations on the line. He explained that he'd made reservations in two more superior hotels, both on an All-Inclusive basis. He had informed the guests of the over-bookings personally and he would be sending compensation to them, via their travel agents.

"By the way, what did you say to Stelios? Because he was livid, but he also took some action pretty sharpish."

"Just the truth mate."

"Well it worked. But be careful, because he's not in the best of moods with you."

SUNDAY – 14TH FEBRUARY

"Hi, I've come to pick up my flight ticket." A middle-aged lady stated at the airport.

Up until this point the whole of the departure had run very smoothly at the airport. I'd had the comparative luxury of a Sunday morning lie-in because I didn't have to be ready for Ravi to pick me up until 05:00, all of the coaches had arrived on time, without any unnecessary problems and the transfers had gone very efficiently. The flight was also scheduled to go on time and the check-in queue had been going down very rapidly indeed when the lady asked me for her ticket.

"What ticket would that be madam?" I asked very politely, but with an obvious look of consternation in my eyes.

"The one I booked about three weeks ago!" she said a little too harshly.

"Sorry, I haven't been made aware of this. Could you just bear with me for a second please?"

I walked over to the corner where we always kept our airport file, cursing Kate, because I could have done without having surprise bookings turning up at the airport.

I searched through our file and there was no ticket whatsoever and no note to indicate that either Kate or anyone else in the office had sold a flight seat. I also checked our manifest and that showed that every seat we had allocated on the flight was full. This wasn't looking good and I had to go back and face a lady who was beginning to go a bit red in the face. My only hope was that she'd lost her original ticket and simply needed me to write out a duplicate.

"I'm sorry I don't have a record of having any flight tickets to issue. Who told you to collect a ticket from me?"

"Ruth!" She commanded.

"Uuuh..uh.." struggling now to maintain my composure, thinking I'd heard the last of that girl's name and wondering what we could do. "When did you book the seat with Ruth, because she's no longer with the company." I knew now that it wasn't simply a case of a lost ticket.

"I'm not surprised if you're as unprofessional as this. Lovely girl she was I might say and she told me that she'd confirmed me a seat on this flight about three weeks back." This happened to be right about the time that she'd left.

The woman was brandishing a note on our headed paper, which I gratefully took and clear as a bell it read, in Ruth's almost illegible scrawl, that she had booked a seat for this woman on today's flight. The only consolation was that she hadn't collected any money off her, because she was instructing her to pay us at the airport in cash.

I wasn't too sure what to do initially, because as far as I was aware the flight for today was full and I didn't know where we stood legally because if Ruth had told her this after she had quit then surely I didn't have to do anything. But if she'd given her the note a day or so beforehand then we would be obliged to find her a flight, which would be a lot of fun. However, my natural inclination to help people, even at this time of the morning, was taking over and I felt sorry for her, plus if we didn't help her it would only tarnish our name a little. I decided to tell her the truth and be upfront with her, hoping that I'd play on her sense of decency.

"I have to be honest with you that Ruth was fired about three weeks ago." A little faux pas, but I needed to get her on side, "and even when she was working for us, she never had the authority to confirm flight seats for guests without going through either myself or a lady called Kate. What I'm worried about is that the flight is full for today, but I'm just going to double check this for you now and if it is I'll see what I can do to get you on another flight, because there are six flights leaving today and I've got some pretty good contacts in the airport."

"Okay. But I better f***ing get on this flight. I've stayed three extra weeks and I was promised a seat by your company, even if it was Ruth, who I still think is a lovely girl." I'd have to agree, Ruth is a lovely girl, but she was a God-awful rep.

The lady continued to remonstrate about how important it was that she get on the flight, but I didn't really hear a lot of it because I was trying to think what to do next. I decided to check the manifests that the flight-handling agent had, to see if they had any seats showing and if they didn't then I'd check with the other charter companies who had seats, to see if they had any 'no-shows'.

Meanwhile Lester had come across, presumably to ask me a meaningless question and I rather rudely brushed him off with a, "not now Lester." Poor lad, he deals with the major things very well indeed, but he always seems to ask the silly little questions at the wrong time. I'd apologise to him later though.

I went over to the office of the flight handling agent and checked my manifest again, which was most definitely full, so I asked them if I could have a peek at the ones for the other tour operators, but they were showing full as well. I asked the agent if he knew of any possible 'no-shows', to which he replied in the negative, but he did say that there was a possibility of a seat on the flight that was due to leave two hours later, which was something.

I came out of the office, looking for the lady and as I reached her, Lester came across calling my name, and again I had to tell him to wait because I was busy. I then explained to the lady the situation with the seats and explained that I would check with each of the other tour operators on the flight, to see if they had any other seats otherwise it would be a case of her waiting on standby. This means waiting for the check-in desk to close and when they do, if there is a seat available the lady could buy it. And finally I apologised. I apologised for my company, I apologised for Ruth's error and I could have apologised for my country and the whole of the Commonwealth, I was so apologetic.

Unfortunately the lady wasn't as understanding as I would have hoped she might have been.

"This is an absolute f***ing disgrace. I've got to get on that flight! I've been promised a seat! You're Useless! You're a f***ing useless company!" she rather delicately exclaimed going into one a bit.

"Look I'm sorry." I said reverting to type, "but getting angry isn't going to help the situation at all. Now.."

"Ceri." Lester this time.

"Don't you f***ing tell me to calm down. I know my rights and I'm getting on that flight whether you like it or not."

"Ceri."

"Not now Lester, can't you see I'm busy with this lady."

"Too f***ing right you should have called me a lady." Which I thought was a bit ironic. But I wanted to explain that the chances were fairly good that she would get a flight that morning, just not on the one that she had been promised.

"Look." I started again, "Can I please check with the other operators first to see if they have any potential 'no-shows' and if they don't I promise I'll stay as long as it takes to get you a seat."

"Ceri."

"Not now Lester!"

"You better f***ing get me on this flight or there'll be hell to pay. And I've got a friend who works for Watchdog." *Yeah, you and everyone else who has a complaint*, I thought.

"Look, just give me two minutes please." I walked off in search of the managers of the other two operators who had seats on the flight. Neither of them had any available and neither of them expected any 'no-shows' either, which meant that I had to face the woman again and presumably learn a few more insults, which I would be able to add to my thesaurus of profanities.

"Ceri, I need to talk to you about some guests."

"For Christ's sake not now Lester, can't you see I'm with an angry lady."

"Sorry," he said sheepishly, which made me feel guilty, but still he didn't go away. I approached the lady, who was by now explaining her predicament to anyone who would listen and it was obvious by the colour of her face, and the way that she was pointing at me, that I wasn't being referred to in the most congenial of manners.

"Hi." I said nervously, "Not very good news I'm afraid. I'm sorry, but it doesn't appear as if there are any seats at all on this flight, but we'll put you at the top of the standby list and I'll also speak to every one of the other tour operators for you, because I know there are a few seats available later on in the morning."

"You get me on that f***ing flight or there will be all hell to pay, you useless f*** idiot." Now, if you want to motivate someone to help you, I have generally found that insults are not usually the most persuasive method, which I felt it was time to tell her.

"Ceri, please."

"Lester, just a couple of minutes alright mate and I'm all yours," I said trying to let Lester down a little bit more gently this time and then I turned to the lady, "Madam, I appreciate the situation you are in, but speaking to me in that manner is not going to help you. I am not obliged to help you, because all you have is a piece of paper with a note written by someone who was sacked a couple of days prior to her writing it, so that is nothing to do with us. Also you have paid us no money for the seat and we have not issued you with a ticket or a receipt, so there is no contract, which means I am not legally obliged to help you. However, I am willing to do so, because I sympathise with you after what Ruth has done, but please stop swearing at me. Now if you'll bear with me for a second I need to have a word with my colleague."

I could see steam coming out of her ears, but she kept her rage in and despite my calm exterior I was shaking like a leaf on the inside. I turned to Lester and beckoned him outside for a minute.

"Sorry Lester, but as you can see I was a little busy mate. Now what was so important?"

"I have two guests who told me last night that they will not be taking their seats on today's flight, because they are going to be travelling around India. Why do people do that? Travel around India, it is such a poor country and we all want to come to your country because it is rich."

"You mean there are two seats spare Lester. You're sure?"

"Oh yes. They told me last night."

"Well why didn't you tell me sooner?" I screamed as I hugged him simultaneously.

"Because you said you were too busy," he replied nonchalantly almost as if he was oblivious to the importance of it all.

We went back in to find the lady and told her we could sell her a seat and I asked how much Ruth had quoted, but the lady foolishly said that she had been told we would tell her at the airport.

The cost of a seat one-way is usually £170, but because some operators sell theirs at £230 and this lady hadn't had the decency to apologise or say thank you yet, I charged her £220 and put the £50 difference into the team 'jolly kitty'. Lester went and informed the handling agents of the name change and I checked the lady in personally, to ensure that we would see no more of her and gave silent thoughts hoping that there would be no more Ruth repercussions. The bloody girl was still having a detrimental effect on the team.

After that ordeal though, the complaints from the people who had been overbooked at the Goan Heritage seemed quite tame and just before 11:00 I was back at The Ranch hoping to get a small siesta.

However, whenever you start to hope that you may get a moment's peace in this industry something will always ensure that it doesn't happen and for me the responsibility of having the mobile phone back was my particular curse. It didn't stop all afternoon.

Most of the calls were from Lester and Sharon who were just ringing to let me know of their movements and as I already know, Sharon is a bit of a 'phoneaholic' and a 'talkaholic'. But one call in particular did stand out and it came from the Goa Renaissance.

One of our guests had fallen down, before she'd even reached the reception desk to check-in, and had twisted her knee. She is seventy-seven, on holiday with her family and in India for the first time. The hotel were only ringing as a courtesy, just to make me aware of the situation in case the guests needed any insurance advice and to let me know what clinic the lady was in. She hadn't even seen her hotel room and it didn't initially register with me how severe this could be. I went back to my late lunch and received a few more calls from Sharon before the bigger picture started dawning on me, and although the guests hadn't asked for any help I felt sure they would do so eventually. I therefore rang Toni, who is now the rep of the Renaissance and told her to give the guests a call, to make sure the lady was okay and to see if they needed anything.

She rang me back at about 17:00 to say that it was more serious than we'd been led to believe and that she'd smashed her kneecap in two and was due to be operated on at 06:30 the following morning. No sooner had I put the phone down from Toni, still trying to get dressed to head into the office, than the lady's son rang from the clinic to say that the operation was going to cost 50,000 Rupees (approximately £700) and how could he sort the money out?

He was intending to get a money transfer to deal with it himself and then reclaim the money from his insurers when he arrived back in the UK, but I took a moment to think things over and then decided the best way would be to get the insurers to pay the clinic direct. I asked if I could take down details of their insurance policy, but the son didn't have his documents with him, so I agreed that I would call his wife, who had the policy with her and take down the details then.

This gave me time to finish getting dressed, there is always something surreal about holding an important conversation when you're half dressed, and then get to the office to call the lady from there. Once I'd taken as much information that I could possibly think of, I typed it all up onto a sheet of paper, so that it was legible, and faxed it through to the guest's insurers.

I wanted to call them and see if they'd received the fax, but knew it would take a little while, so called Gina in the meantime to let her know that I was going to be late for our special Valentines Day date. She'd planned a romantic night in with room service and watching 'Romeo and Juliet', which is probably no different to many of our other nights in, but she was disappointed with me and I sensed she didn't quite believe me. I didn't need her special brand of clinginess and felt she should understand a bit more, seeing as she is in the same industry, but as I'm coming to understand, the Clingfilm love she gives is part and parcel of her package. As the locals would say, 'what to do?'

I called the insurance company about an hour later, which by then would have given them ample time to digest my fax, to see what further details they needed and also set up a claim file. After the usual formalities of getting put through to the correct person who is handling the case, I was able to explain that the lady was being operated on the following morning and we needed to confirm the clinic would receive the payment before they could go ahead.

"Oh, we've got plenty of time until 06:30." The girl stated and seemed to be in no apparent rush to get their local assistance company down to the clinic. She did ask me to get hold of the treating doctor's phone number, which in itself wasted almost another hour. His number wasn't in the phone book, which was not very reassuring nor in Directory Enquiries, but I was able to track him down via a friend of the first doctor who was called out.

A little exhausting, but I was able to ring back the insurers with the relevant number who said that they would get in touch with him before confirming that they would allow the operation to go ahead. I confirmed to the young girl that when I said the operation was at 06:30, it was at a Goan 06:30 and not a UK timing.

"Oh silly me," she exclaimed, "That would have put the cat amongst the pigeons wouldn't it?"

This done though, I'd achieved as much as I feasibly could and it was now in the hands of the doctor and the insurers. Unfortunately it meant that I didn't get to leave the office until 21:30, which meant I didn't get to Gina's until 22:30, which was half way through the film and the food she had ordered had gone cold.

As had she.

TUESDAY – 16TH FEBRUARY

For anyone who knows anything about Goa, the highlight of the social calendar is the final night of the carnival celebrations, which culminates in the all night 'Red & Black' party in the streets of Panjim.

The carnival lasts for five days and processions are held in five of the principle towns, with glorious themed, night-time events that bring to a climax the multi-coloured festivities. This year the bulk of the party going has passed me by, primarily because of my workload and responsibilities, but also because I've been trying to spend some time with Gina. But I had been saving myself up for the Red and Black event, which is always a great occasion.

Before I could don my glad rags though, I had to get through a couple of days work, which were thankfully run of the mill where I spent most of the time in the office. In that time I'd confirmed all of the coming weekend's arrivals and departures, still being a little nervous after the previous week's fiascos. I'd also tied up a lot of loose ends and of course attempted to stay on top of the insurance case. The lady had her operation on Monday morning as planned and the insurance company had agreed to pay the clinic direct for it. This was a bit of a result for me, because the guests were grateful at not having to find a way of getting £700 transferred over to India, but most of the work was down to the Insurers and Toni.

Toni has been excellent throughout, and although I'd made a special visit from Panjim on Monday to see the daughter in law, she'd spent a lot of time with them, explaining the finer details of the insurance procedure and providing a lot of comfort. With that out of the way, all I had to do was make preparations for drinking until dawn and if she wouldn't show, then I'd drink until the sun comes up. I had a good two-hour siesta in the early evening and then donned my lucky clothes of lucky boxer shorts; lucky black boots; lucky black jeans; lucky aftershave and brand new, shiny, satin effect red shirt, with huge collars and a black bandana. I had no idea what effect I was aiming for, but I was ready for a long night of drunkenness and debauchery of the highest degree. I ordered a beer from The Ranch bar whilst I waited for Gina to turn up.

True to form she was only two hours late, arriving at my place at 23:00. But there wasn't too much cause for panic, because the party starts at 22:00 and goes on until the sun rises, which gave me plenty of reason to rejoice at the fact that I have never come across a race that can party like the Goans. So after a quick dinner we headed to the venue, which is in the heart of Panjim city. To create it, they actually cordon off three streets, put in some makeshift bars, which are sponsored by the local brewery, erect a stage in the centre, and one of the roads transforms into a massive dance floor which can hold up to a reported five thousand people. Entry is complimentary for ladies and is only 200 Rupees for men. When you consider that amounts to under three quid to get in and a pint will work out at roughly forty pence it is a bargain that will induce revelry and merriment all round. The other fantastic thing is that there is never, ever, the slightest hint of trouble, because everyone just parties with a smile on their face, which is a little ironic seeing that Red and Black are supposed to be aggressive colours. The only proviso for the whole evening is that these are the only colours you are allowed to wear.

Two years ago, when I first visited Goa, I had the most fantastic time at this event and met a beautiful Danish girl called Ulla, who I got on with so well I ended up dating for the next five months. She works for a Scandinavian tour operator and I know she is currently based in Kerela and spends her summers in Sorrento, Italy. She and I developed a fairly intense relationship that season, although I had my suspicions that I wasn't the only one she adored, but it resulted in her asking me to go and visit her in Italy when I had some spare time.

As luck would have it I was free in the month of May, so decided to pop down and surprise her, which fell a bit flat on its face because she didn't seem too overjoyed to see me. Still we had two weeks to work on the relationship and I had some fantastic sights to go and see. The second night I was there she was due to guide a long evening excursion, so I went out and made my own entertainment. This involved sitting in a bar watching Inter Milan lose the UEFA cup final and getting slaughtered with a group of Italians, to the extent that I didn't crawl in until 05:00, much to her annoyance. She didn't speak to me for the whole of the next day and night I was there, so I decided to pop over to the island of Capri on a sightseeing visit the following morning and would return in the evening for a romantic dinner, which she had planned.

However, when I arrived in Capri I was so captivated by the place that I trekked from one amazing sight to the next, completely oblivious to time and transfixed at the beauty of the surroundings. This is why I missed the last ferry back and had to stay over night in a quaint little pension, which heightened tensions in Ulla's apartment even further.

When I got back, overjoyed at my tiny little adventure I had no one to share it with because she wasn't talking to me again. We didn't properly reconcile until about three days later, in which time I'd explored Pompeii, doing my Frankie Howard impressions to bemused Americans, and I'd also been wandering around the streets of nearby Napoli. With a week or more still to go, we agreed that we weren't getting on that well, but would make one final effort to have a romantic night out. We went to a glorious little restaurant in the midst of the cobbled streets of the old town, where by chance a group of Scandinavians were enjoying a meal, and by even bigger chance a guy I had known in The Gambia was sitting. We exclaimed pleasantries and agreed to meet up for a drink later, thus stretching Ulla's patience to the limit. It was actually stretched so far that we, or rather she, decided that I should catch the train back to Switzerland to go and stay with one of my mates up there, which all happened in a blur the following morning.

The point is, although my track record with women isn't that great, I had a fantastic time at the last Red & Black and I'd drunk until mid morning with some wonderful people, which had led to a great big adventure and I wanted more of the same this evening.

For the past two weeks I'd been forewarning Gina that I would be staying up throughout the night and that I was going to have the biggest party of the season. She wasn't too impressed by this, but I'd missed out on a couple of other events to be with her and as I kept saying she was more than welcome to join in. I was thinking to myself, *What the hell! I've been working very hard recently, it's my day off the next day and I don't party half as much as I used to.* It was about time I let off a bit of steam.

Once inside the cordon, I started as I meant to go on by quickly getting onto the whisky chasers. Although I was deliberately pacing myself, I was very happy in a short space of time, which could have been down to the adrenaline that had been building up inside of me and was coursing through my veins. Within an hour I was even on the dance floor, which is a rarity in my case because when you move like a white man, it's best to watch from a distance. But in the process of moving through the crowds I'd also lost Gina.

The evening was going very well, most of my friends were out, slowly going down the same road that I was and after a while I needed a breather. I was sitting chatting with one of my mates, sharing a beer when we both noticed an attractive girl, not so far away at the edge of the dance area. She had long, fine white hair, which fell gently below her shoulders, was about 5'9", with a cute face, slim figure and strong shoulders a bit like a swimmer's.

"She's a bit of alright." My mate commented, so I took a second glance and couldn't believe my eyes, because staring back at me was the girl who I'd spent the last Red & Black with. Ulla had come up from Kerela, presumably for a holiday and she was now in front of me at this momentous event again.

I dashed over to her, tapped her on the shoulder and she turned, stared for a second in confusion and then screamed, "Ceri. Oh my big love!" She always was one for the over dramatic statements of affection.

She gave me a big bear hug and we went through all of the usual 'How are you's? Where've you been? What are you doing here? You're looking great? etc' and then decided to go and grab a drink and chatter for half an hour, which stretched to an hour as we got so lost in catching up.

But the one thing neither of us mentioned, or dared ask, was the question about boyfriends or girlfriends.

It was amazing to see her so unexpectedly, especially seeing as I had been reminiscing about her earlier in the day and just when I started to think some rude thoughts and how things could get complicated, I realised that I hadn't seen Gina for ages. Thankfully, because the arena is large and so crowded, she hadn't seen me talking to Ulla, because that would have upset her greatly and we would no doubt have had an argument over nothing. But out of a slight pang of guilt I told Ulla that I would catch up with her later on and went off in search of Gina.

As it turned out she was on her way to being even more inebriated than I was and wasn't in the best of moods at all. Another coincidence is that she too had met up with an old flame, although I kept my discovery as a little secret. She'd joined up with the reps from her company and with them was an old boyfriend who was out on holiday, and more importantly still had strong feelings for her.

Whereas I hadn't told Ulla a thing about Gina, Gina had told this guy all about me and probably a bit too much. From what I can gather she let slip that she loved me, but that I wasn't giving enough back in return. He in return, had seized his opportunity to berate my claims on her, told her she should be with someone who loves her and that she should dump me for him. This of course had upset her, because he was criticizing the guy that she adores, but I'm ashamed to say that I wasn't interested, because for this night I just wanted to carry on drinking.

"Ceri, take me home." Gina demanded.

It could only have been about 02:00 by that time and I had only just got started. This stirred an element of resentment in me, because I'd given up a few nights for Gina recently and I wanted this night on the town and more importantly I wanted her with me. But she was in a bad mood and wanted me to play the loving boyfriend and to go home and cuddle her and give her lots of reassurance.

"Come on Ceri. Take me home or stay here with your friends." By now most of her friends were trying to listen in to our exchange and I resented being shown up in front of an audience. I know I was wrong, but Gina had pushed me to a line I didn't want to walk, so I gave her my room keys and 100 Rupees and told her to get a taxi. She walked off in a huff, some guy in the middle of the crowd shouted something about me being a selfish bastard and that he'd treat her better than that, and I headed off to the nearest bar to find a beer, a whisky chaser and Ulla.

Ulla was with another of the Scandi reps, a good mutual friend of ours called Tor (what a great name) and I joined them in some frenetic drinking games, which I knew was a mistake. The three of us carried on drinking until about 08:00, when the venue shut up shop ready for the town to go about its normal day's business.

Despite warnings some of my better friends had been giving, we headed back to Tor's apartment in search of more booze and some food, but as I was to also find out it was where Ulla was staying.

By this stage I was getting a bit tired and they directed me to a bed, where I crashed out for a bit while they made some cheese, onion and corned beef sandwiches. What felt like hours later, but was a mere twenty minutes, Ulla woke me up with some food and another beer, which I duly gulped down, trying to take in my surroundings.

Throughout the course of the night she and I had been flirting, because even as friends she and I are very tactile people. But now, by the way she was stroking my arm and my chest I realised she wanted a bit more, for old times sake. Tor had gone to bed, so I got up and headed to the toilet, where I spent an age having the longest pee in the world, rinsing my mouth out with water over and over, as well as racking my brains in unison.

Despite still being very drunk I realised I had a couple of options. I could make my apologies and leave now, return to The Ranch and hopefully find Gina there, thus saving the most fantastic relationship that has happened to me in a long while. Or I could go back into that room and have a fling with an old flame, which would be meaningless, but would probably destroy my relationship with Gina.

I made up my mind and chose the sensible option. So I walked back into the room, bent down to pick up my shoes and saw Ulla lying on the bed in just a g-string and bra.

"I have a problem getting these off." She stated coolly. The way Scandinavians do, because everything to them is so matter of fact.

Her hair was flopping onto her shoulders, but my attention didn't stay there for long, because her firm figure was glowing with a slight suntan and she looked more beautiful than she ever did when we were together. I closed my eyes, tried to be strong, thought of Gina, and made my mind up.

I climbed into bed and we proceeded to enjoy some of the most amazing, drunken lovemaking, but again we couldn't perform like film stars. There was no way, after all of the alcohol we had devoured that I would be supremely erect; we would copulate like Olympic athletes and that we'd have wave after wave of multiple orgasms between us. Instead I was mildly erect, so she had to help a lot, we bumped into each other clumsily, and I couldn't find her private whereabouts, which was before I fell out of the bed.

But when I climbed back in we giggled, I slipped off her g-string and then called her by the wrong name, but she didn't notice, because she was struggling to remove her bra strap.

I rolled her over so that I could undo it for her and thought I'd playfully bite her left buttock. But when drunk you don't know your own strength and I bit a little bit too hard; she screamed, turned round to slap me, but caught her elbow on the wall, which caused even more pain to her, which I secretly hoped she liked, because that was the only way I could have been turning her on.

She didn't like the pain, so I gave her a cuddle, which turned into a kiss and some drunken fumbling and thirty minutes later we were lying alongside each other, with sweat laden bodies, stroking each other's arms wishing that we both smoked. Despite the clumsiness it was enjoyable, but when she was agreeing with the lord for the fourth or fifth time, the mixture of the cheese and onion sandwich, varied doses of alcohol and having to hold my climax kicked in. She bit my shoulder. I let out a little yelp, but she closed her eyes, grimaced and vociferously agreed with the lord once more. I farted.

WEDNESDAY – 17TH FEBRUARY

I eventually managed to run away, after another equally romantic session, complete with alluring belly farts this time and stumbled into The Ranch just after midday. I was still pissed, smelling of sex, scratches were burning my back, I was wearing the previous night's clothes and doing my best pub singer impression.

I stumbled into my room, to be greeted with a note that was lying haphazardly on my bed, which read:

"CERI, YOU F***ING BASTARD!

I HOPE YOU HAD A GOOD NIGHT!
G."

Oops.

She'd written the note on the back of a photo lab receipt, which was good because I thought I'd lost that.

FRIDAY – 19TH FEBRUARY

Ceri. I have something to confess."

"Yes Gina?"

"Well," she said avoiding eye contact, "you know how you didn't come back the other morning?"

"I did come back! I was just late!"

"Whatever." She agreed, wisely avoiding wasting her time on that argument, "you can understand how upset and angry I was?"

"S'pose so," I mumbled, wandering what was coming, although I had a fair idea.

"Well. I did something I shouldn't have and I have to tell you."

I was now beginning to realise that she'd been with another guy. Her old flame is still out on holiday and I didn't see her on Wednesday or Thursday night, so she could quite easily have done so. She also said that she was hoping to catch up with him at some stage, ironically something I had no problem with. The peculiar thing is I didn't how I felt at this realisation. There was an element of relief that I wasn't the only naughty one, but also a little selfish anger that she would dare do something like that to me and even a bit of confusing jealousy, because I wanted to be the only one that was naughty.

"Go on." I snapped a little too harshly.

"Ceri, promise me that you won't be angry or cause a scene."

"I can't promise anything Gina, not until I know what you're trying to tell me."

"Oh Ceri, please don't be like that?"

"Okay Gina, I promise." *Just hurry up and get on with it.* I wanted to shout.

"Well, you didn't come back and I was upset and thinking of all the things you could have done and I convinced myself that you were with another woman and....... Well.....I'm really sorry!"

"Go on." Which meant, *put me out of my misery now please*.

"Well.."

I wish she'd stop saying 'well' and get on with it!

"Come on Gina. Get on with it!"

"Well....."

"Gina!!"

"I read your diary!" she blurted at a hundred miles an hour and then turned away from my gaze.

"Is that all?" I said, laughing hysterically, "there's me thinking you've been with another guy and I'm beginning to get angry and jealous and confused and, and all sorts of weird things I've been feeling and I don't know what, and all you've done is read my diary? Ha, ha, ha, ha, ha, ha, ha..!"

"But I shouldn't have, but it was there and I wanted to get back at you and find out what you've been up to."

"That's okay, you're forgiven. I've said all along you can read it if you want." *Thank Heavens for that* is what I really meant. I now knew that she didn't know about Ulla and if I could keep my big mouth quiet for a few weeks, she'll never know and I won't have stupidly ruined our relationship.

I am ashamed to admit that there is still a smidgeon of male pride in having slept with Ulla, because how often does an attractive Scandinavian put it on a plate for you? But I am realising more and more that what I have done is wrong and I am beginning to regret my actions immensely. Mainly because I'm realising that I don't want Gina to find out and I don't want to spoil the relationship we have, which means that I must like her a lot more than I ever realised. I'll have to ride the current storm for a few days and let her get over her sulks at me staying out so late, but I also need to make it up to her a little bit and show some affection, it's just hard to overcome my usual commitment anxieties. Still I can work on them gradually, because I seem to be over the worst of it for now.

"Alright then you bastard. Why do you fancy my best friend?" she demanded to know, this time holding my gaze with a fire in her eyes.

"You what?" I stammered in return, but obviously knew she'd read a sensitive bit.

"You know!" her eyes boring deeper into me, "on December the 29th you wrote you 'Fancy Terri Big Time!!'"

That made it much clearer, as if I didn't already know, which meant that some quality bullshit and smooth talking was desperately needed.

"Uhhm." Good start Stoner.

"I'm waiting."

"Well…" I was astounding myself with my wit, my charm and the debonair ease with which I could talk myself out of a situation. I wanted the ground to open up and swallow me whole and I would rather have gone through a whole Christmas at the SJM again, than explain this one away. But I gave it my best shot anyway.

"Terri can be quite attractive at times. I mean sometimes you see her when she's dressed up and she can look quite stunning, but on other occasions she can look a little bit rough. Plus there's the attraction of her being your best friend." *Whoa there Ceri. A little bit too much honesty for your liking.*

"What do you mean, that attraction of her being my best friend?"

"Well. Guys, we often fantasize about what we can't have and.."

"So you fantasize about Terri?"

"No!! I find her attractive Gina, like I find a lot of other girls attractive, but I fantasize about you only and I want to be with you only. But like all other guys I still look at women and form an opinion on them based on how they look first and like all children, that guys really are, I want what I can't have. But when what you can't have is laid on a plate it's not so desirable after all."

And if there were an audience I would have stood up and milked the applause, instead of turning my head away sheepishly from two lesbians at the next table, who were giving me an evil stare.

"So you don't fancy Terri?"

"No." *Yes I do.* "I think she can be attractive at times, but that's it!"

"And you're happy with me?"

"I want nothing more Gina!" *Except for alternate threesomes with you and Terri, then you and Kylie, then you and Anna Kournikova.* I was laying it on a bit thick but I think she accepted it for now.

"Good!" she said, knowing she'd got me where she wants.

For the rest of the evening we discussed our relationship and backtracked over the same old ground that we'd covered over the past two months. I was cautious not to be too much like my true self, whereas Gina tried to utilise her current upper hand status and she attempted to trap me into committing myself to a life long relationship, with babies, a three bed semi, Vauxhall Cavalier 1.6GL, a Labrador, holidays in a villa in Spain, foursomes with our 'coupley' type friends, meals at swanky restaurants, shared bank accounts, the destruction of my treasured video collection and weekends at her mothers.

I, on the other hand, as cautiously as possible tried to intimate that I still want to take it one step at a time. I did give her a huge clue however, when I said that I want what I can't have and I reiterated the point repeatedly, but I don't think she clicked on to what I was getting at.

After some tentative, rather than passionate, lovemaking we went to sleep on opposite sides of her huge double bed and I still wasn't sure if I was relieved, or not, that she hadn't slept with that other guy. But then who cares, so long as I'm off the hook?

WEDNESDAY – 26TH FEBRUARY

Last evening was quite relaxing, although a little tiresome, trying out a new excursion, which is a tad strange for this late in the season. I suppose it is one of the perks of the job, getting to go on all of the trips for free, because as we are frequently reminded, if we know nothing about something, then how can we sell it? But with Gina leaving on Friday, I would have much rather preferred to be in the South of Goa, treasuring the time I have left with her and secretly trying to atone for my error a week ago.

However, I do quite maliciously enjoy the resentment that some of the more narrow-minded guests feel when they take the attitude that they pay good money for these trips only for us to enjoy them for free, which couldn't be further from the truth. But I was determined to have a great time and enjoy the backwaters of Goa, which is at least innovative.

The trip in question is an overnight stay on Goa's first and only rice boat and is the only one outside of Kerela. Toni was also along for the ride and she too would like to have been at Gina's do, but we did have the pleasure of cruising along the river Mandovi and witnessing some of the amazing sights of river life. The boat itself is very well built and ever so comfortable, with four nice, spacious rooms, on two separate levels, each with the most comfortable beds I have lain on in ages. The service was excellent, the food fantastic, with a never ending supply of drinks and a glorious buffet for the main meals.

Because there are no stops though, all you can do is sit, read, eat and drink. This is where it became a little tiresome for Toni and for me, because we would rather have been with our respective partners and especially because Gina's company was holding an official leaving do for her in the evening. But we do have the consolation of her unofficial, and promisingly more riotous, party on Thursday to look forward to.

After what seemed an age of sitting on our lower deck, reading, sipping tea, listening to the couples above us, ordering more tea, wishing our partners were with us and reading some more, Toni and I had exhausted every semblance of conversation between us. We therefore decided to head up a level and make polite conversation with the four guests who were also on the trip, but were thankfully none of ours. But, as is always the case, they found out we were reps and the same old thing happened.

After a few pleasantries of hearing, 'that must be nice' we then had to answer the same old tired bunch of questions that we've been answering since the industry began and once you've been in the industry for more than a couple of seasons it becomes wearisome to say the least.

"Oh that's interesting. Who do you work for? How long have you been a rep? How old are you? How did you become a rep? What qualifications do you need? What did you do before you became a rep? Do you enjoy it? Do you miss home? What do your family think? Are you married? Are you single? Are you straight or gay? It must be a lonely life, is it? Where else have you worked? Where are you going to next? Where's the best place you've worked? Where would you most like to go? What will you do when you finish? When will you get a proper job? It's not a career is it? Can you help me with this problem I've got? I know it's your day off but? Our rep's lovely/crap, do you know him/her?"

As soon as we'd spent an hour or so going through the whole routine of nauseating question and answer, I was ready for bed and to get away from the terminally boring monsters that were above us and almost looking forward to going back to the office.

We were dropped off by about 15:00 on Wednesday, tired, stuffed, bored and being snubbed by the other guests and because Toni was heading South and Kate now has the car back I had to decide quickly if I needed a lift.

"Hi." I said to Gina as soon as I got through to her.

"Hi."

"It's me." I rather obviously pointed out.

"I know. How are you?" she muttered almost frostily. Something didn't sound at all right here.

I knew she had been out on the booze the previous night and probably didn't get home before 05:00, but without fail Gina has always been so talkative, even when she's angry with me. So why the silence now? Something major must have happened or something major must be wrong.

"Fine," I answered. "How was last night?" I inquired hoping I could draw some form of conversation out of her.

"Good. Got drunk. Didn't get in until six. Have a hangover." This came across even icier than the waters the Titanic sailed in.

"Good." I carried on trying to sound upbeat and hopefully draw some response out of her, "I'm glad you enjoyed yourself. Toni and I wished we were there with you, instead of being stuck on a boat doing what I would suppose you could call work."

"Oh."

Oh come on Gina! I wanted to scream. *What's up with you? Have I done something wrong, because you said it was all right for me to miss this party because it was a company do and I'd spend the next couple of days with you. Or is it because it was a company do and that guy was there, your old boyfriend, or that someone has gone and said something to you, or even worse you've gone and done something that I'll regret!*

But as always I'm never any good at confronting situations in a relationship, much like I am with my feelings, so I continued to bottle up what I wanted to ask in the same way that I bottle up my emotions.

"Can I come down tonight?" I eventually murmured, chickening out of anything close to what I wanted to talk about.

"Ahh, no. Not right now. I've err got to go to uhhm Bogmalo! To see Terri and say goodbye to some people."

"But I thought we'd arranged that I'd come down?" I pathetically whined.

"Well, not just now I have to go to Bogmalo and pack and, and things."

This sounded like a major brush off and was very alien to anything that had ever gone before in our relationship. I wanted to charm my way into going down to see her, but I was flummoxed and I didn't know what to say at this juncture, so I opted for a bit of time to compose myself.

"Maybe later Gina?"

"Yeah. Maybe."

"I'll call you."

"Yeah."

"Bye."

"Bye."

And that was that, the worst phone conversation I'd had in a long time. I sent Toni off on her own, fearful of the response I'd get from Gina if I just turned up on her doorstep and I hoped that she had the most humongous hangover and would feel better later on.

She rang me back later on, by which time I was back in The Ranch and the conversation headed along exactly the same lines, when I eventually mustered up a modicum of courage and asked, "You're not going to Bogmalo, are you?"

"No." Again enough ice to freeze half of Asia.

"And have you done any packing?" I gently probed, trying hard, but not too convincingly, not to be too pushy.

"No. But I will!" and she was equally unconvincing.

"Look Gina, I want to come down and see you! I've missed you the last couple of days and I want to spend some time with you before you leave."

"Sorry Ceri. No." *What?! She's always wanted to see me. With two days to go she can't be saying no!*

"Gina?"

"Look Ceri, what's going to happen when I leave?" And again she brought up the same old chestnut that has been destroying our relationship from the start, because it never fails to send a shiver of fear down my spine, exactly as it did when she started that last sentence.

For what seemed like the hundredth time a familiar set of thoughts went racing through my bemused cranium, replaying every moment of our brief but beautiful liaison to date. Yet again I thought about how we'd clicked almost instantly and have both had strong feelings for each other, however we both reacted completely differently, which has been the cause of every problem we've had ever since.

This is where the seven-year age difference really comes to the fore, because after the first night she has thrown herself full on into the relationship and has been planning the rest of our lives together. This is very flattering, but completely the wrong thing to do with me, something which she hasn't learnt at all, despite my less than subtle hints.

Unfortunately, unlike a lot of people I know, I won't lie and tell someone I love them unless I am 110% sure and I won't look beyond the next corner, which obviously upsets Gina who sees the next corner as nothing but a distant memory, considering the rate at which she has hurtled ahead. So while she has been careering down the hill at full speed, I've been slamming the brakes on and neither one of us has had the courage to try and meet in the middle. This has led to an awkward stalemate between two people who care ever so deeply about each other.

But in answer to her question I tried to explain that I cared deeply about her, that I wanted to give it a go and that it was possible that it could work between us, but I wasn't prepared to commit myself to her forever and give up my whole life on something that may not succeed when she leaves Goa. I wanted it badly, but I also wanted to wait and thought we should still take everything one step at a time. But she thought differently.

"Look Ceri, it's obvious this isn't going to work when I leave."

"No Gina. It can. But just don't force me into something I can't guarantee. I need more than just hope."

"But I need more than that Ceri and that's why I know it won't work."

"Gina."

"Ceri, we both know it and that's why I don't want to see you."

Silence from my end.

"Ceri??"

"Yeah."

"Do you understand what I'm saying?"

"Of course I do. You're throwing away something beautiful and you're never going to see me again." I spluttered none too eloquently.

Why is it that we can't copulate like film stars and we can't argue like them either? I've seen loads of films and memorised loads of fantastic lines and responses, yet when the time comes I never seem to be able to deliver the right answers and degree of control. Also, unlike film stars, I never seem to be able to get across what is on my mind.

"It's not like that Ceri. I want us to be friends."

Silence from me again. I'd now decided that because whatever I'd say was bound to be wrong, I should try another tack and remain quiet to see if I could elicit a response that way instead.

"Ceri. Are you still there?"

"I've got to go now. Bye." *And where on earth did that petty piece of inspiration come from Ceri? Stupid. Stupidy. Stupidest.*

And all the while Savi, the receptionist, had been listening in and grinning.

"Your girlfriend leave you?" he asked, the nosy little bastard.

I grabbed some cash and went into town to spend some money on some trainers or a replica football shirt or anything for that matter that would help assuage my misery. But that didn't work, because not only are girls better at arguing than guys, they also shop better when they're angry. I merely ended up back at The Ranch, empty handed and more frustrated than before I went out, with Savi still grinning at the demise of my relationship.

By 21:00 I mustered up the courage to call her back, having wisely decided, I thought, against dashing down there on my moped to be humiliated in person. I called with the aim of clarifying that we were indeed breaking up but all it served to do was prove that she wasn't drunk and that I wasn't imagining things, and of course it tortured my fragile ego a little more.

"Gina. Is this it? I mean we are breaking up and you weren't drunk earlier?"

"Yeah. I'm sorry." *No you're not*, I thought, *you're just insecure about reaching your thirties and still being single, even though you're only twenty-four.*

"So you're going to leave it with a bad taste in the mouth?" Cheap shot I know, but anything is worth a go at this stage.

"Look Ceri, you know why I'm doing this, so don't make it any harder than it is already." Why do women always say that? They're the ones doing the dumping and they still expect us to be gentlemanly and make it easier for them.

We then proceeded to have about five minutes of Gina explaining again why she was leaving me, when all I could respond with was dramatic silence, because I'd run out of things to persuade her with, except for my trump card. I had to play my joker, something that had been held back for just such an occasion like this and I had to tell her that I loved her. I'm not sure if I do or not and it could be cruel if everything doesn't work out, but as far as I could see it couldn't fail and anyway, drastic situations call for drastic measures.

"Gina.." I let it linger for good measure.

"I know that 'Gina..' Ceri, so don't even think about telling me you love me because it just won't work. If you really loved me you would have said it long ago and shown it to me more often, even by coming down here tonight to fight for me." *Shit she reads me like a book! And double shit I was wrong and should have gone down to see her! So that's it then!*

'So that's it then?"

"Yeah." She said softly, "I'm sorry Ceri."

"Yeah." *Like hell you are!*

"I'll call you tomorrow Ceri." And all that was left for me was to be gracious in defeat, show a bit of humility and ensure that we part as friends. "F*** OFF!"

What hurts a lot, on top of being rejected, is the timing. Two days before she leaves she decides to do it, when she could have just let it fizzle out nicely and we'd have stayed in touch with some nice memories, or maybe that is a weak guy's way out of these things. I know deep down though that it's my fault and that if I'd committed myself a bit more, lied and told her that I loved her and not pushed her away when I wanted to open up, we'd now be spending two blissful nights together and looking to the future, instead of parting with a very bitter taste in the mouth and the worst of memories.

I went to my bed that night angry at myself for not letting her love me, despondent that I may never get another chance at love and most of all sad that I'd let someone so fantastic slip away. I fell asleep to the sounds of the Eagles and ironically my favourite track of theirs, Desperado.

"Desperado, you should come to your senses….

….. You should let somebody love you!

Let somebody love you!

Before it's too late!!"

THURSDAY – 27TH FEBRUARY

I spoke to no one I didn't have to today.

I took the girls' liquidation and buried my head in paperwork. I was hurting. Despite everyone's pleas, personal pride didn't allow me to go down to Gina's leaving party and I didn't call her to make any pathetic sounds at reconciliation. I did however, drive 40 kms there and 40 kms back, on my moped, to drop off a card at her hotel. There isn't a lot of choice in such things in Goa, so I had to make do with the following:

Cover: The reason I'm crying
Inside: Is because you're goodbyeing!!
And I wrote:
You never knew how crazy I am about you.
Sorry it had to end this way.
Luv Ya.
C.
Even in a card I still can't write the 'L' word properly.

WEDNESDAY – 10TH MARCH

After a very drunken, lecherous night at our delayed Christmas party and subsequent sojourn to West End nightclub, I woke up at around midday with the familiar smell of stale farts and furry mouth syndrome permeating their way around the room. They were competing with a throbbing cranium and prop forward stomach to see who could inflict the greatest amount of pain on me. The stomach won and I spent what seemed like half an hour on the toilet, spraying the porcelain a darker shade of brown.

As I came out I banged my shin on the side of the bed yet again and marvelled at how my clothes from the night before were folded, in neat little piles on the room's one and only chair. I was then forced to return to the toilet and in between painful groans I had time to muse over the fact that no matter how drunk I may get, I always fold my clothes immaculately, instead of throwing them onto the floor like normal people do.

Some drastic measures of recuperation were required, so I headed off to the confines of the private beach at the Cidade De Goa, complete with beach volleyball, personal stereo and a tacky Clive Cussler novel. This didn't help that much, because no matter how much water I forced down my throat or how much time I spent cooling off in the sea, my less than perfect condition meant that the 100-degree heat was way too painful.

Instead of burning myself like I did a week previously, which has caused my entire top layer of skin to peel away, leaving a milky glow on the surface and me standing out like a luminous pole on the beach, I decided to do something that would make me feel better about myself. Seeing as I don't enjoy shopping and I was hurting too much to go in the gym, the only thing I could think of was to get a sharp new haircut and have a head massage to boot and I prayed that I wouldn't surface with the almost obligatory side parting.

I don't know what it is about side partings, but every Indian I know has one and every time you go to the barbers they cut your hair with an aim to squeezing in the aforementioned parting. Having spent most of the season trying to grow the top of my hair longer, to the extent that it reaches down to the tip of my nose these days, I wanted to encourage this and therefore asked for a short back and sides and a slight trim on the top, hoping that I wouldn't end up with a Bobby Charlton comb over.

Sadly my allotted man in charge of the scissors didn't understand a word of English, so he called over a colleague and I repeated again that I wanted a short back and sides, with just a trim on the top and definitely no side parting. He then translated this to the first guy and wildly gesticulated about a side parting. The initial guy then set about my hair with a gay abandon, shearing up the sides with a toothless comb and rusty scissors that were tugging at the roots a little too fiercely. But after a while I got used to the gentle little tugs and the haircut settled into that relaxing feeling, which overcomes you when a strange person is stroking your head. He also kept tapping me on the shoulder every time my eyes started closing and smiled at me with a huge childlike grin, as if he were a child seeking reassurance for a superb piece of colouring in.

I happily drifted off into my own world, reliving my failed attempts at trying to snog one of the Scandinavian reps the night before and subsequently feeling a little guilty as I thought of Gina. This was very therapeutic because I was feeling a huge weight lift from my shoulders as I floated into a sensual abyss, but in doing so I made the mistake of not paying any attention to where he was cutting. When I opened my eyes, expecting to see a George Clooney look-alike staring right back at me, I was shocked and a little dismayed to see that he had given me a number three on the right hand side, all the way up to a line just above my crown, shearing into some of my treasured locks. But on the left hand side, he'd only cut up as far as an inch above my ears, leaving plenty of growth on that side. And yes, he'd brushed it into the obligatory side parting, of which the esteemed Mr Charlton would have been proud.

"No!!" I exclaimed. Terror seeping through my vocal chords, "I said I didn't want a side parting!" This had only fallen on deaf ears though, because the lad couldn't understand what I was saying and merely smiled back at me through the mirror.

I called over his friend and explained that I didn't want a side parting and that I wanted to keep the length on the top of my head. He nodded in what seemed like definite understanding and instructed my barber to do as I said. Or rather I desperately hoped he had done. The lad then continued and tried to genuinely rectify the situation, by cutting away furiously at the left hand side. But he grossly misjudged how far to go and exceeded the level that was on the other side of my head, thus cutting further into my beloved locks and treading a line that was very close to giving me a Mohican. He then had to rectify the right hand side, which thankfully was spot on and I was left with some semblance of hair left on the top of my cranium.

That done, I thought there was no way that he could mess up the trim on the top, so I settled back down again, my temperature lowering, while all the while he still continued to smile at me in the mirror. To his credit he did a perfect trim on the top and just about saved the day, before he brushed all my hair forward. I made a frantic gesture, trying desperately to indicate that I didn't want a side parting, fearing that was what he was leading up to and he carried on smiling. He then took out his scissors, grabbed hold of the hair at the fringe and snipped it off about two millimetres away from the root. This meant I had a huge clump of hair on the top of my head tapering into a fierce fringe in the front, which made me look like Blackadder the First after a night crawling through a hedge.

I screamed again, and again the other guy came over. I again explained that I only wanted a trim on the top and no side parting and he in turn explained that customers who do not want side partings usually have their hair very short. Because I wanted to keep mine long on top they'd decided between them to just cut the fringe short, because in their endearingly convoluted logic there was no way I could have meant keep it all long on the top with no side parting.

The only thing left to save the day was for him to give me a number two cut all over and cut away nine months of carefully cultivated hair.

Instead of walking away looking like Chris Isaac, with a stylish quiff, I ended up more like a battered version of Richard Gere from an 'Officer and a Gentleman'.

To compensate matters a little I had a soothing shave with trim for a newly grown goatee, which was immaculate, and the head and face massage was even better. This meant that I couldn't begrudge paying a total, somewhere in the region of sixty pence. After he tidied up, put the anti-wrinkle cream on my forehead and moisturiser all over my face, he then smeared some strong mould, hair gel onto the left hand side of my head and still managed to give me some semblance of a side parting.

SUNDAY – 14TH MARCH

There was only the one meeting this evening but for quite a large crowd in the Cidade De Goa, where I was hoping for a good return to generate some much needed spending money. I should be so lucky.

I'd booked it for 17:00 and had arranged chairs and welcome drinks in the small garden area at the rear of the hotel, which is a pleasant little spot and nice and intimate. However by ten minutes past not a soul was to be seen.

I wanted a full turn out, because it meant I could do a stand-up meeting and really go to town with my sales pitch and 'wow' them with a new routine I had been working on. Plus we'd received a fax from Stelios George yesterday criticizing our sales levels and we all desperately wanted to increase our per heads. But by twelve past, there was still no one around.

Unlucky thirteen minutes past remained true to its reputation, as I still didn't bump into anyone who may have remotely looked like a guest. I was becoming concerned that maybe I didn't tell anyone about the meeting on the coach on the way in from the airport.

But to assuage my anxiety a little, one couple turned up at fourteen minutes past. I duly walked them to the garden area, asked them to take a seat, gave them a welcome pack and a complimentary welcome drink and was dismayed to see that no one else had accidentally stumbled across the venue. They did however confirm to me that I had mentioned the meeting on four occasions, on the transfer in, so I had no real cause to doubt myself. I returned to the lobby at exactly quarter past and again no signs of any lost tourists absent-mindedly searching for a dashing rep. Or even any tourists looking for me.

At seventeen minutes past and thirty-two seconds, I knew because I was nervously boring holes into my watch, another couple came along and without saying hello, they started indulging themselves in a massive tirade against the hotel. They were obviously tired from the journey out, which heightened their irritation and made their Cockney accents even coarser. The gist of their complaint, as far as I could make out as I listened half-heartedly in between anxious glances for other guests, was that they didn't think the hotel should be rated as a five star and that they didn't like the flight.

"It's a facking disgrace you advertising this 'otel as a five star!"

"We don't advertise it as a five star." I calmly replied, whilst looking over his shoulder for possible signs of any other guests. I also engaged my smarmiest of smiles and because he was so wrapped up in his own feelings of discontent, he didn't spot it at all.

"If you look in our brochure sir, you'll see we don't have any star ratings at all, which means that you have to read the description of the hotel, which in turn, I think you'll find is very accurate."

"But this ain't up to five star standards."

"I completely agree with you."

This stumped him for a moment, because he was looking for a fight. I love it when this happens, because nothing winds people up more than us being nice and helpful and they've got all this pent up rage, which has built like a monsoon, and they've got no reason to let it loose. It just sits and simmers away eating at them as they're forced to be civil.

"Yeah. Well it ain't and I'm not 'appy wiv it." He tried to recover. But because we could sense he was calming down a bit and may be prepared to listen to reason, his wife decided she had to get her two pennies worth and blurted, "We wanna move!"

I then glanced over at her and noticed that she was standing in the middle of reception with a Bet Lynch style, leopard skin bikini, with a white, see through shirt over the top held up by one solitary button. They were both adorned extravagantly with thick, chunky gold earrings, rings, bracelets, chains and anything else Mr. T couldn't carry. As another rep commented later on in the evening, 'mutton dressed as lamb', or rather market traders dressed as humans, who weren't fit to be in a five star hotel anyway.

At this point I was tapped on the shoulder by another guest, which was a welcome break for me to gather myself, and after he introduced himself I sent him down to the garden to join the other, patiently waiting, couple. By now it was 17:22.

"Alright" I said, turning back to the couple, "it's no problem to move you hotels if you want, but I'm afraid I can't do so until tomorrow, because with today being a Sunday all the hotel reservations staff are off and I'll need to check on room availabilities. But if you're looking for an improvement the only two hotels I think you'll like are the Goa Renaissance and the Leela Palace.

"Now we'll have to charge any price differences and of course the hotel here will charge a three night cancellation fee."

"Money ain't no problem! Is it doll?" he blurted and then allowed me to finish.

"So what I suggest is that you go and have a look them both tomorrow, while I find out about availability and I'll then meet up with you tomorrow night."

"Yeah. Alwight then. Triffic, you're a diamond geezer!"

Off they went, still muttering the words 'five star' and 'fackin disgrace' and they left a wet trail from their swimming costumes through the whole of the reception, much to the bemusement of some of the older clientele. I was able to go and start my welcome meeting only twenty-seven minutes late and with only three out of forty-eight people. Even as I walked down to the garden I knew that the 'barrow boy' couple wouldn't move, because they just wanted to get a few things off their chest and assert their authority, but they would probably come and sit with me every night to tell me what a great time they're having, how much money they're spending and complain at every available instance about the hotel's star rating, which we don't advertise.

Not surprisingly the meeting was a general chat, because there is no way that I'm going to produce my full routine for just three people. A shame because I was geared up for a bit of showing off, plus I had prepared my map and a great selection of props as well as having thirty-five surplus welcome drinks. Surprisingly though, I hit my sales target, because a couple who had sat there patiently for twenty-seven minutes booked the Jungle Book and the Taj Mahal tour, which is over a thousand pounds worth of business.

Triffic!

MONDAY – 15TH MARCH

In the past couple of weeks I've been struggling to get any decent sleep at night, which has been making me very drowsy during the day and my appetite has rapidly diminished. When this has occurred in the past it has either been because I'm excited and busy or because I'm feeling the effects of some nervous tension.

Kate seems to think it's because I'm missing Gina, but she always was a romantic. Although I do miss her I know that's not the reason, because I've put it down to a severe lack of motivation and the fact that I'm not enjoying myself as much as I have done in previous years. I have to admit that things have taken a turn for the better and have gradually been improving since Christmas time, but I am not as satisfied with my own performance compared to what I've achieved in the past. Also, because I'm finding the work very easy at present, I feel as if my skills, experience and energies are being wasted. The other thing that could be taken into account is that I'm the only member of the team who has been here since the very beginning who hasn't had any time away from work at all in the past six months. This isn't unusual at all and I have certainly worked much longer stints, but because business visa regulations state that I must leave the country within the first six months of my stay, it looks like I might be having a few days off in a week or two's time. Before I can think about time away though, I still have to concentrate on giving a good service to the guests who are currently in resort and this evening in the Cidade De Goa could be described as a visit of two halves.

The couple who arrived on Friday and who have been to Goa three times before duly came along and asked to move down south to the Holiday Inn. It helps that they're here for three weeks in total, so we arranged for them to move from this coming Friday, giving them an even two weeks in their new hotel and avoiding the Cidade De Goa's cancellation fee as well. They were very pleasant about the whole matter, especially seeing as the move wasn't costing them anything and we shook hands and they left with a smile on their faces. This certainly made me happier and I felt better about myself. But not for long.

Shortly after they'd left, Cockney Barrow boy who was still dripping with gold, came and positioned himself right next to me for the duration of my visit. He didn't say 'hello' or offer a 'how do you do?' or even a 'watcher.' He merely looked right through me and said,

"This is still a fackin crap 'ole, but we'll stay here becoz we're only here for one week and we don' wannna waste a day movin' 'otels now, do we?!"

I thought that was fair enough and made sense, which I politely intimated to him. Because he had also complained about the standards on the flight I said I would try and arrange legroom seats for the two of them, especially seeing as he is 6'4" tall. I also hoped that he wouldn't bore me to death with the details of why he doesn't like the hotel if he's decided to stay on and even though he was fully clothed, I hoped his wife would be too when she appeared as well. He didn't offer any thanks for the legroom offer and much to my dismay he launched into another vitriolic tirade about why he doesn't think the hotel should be locally rated as a five star. I spent forty-five minutes being boringly sympathetic, repeating the words 'yeah' and 'I understand' at random points in the conversation and trying to avoid the reception staff's gaze as they were doing impressions of someone selling fruit, behind his back.

The only productive thing that I could take out of seeing him for so long and hearing him for what felt like three times longer, was that by the time I managed to get in the gym, I was seething with frustration. As a result I worked out harder in that hour and a half than I have done all season and eased a lot of my minor tensions. This helped refuel my appetite and later on I was able to stuff my face with Butter Chicken as I read a British newspaper, which I'd acquired earlier in the day.

There was one interesting article in it, which reported that the policemen on the scene of the Dunblane disaster would be receiving £10k and more, as compensation for doing the jobs they're trained to do. Yet I've lived through one military coup, one massacre where sixty-six people were shot in Luxor, a bombing in Sri Lanka and two guests who have died while I was on the scene and all I get is a bucket load of paperwork, an hour in the gym and forty quid commission a week.

It makes me wonder why I still do the job sometimes? It's certainly not for the delight of seeing Cockney barrow boys wife wearing a leopard skin bikini and supporting a mountain of gold that would wipe out the whole of the third world debt. After a visit of two halves, I needed a full ninety minutes in the gym, but I'd much rather have a footballers weekly salary in compensation. I need a break.

TUESDAY – 16TH MARCH

I'm not the only one who's been feeling the strain and the rest of the team have all intimated that they'd like to get away from the guests for a while. Apparently it's silly season for people like 'Cockney Barrow Boy' to come to Goa for this couple of weeks of the year. But to compensate us a little and reward us for our efforts over the season, Kate has arranged a 'jolly' for us all.

Kate to her credit has been determined to make sure that all of her team see every bit of Goa, and India that we want to and also enjoy ourselves to boot. Especially considering there wasn't as much fun as there usually is through the early segments of the season. This makes a lot of sense as well, because after all travel is usually the principle reason that reps get into the industry, so we are in theory doing what we initially set out to do.

Our Reward? We're being taken on a two-day, one night sojourn to Shanti camp to experience the Jungle Book trip, which we've been selling for the past six weeks or so and is a variation on the Shanti camp we enjoyed at the very beginning of the season.

Because amongst the five of us, we've all done the waterfalls section, the spice garden and all of the incidental little stops along the way at least twenty times between the lot of us, we missed them all out and headed straight to the rural camp. We went through the check-in formalities, which still took the usual twenty minutes even here in the wilderness, and then headed down to the nearby stream, with our old mate 'John the guide' and a crate of Kingfisher beer, plus some 7UP for the girls to make shandies.

The area is still as beautiful as ever, with spectacular scenery from the camp looking up into a dark green mass of hills with trees clustered tightly upon them. Water runs all the way down in some fast flowing streams over the rocky paths and at the bottom are the lush, bright green rice fields, which are coming into season and blooming fantastically. Luminous green stalks protrude in abundance from the earth and a myriad of colours permeate through at the border of every field, as wild purples and free reds strive to be seen. It's still amazing to see the seemingly frail old ladies hard at work in the fields, while the men sit under trees all day long, smoking cigarettes and directing operations.

The stream we settled on had a mini-lake, which we swam in for half an hour until we discovered some delightful effects of the water levels becoming low prior to the rain season. Amongst the rocky paths and big boulders were an abundance of mini pools and pockets, which were up on one of the higher plateaus and they created what looked like personal baths. Needless to say, we made that heavenly spot our base for the day. We wasted a glorious afternoon chilling out in the pools, soaking up the sun and listening to the sounds of Kingfisher beer bottles being guzzled, which intermittently broke through the chorus of birds and monkeys at play in the trees.

We made sure that 'John the guide' stayed with us for the rest of the day and I for one envied him his job, being lucky enough to come up to these parts every day of the week. We talked about what it would be like sleeping under the stars, especially seeing as I had done it for a fortnight in Yugoslavia with some mates when I was twenty-one, but John advised us against it, because of a minor problem with snakes.

When we returned to the camp in the very late afternoon we were legless, hungry and unbelievably relaxed. After dinner and another beer, we took a stroll down to the nearby temple where they do the yoga and meditation in the daytime, but which is simply very pretty and tranquil in the darkness of night. Memories of my sprint back last time I was here came flooding back, but thankfully my bowels held out and my sphincter remained tightly shut as we looked up at the stars. As I pointed out the Plough, The Southern Cross and Orion's Belt to Toni, we saw a shooting star and I wished for the first thing to enter my mind. I wanted Gina to get in touch.

After consuming copious amounts of Kingfisher and singing the obligatory 'La Bamba' around the camp fire, I went to bed still thinking about Gina and how it would have been nice for her to join us in this romantic spot. I realised that I really enjoy what this job provides sometimes and after today I've as good as decided that I'll probably do one more season. John didn't make it to bed. He fell asleep under the stars.

WEDNESDAY – 17TH MARCH

I passed on the sunrise yoga session and lay in my hut until 10:00 when John decided I had slept enough, seeing as he was awake at 05:30 to get the rest of the tourists up. We strolled up to the top of the camp for a cup of tea with Sandip.

Sandip had promised us all a ride on Babu the elephant, if she was feeling up to it later, but first off he insisted I take my turn with an Ayurvedic massage. He detailed the rules and gave me a brief run down, explaining that the massage comes from the South Indian state of Kerela and uses the soothing effects of oils to rejuvenate the body. One of the conditions is that you must be completely naked and there is to be no giggling or doing anything untoward that may distract the masseurs, who take their job very seriously having spent three years learning the specifics of this type of massage.

Because it was complimentary, he insisted I take advantage of the full body. I quite readily agreed because I was still aching from Monday's work out and I wanted to rid myself of any stiffness before a coming evening's game of football, which was a hastily organised grudge match between our agency and their biggest rival.

I was led into the cordoned-off hut, which houses two separate massage rooms, a small office and one communal area for hanging clothes, relieved that no one else was there in a state of undress. Actually everything was in keeping with the rest of the camp, because the hut was built out of the same materials as the living quarters, complete with cow dung floors and home made wooden divides, which lends to the authenticity of the area. Sandip told me to hang my clothes on a nearby line and wait for my masseurs to come in.

I'd hung up my T-shirt, kicked off my sandals and was gingerly undoing the belt to my shorts, not wanting to be standing naked in a strange place without any form of direction. I was pulling the belt back and forth, trying to decide if I should take it off or not and secretly pretending to regale myself in a striptease. I turned to face the wall, pretending my back was to the audience, I wiggled my bum a little and stuck it out, then whipped the belt off and held it in my teeth, all the while humming the striptease tune. I undid the button on the top of my shorts, pulled down the zip, threw my head back then spun around to be faced with two giggling little Indian ladies, who had entered the area a bit too quietly for my liking.

I pulled the shorts back up and tried to suppress the embarrassment, which was clearly showing in my face. As I hopped from one foot to the other, slightly uncomfortable and making sure they hadn't seen anything that would have embarrassed them, I noticed how pretty they both were and also how they hadn't washed for a couple of days. I smiled at them and they smiled politely back, staring at me almost expectantly. I wanted to take my clothes off and go into the massage room, but I couldn't do it while these two ladies were here, so I coughed and then decided it would be safe to speak.

"Is masseur coming?" I asked in very slow English, knowing that if they were from Kerela their English wouldn't be as good as a Goans.

"Yes." One of them mumbled in reply, so I relaxed and prepared for a little wait.

"When is he coming?"

"Yes." The same one almost whispered and I realised my suspicions were right in that they couldn't speak much English. There was a quiet stalemate with the girls smiling expectantly and me continuing to fiddle with the button at the top of my shorts and sheepishly looking at the floor.

I looked at the floor for a couple of seconds, then up at them, but they hadn't changed their expressions and were still smiling, so I looked at the floor again hoping that next time I looked up, they would have gone and the masseur would have appeared. It was then that the other one spoke.

"Clothes please?"

And that is about the moment when it dawned on me that they were looking at me expectantly because they were the masseurs. I wasn't getting a guy to do it, which was a relief in one sense and filled me with trepidation in another.

First I had to strip in front of two very attractive ladies and then I had to be rubbed by them and try and maintain my dignity throughout. *Remember* I kept repeating to myself, *no giggling and nothing to distract the ladies.* I glanced at them again and as nonchalantly as possible took off my shorts and boxers in one swoop, making a conscious effort to face the ladies as I bared all, to show that I did this all the time. Sadly I looked as casual as a teenager seeing a naked woman for the first time and almost tripped over as I stepped out of my shorts. To their credit, they didn't even notice because they obviously do this all the time and they told me to go into the room and lie on my back.

While one smeared oil onto my torso, the other started working on my left arm and they pummelled and rubbed away, at a well worked, precise co-ordination. Thankfully the idea of the massage is to relax the muscles and this is not done through a sensuous touch, but with hard, practised hands applying a fair bit of painful pressure on the relevant parts of the body. I had to admire their professionalism and I could sense my muscles beginning to relax from the pressure. If only I wasn't suffering from trying not to distract the ladies.

I had to constantly keep thinking of unpleasant thoughts, because I had a semi erection which was threatening to become much more prominent if I couldn't keep him under control. I kept trying to pretend that the ladies were ugly men and I thought of anything I found unappealing, which included Manchester United, rotting corpses, maggot ridden food, Vanessa Feltz and my old English teacher from the sixth form offering to fellate me, which just about did the trick.

But despite pretending two men were doing the rubbing, every time I opened my eyes I kept seeing two very attractive Indian ladies rubbing oil onto my naked body in a tropical wilderness. This just so happens to be a particular fantasy of mine and every now and then I'd forget about Manchester United and Vanessa and I would start waking up. To their credit, they continued to pummel and rub as if I wasn't even there and they were oblivious to the torment I was going through as I made every effort to simply relax.

The ladies worked my shoulders, chest, arms and upper body, then moved down onto my legs. Whilst they were doing my thighs, one of them accidentally and ever so faintly rubbed my right testicle. Heaven seemed to explode around me. The grim walls became glorious spring meadows full of daffodils, the ladies were suddenly clad only in discreetly placed rose petals; Vanessa Feltz became Anna Kournikova; Man Utd became me lifting the Champions league trophy with Swansea City and my John Thomas stood proud and erect like the Eiffel tower looking over Paris. He promptly decided that he was going to remain there for the remainder of the session.

My face went a deeper shade of Cerise and my fingers clenched the side of the bench, but again to their credit they carried on as if nothing had changed. They continued to ignore my prominence and I closed my eyes to pretend it wasn't happening.

But I was secretly hoping that one of them would accidentally flick me again and rub it a bit more, and a bit more again, and they'd hold it and they'd rub it simultaneously. Then they'd kiss it and tell me how wonderful I was, and I'd be able to speak fluent Hindi and they'd stroke sensuously along the inside of my thighs. I'd tell them they looked beautiful and then they would rub my member harder and rub some more and together, more and more and, no!! No. No. No. No. Vanessa Feltz, Manchester United, My old English teacher, not the nice one from year four, the ugly one from the sixth form.

They spent about twenty minutes on my front, then I had to re adjust my prominent tackle and then had another twenty minutes of thinking perverse thoughts about Vanessa Feltz and wishing I'd never done an English 'A' Level in the first place. It was a tortuous period where I couldn't truly relax and to make matters worse, I spent the last five minutes trying to suppress a fart as they were kneading my buttocks.

When they had finished and I could breath a sigh of relief, they stood up and wrapped a towel around my waist, then both of us stood up and I had no struggle whatsoever with a rejuvenating head massage, whilst sat in an uncomfortable wooden chair.

After putting my clothes back on, on top of an oil soaked body and with my embarrassment slowly starting to subside, I thanked the ladies. They smiled and said 'thank you' in return and then looked at each other and giggled, which was my cue to sheepishly walk over to Sandip who ordered me a hearty breakfast.

"Sandip." I said between mouthfuls of scrambled egg, "I've got a small complaint to make about the massage."

"Go on."

"The poster outside says it's a naked massage. But the girls weren't naked!"

We arrived back in Panjim in the latter hours of the afternoon with enough time to spare for us to pop into the office and collect any messages. To my great surprise and even greater delight I found a letter from Gina, which must mean there is something in those shooting stars after all. I read it very quickly because I was anxious to get to the football ground and join the rest of the team, but it didn't say a great deal anyway. She merely said she was sorry that she missed me before she left, that she's sorry we split up and that she misses me, but that our parting was for the best and can we be just good friends. The rest was four pages of general gossip and a final 'I miss you'.

I shoved the letter into my bag with the intention of ringing her later that evening, dashed home to get changed into my football gear, complete with a pair of £4 moulded stud boots, and was pleasantly surprised to see that the agency had splashed out on a brand new strip. We were of course adorned in the company colours of navy blue jersey, navy blue shorts, our own socks and I was pleased to see they had reserved for me my customary, and lucky, number ten.

The game only started thirty minutes late and was an untidy, disorganised, scrappy affair. Both teams had a strange mix of players, with each having a couple of decent people who could knock the ball about a bit and an equal number of office boys with two left feet. I quickly became very frustrated at trying to play a neat passing game, when each time I would lay the ball off to one of my team-mates I could guarantee that he would either try and take on the whole of the opposition or kick it miles into touch. By a sheer stroke of good fortune we won 5-1 and I scored two, made two and received a dead leg from one of my own team.

The first of my goals, the one which broke the deadlock, was very Michael Owenesque. I picked up a loose bouncing ball, which was hardly surprising in itself because the ground was like concrete and they insist on pumping the ball up so hard that it bounces like a space hopper and is almost impossible to control. I was just inside the opponents half, so knocked the ball ahead of their rather clumsy and overweight centre half, ghosted past him like a young gazelle and volleyed the ball with my weaker left foot into the roof of the net, when in fact I had aimed for the bottom left hand corner.

After scoring, I nonchalantly turned around, as I would at an empty Pembrokeshire League rain sodden ground, to be met with a wall of sound. The Indians get a little bit fanatical about their sport and over two hundred people from the industry had turned up to watch the game. The crowd cheered constantly throughout dull moments like throw-ins and so they were positively dancing and blowing their horns when I scored. It was unbelievable, for a friendly as well, and helped me forget the sweltering heat and rock hard surface, which was hurting my back a little.

My second goal was a free kick from thirty yards out, which I drilled diagonally into the keeper's bottom right hand corner. I didn't actually hit it that sweetly, but it went through a crowd of legs and beat the bewildered guy in goal with its second bounce, which kicked up off a stone or something that stuck out on the six yard box. I walked back to the centre circle rather sheepishly, whilst my own side mobbed me as if we'd won the FA cup, as opposed to going four up against a bunch of duffers. The crowd went delirious and erupted into a wall of car horns and wild cheers.

Afterwards I hobbled home to shower and change and then headed back into the office to make a couple of calls. The first was to Stelios George who wanted to speak to me about Kate's leaving date and whether or not I could look after the resort after she leaves. The conversation was its usual difficult affair, but the general upshot is that Kate can leave on April 4th, Toni can go on the 25th, even though our parent company need her on the 18th and Sharon can stay until the 30th, the day of the final charter. I in turn will stay until the very end and will fly home a week later after the season finishes, hopefully on a schedule flight, but more likely via the Maldives on that particular charter.

He also sounded me out about the Head Rep position in Sri Lanka for the summer and then returning to Goa for the following winter, although he didn't intimate in what capacity. It did take me by surprise though, because usually I'm told what they want me to do next after I've arrived back in the UK, but it is quite tempting and I'll sit on that until the offer is set in stone. It does give me a lot of food for thought and has got me thinking again. As a result I've now started considering getting into management and doing a couple more seasons, which is a big difference to my feelings around Christmas time.

The second call I made was to Gina, and thankfully, or not as the case may have been, I managed to get through to her straight away. I'd decided beforehand that I was going to say a few, much needed words to her; I wanted to tell her that I missed her, that I wanted her back and wanted to make a go of things and I also wanted to say that I was sorry for acting like a jerk, but it was just me being my usual scared self. Maybe she could then come back out on holiday, I'll try and mature and we'll see if we can make a go of it. After all we'd always found it easy to talk to each other, even if we didn't always say the right things.

All I could muster though was inane chat about the weather; gossip in the industry and a bit of a stunted conversation about the football. For ten minutes this carried on, all at the company's expense, until eventually I heaved one of my obligatory deep breaths and decided to take the bull by the horns.

She must have recognised the intake of air, because I sensed her tighten up a bit and even as I muttered my first meaningful words I knew they were out of place.

"Gina. I miss you!"

"I miss you too Ceri," She said almost defensively.

"You know I have a hundred and one things I want to say to you?"

"Oh?"

"But."

"But, Ceri?" and but was the key word. I could hear her saying in her mind 'But what?', 'But what about you not wanting me?', ' But what about you never telling me you loved me?', 'But what about you not being prepared to make a commitment when it matters?', 'But, But, But, But!!"

"Oh, never mind Gina. Bye."

"Bye Ceri." She said with a deep-rooted sense of relief, which was probably the moment that I realised I wasn't going to get her back.

I had been so confident that we would get it together, because at the end of the day I knew she was crazy about me. But (that key word again) I hadn't banked on her having this much strength. The ironic thing is that if she had been this distant and this strong at the beginning, I would have made much more of an effort and we would probably be blissfully in love right now.

"Miss you." I said quite feebly.

"Miss you too." And then a distinct sound of the phone clicking off. Stupid! Stupidy! Stupidest!!

Yet again I'd bottled up what I truly felt and I couldn't make any sense of it. Maybe it was fate that my tongue was tied right at the moment that I wanted its use the most. Maybe we weren't meant to be. Maybe I'm not meant to meet that someone special. Maybe I'm destined to be a lifelong rep, seeing all of my favourite parts of the world, making some great friendships and living a shallow, hollow life.

I went home and wrote her a twelve page letter, telling her everything that I couldn't say over the phone and as soon as I'd finished I felt almost liberated, as if I'd closed a chapter and was ready to move on. As I slept I heard the sounds of the Eagles track 'Desperado' running through my head and not the cheers that greeted each of my goals.

My back was killing me.

SUNDAY – 21ST MARCH

I'd been dreading today. Having to do a Renton Manor welcome meeting, where we're supposed to be bombarded with complaints in Sharon's absence, had been playing on my mind for a couple of days and had gradually started to reform some of those long banished dark clouds.

I don't really know why I've been so worried, because I've handled every conceivable situation this job can throw at you and there is no way that this hotel can be as bad as the SJM earlier on in the season, or even on a par with past hotels that I've repped. But Sharon, who is off on a shopping jolly with Kate, has made it sound worse than Faulty Towers and if she is to be believed, every spare moment is spent under siege from a battalion of disgruntled Billies. But I just couldn't fathom why I was getting so worked up about one simple late saver hotel. I've obviously been believing too much of what I've been hearing recently and maybe I'm just a born worrier, which I suppose has an advantage in that it makes me work harder. First of all though, we had to get through the morning airport run with a depleted number of staff.

To their utmost credit all of the local boys worked exceedingly hard, from the handling agent by ensuring the check-in procedure was fast and efficient and also complying with all of my seat requests for this week, to our transfer reps who arrived on time and hung around to help the guests.

Also the seats I'd requested for 'Cockney Barrow Boy' were allocated, much to my relief, but when he went to the check-in desk he didn't ask for them and was therefore given seats in the middle of the aircraft. He immediately came over to me effing and blinding again and I calmly went and got the seats changed for him. Yet again I received no 'thank you' or even a 'cheers mate', just a curt and offhand, 'I should think so an' all!' Quite frankly he's a rude bastard who I was glad to see the back of and I hoped I wouldn't have the misfortune of coming across anyone else like him during the rest of the season.

Despite the 'Barrow Boy's' ignorant touch, the rest of the departures went along nice and smoothly. The flight was only twenty minutes late and the luggage came through quicker than it has done all season and we were out of the airport by 08:30 and I was back at The Ranch by 10:00 for a couple of fretful hours kip. Just to make an effort to put me in the right frame of mind for the coming evenings meeting, I spoke to as many of the Renton Manor guests as possible and one couple in particular stood out. They were dripping in chunky gold, even more than 'Barrow Boy' had been and walked right up to me and said, "Where are we fackin' staying then?" in the broadest Cockney accent I've heard since, well since 'Cockney Barrow Boy' an hour earlier.

They gave me their names, which sounded a few alarm bells and I looked at my flight manifest in despair. I desperately hoped that it couldn't be so.

"Uhhm, have you had any relatives in Goa recently sir?" I very nervously asked, but just by looking at his face, his cold ignorant expression and hearing the jangle of gold on gold I already knew the answer.

"Yeah too right. My sans just leavin' today and he called me last night. I 'ope we don' 'ave a shit 'ole like what ee did?!"

So having got rid of one obnoxious and ignorant bastard, I only had the misfortune of having his dad come out. Worst of all the son had complained about a good standard of hotel and his dad, who is supposed to be even more particular, had come out on a late saver and was staying at the Renton Manor.

"We'll have some problems there Lester mate." I said whilst turning to look at my colleague after I had sent the guests off to their bus.

"Why, who are they?"

"Just trust me. Oh fackin' 'ell!"

I woke up after my siesta at 13:00 with a dry taste in my mouth, so forced some food and drink down. In an effort to pick me up I put on my happiest tape extra loud as I changed into my uniform and prepared most of my spiel for the coming meeting. I drove up to Arpora in a cold sweat and also travelled pretty slowly, doing my utmost to convince myself that everything would be okay and trying to repeat positive thoughts over and over.

When I arrived, Lester was already in reception and was in the process of sorting out the chairs in the car park behind reception, which is the only place that we're allowed to hold the meeting. I put my bag down, introduced myself to the front office staff with sweaty palms and tried to gather as much information as possible about the hotel, because we were doing a significant meeting 'blind'. As I was chatting to the receptionists, I was tapped on the shoulder, turned round and was face to face with 'Cockney Barrow Dad'.

"This is fackin' shit. We want to upgrade!" which was more of a demand than a request.

I was hardly surprised, having expected this since the moment I arrived, but his timing couldn't have been worse, because other guests were starting to arrive and I didn't want him influencing them and spoiling their holidays. I therefore explained as quickly as possible the usual routine of not being able to move until Monday because reservations staff are off on a Sunday and of course any upgrades would have to be paid for. He said he understood, but still demanded to be moved as soon as possible. In the meantime his wife, who also had a leopard skin swimming costume and plethora of gold, was going on about having seen a cockroach on the road, claiming there's lots of poor people and that the streets are dusty and it's not what she expected. Apparently she thought Goa was going to be like the Algarve or Lanzarote.

I couldn't really answer any of that, so kept my mouth shut for a moment, thus keeping in an abundance of sarcastic comments that were chomping at the bit to ridicule the ignorance of the couple. We agreed that I would contact them first thing the following morning with options of where they can move to and what the price differences will amount to. Then true to form, just like his son, he said, "Money don' matter. Do it doll?" before going behind the reception to sit in the front row of the meeting scowling at me all the way through. Exactly what I needed before a session, which I had worked myself into a nervous frenzy for as it was. I went to the toilet, took half a dozen very deep breaths and said, "Fack it!" to myself and then Lester and I did the best joint meeting I have ever seen or heard.

Ironically the miserable attitude of 'Cockney Barrow Dad' served to act as a stimulant. He glared at me all the way through and that simply wound me up and I thought, '*to hell with him*' and decided to give every one of the other sixty-two guests a fantastic show. As a result the guests were eating out of our hands. Lester and I played off each other extremely well, they laughed at all of our jokes and little stories and at the end we had two long queues of people wanting to book excursions and we even received compliments on the quality of the meeting, which is rare indeed. At least half a dozen couples commented on the fact that they were unsure about the hotel and the surrounding area, but because we were so enthusiastic and positive we'd changed their whole mood and they were determined to enjoy Goa as much as we both do. In fact we didn't receive a single complaint, which also seemed to wind up 'Cockney Barrow Dad' even further.

He won't be getting any legroom seats.

THURSDAY – 1ST APRIL

April Fools Day and it most certainly felt like it with some of the jokers I had to deal with who work in the hotel Dona Santa Maria. I'd got into the office nice and early and was determined to be completely prepared for the gang when they came in for liquidation later on. At about 08:15 I received a phone call from a guy in the UK who was trying to get hold of his sister, who in turn was holidaying in the Dona Santa Maria, which he assured me was nothing serious or for her to worry about. For some reason every time he had called the hotel the reception staff claimed there was no-one staying in the hotel under his sister's surname, so that was why he was trying us that early in the day, to try and get some help in locating her. I promised to do what I could for him.

The hotel reception couldn't locate the girl's name on their register nor that of her friend who is with her, so I was passed to Reservations to find that they had no record of them either. They then hung up on me so I had to call Reception again who double-checked the whole of their Sunday arrival sheet and all of our rooming lists. Still they couldn't find the girl's name anywhere. I was starting to become a little concerned that something may have happened to them, so I checked with Toni to make sure they'd arrived, which she was able to confirm because she'd taken them in on the arrival transfer the Sunday just gone. I called the hotel back again and went through the whole routine, frequently being kept on hold for long periods, and I still failed to discover the girl's room number or even where they might be.

In the end I insisted the hotel should fax to me their full list of our arrivals for the most recent Sunday, which they struggled to do within forty-five minutes. I then checked their list of names against ours and was left with a party under the lead name of Kelly Thomas, who were the odd ones out. I rang the hotel yet again and told them to get a hold of their registration form for the party with this name and read both of the names out. It transpired that the reception had seen the Christian name of Kelly and assumed that it must have been the surname, because they had had a guest in the hotel two weeks previously whose Christian name had been Thomas. The guests were therefore registered in the hotel under the name of Kelly and not Thomas, ie Thomas Kelly. This caused an awful lot of consternation for the girl's family, took one hour and fifty minutes of my time to discover and is a feature that is regarded as the norm in Goa.

Continuing the April Fools theme I also had my appraisal later on in the day with Kate, which I had fully expected to be a joke. Appraisals are generally supposed to be done midway through a season and also towards the end and they quite obviously assess our ongoing performance levels, look for areas where we can improve and also determine our suitability for future positions and destinations.

My personal opinion on my performance so far this season is not particularly high, because I know that I haven't done as good a job as I am capable of doing (and have done in almost every previous season). I have to take into account the fact that I haven't been as motivated as in previous years, there have been no new challenges and I have been most definitely underused by the company. This means that I've been stagnating, slowly receding in levels of performance and have therefore not produced the best work that I'm capable of.

Kate, thankfully, has other ideas and has given me an excellent appraisal. In her words I am basically capable of handling anything that this job can throw at me. Whatever I've been asked to do I've achieved easily, to a high standard and without any noticeable complaints, but that's because I bottle everything up and transfer any moans into my thoughts and my writing. I'm well organised; paperwork is always immaculately presented; I'm positive with other members of the team; good at communicating and training; have great patience on the surface; have a fantastic rapport with our suppliers and am calm in a crisis. She inserted all of these points and more, complimenting me on my efforts throughout the season, because my knowledge of our company and our operations has saved her an awful lot of trouble and inconvenience. She also left more than a few strong hints to the company that they are at fault for not motivating me and that I should have been promoted long ago, which is actually very true. However, I should shoulder a good proportion of the blame for not pushing my case often enough. Overall it was a very positive and pleasing appraisal, something that I will be able to take with me everywhere I go and it has put me in a very good frame of mind to finish the season off. This is just as well, because Kate leaves on Sunday and I am in charge, without the pay rise, for the last four weeks.

SUNDAY – 4TH APRIL

Kate left today, but I wasn't in a position to properly to see her off and offer my farewells, which was a little sad and completely down to the fate I've been tempting in recent weeks.

Seven days ago when I was covering anther meeting for Sharon, I was boldly explaining to more than one couple that it's been a very peculiar season illness wise. Each of the couples had asked what was the likelihood of suffering from something like 'Delhi Belly' because they had heard some bad stories from friends who had already been out on holiday.

I offered the usual warnings of staying out of the sun; not drinking alcohol during the day; getting plenty of water inside them; wearing a hat etc and explained that if they were sensible then the chances of being ill were minimal. So far this season we've hardly had a single case of any guest suffering from any severe illness. It has been the reps who have been dropping like nine pins in a bowling alley and it has been friends and colleagues of ours who have had to return to the UK to recuperate, or spend a couple of nights in a clinic on a drip. In fact, I explained to them, it seems to have been everyone except me. Until Saturday, that was. I've also been proudly boasting to anyone who would listen about my record of nil absenteeism in this industry, compared to the bad old days in insurance. So it was only right that I eat a portion of humble pie and get some feel for what others have been going through.

On Friday night I'd gone out for a farewell dinner with Kate and a few friends, including Janice who I enjoyed catching up with and sadly lamented the fact that she had a new man in her life, and afterwards we went onto a bar in one of our hotels in town.

Inside the bar they had the air conditioning on at its lowest temperature, even though there were only half a dozen people in there. We were freezing, to the extent that we were all wearing jackets done up to our throats, which shows how cold the bar was when you consider it was over ninety degrees outside. No amount of pleading with the bar staff could get them to reduce the effects and I almost struggled to finish my beer. It was so chilly I could feel it slide all the way down my alimentary canal. On three occasions I had to go to the toilet, which was like walking from a freezer to a furnace and back again, because the temperature outside was hot and humid and played all kinds of havoc with my defence systems.

By about 01:00 and two beers apiece, Kate and the others went to get another round in, but I made my excuses and left because I felt as if I had a dose of flu in the midst of a British winter. I shivered in ninety degrees worth of a tropical Asian heat all the way home on my moped and then continued to do the same when I scrambled into bed. I banged my shin yet again and lay underneath a sheet and two blankets, with the overhead fan turned off to boot. I hoped that this was still the lingering effect of the air conditioning and the fact that I was tired at the end of a long season and by the morning I would be feeling my usual ebullient self. After two hours of a deep sleep, I awoke with a start to find myself in a cold sweat, with the blankets feverishly gripped around my torso and held tightly up to my chin.

My teeth were chattering, almost like they were being operated by batteries and I had an excruciating ache in my midriff, even fiercer than I had on the occasion when I was caught short at the beginning of the season. It was rapidly coursing its way around my entire body, giving warning that I had a matter of seconds to reach the toilet.

Being experienced at the getting caught short scenario, I was out of the bed and into the bathroom in one swift movement, avoiding the obligatory shin bashing and within two point four seconds I had shoved my head into the mouth of the not so welcoming porcelain bowl. I was naked, with a sheen of clammy sweat running all over my aching limbs and I was noticeably devoid of any strength as the first load launched itself, out through my mouth and violently sprayed the sides of the toilet.

This was closely followed by a second, third and fourth bout of such intense vomiting and the bug inside obviously had no intention of letting me get my breath back. It was not only content with sending gushes of Mutton Rogan josh through my usual orifices. Because in its rush to rid itself of my very sensitive insides, which were by now burning like a red hot poker, it was forcing itself out of any available orifice. Sweat was flowing through the pores in my skin. An ugly yellowy grey mixture was launching itself, like something out of the Monty Python sketch with Monsieur Creosote, and the bug also delighted in squeezing lumps of meat and vegetables through my nasal passage in its desire to be the first to reach the sanctuary of the porcelain.

After twenty minutes of a non-stop convulsing torture, I calmed down a little bit and was able to get my breath back and start what I hoped would be a steady stream of groans for a few minutes. I had been denied this pleasure for the preceding moments. It was then that I felt a soggy patch on the floor where I was kneeling and as I looked down between my legs I noticed that a mixture of excretion and sick had passed through my rear passage as well. My sphincter had obviously opened its rear gates, without having the decency to inform the other parts of my body, which were fighting a losing battle with the regular nausea.

Fortunately my bathroom is so small that the toilet is almost under the shower and if I'm not careful I can bang my head against the sink when I'm in the usual sitting position on the toilet. This meant I was able to turn on the shower and clean the mess up, by flushing it down the gaping hole in the corner, whilst also taking up my position for the evening of sitting on the toilet and simultaneously burying my head in a large green bucket to protect myself for any further eventualities. The bucket was green on the outside at least.

I remained there for over an hour before bashing my shins, crawling back into bed and hiding under the covers to shiver myself back to sleep, because the incessant teeth chattering had returned. Only sleep didn't come, because that was when the hallucinations started.

These lasted for a couple of hours and scared the living daylights out of me. They started with me believing I was in the middle of a game of Tetris, lying at the bottom of the screen and all of the odd shaped blocks were coming down to crush me if I didn't move into the correct position in time. As a result I dived about my bed frantically, curling myself into a ball to be a square, twisting to avoid the 'L' shaped ones and straightening out to escape anything else. The longer I resisted the higher the wall became and just as I reached the higher levels and could see the game ending and darkness start to overwhelm me, huge, human sized, luminous green frogs came bounding through the room, dropping saliva and an oily film all over my bed and threatening to swallow me whole. I had to bounce around the bed to avoid them, but my muscles ached way too much to do that and my sheets became more and more damp, which made it difficult for me to fathom if it was from the saliva or my sweating, but it repulsed me nonetheless. I threw off the sheets to lie on a bare mattress and as my body could move no more, one of the frogs swallowed me whole and I was lying in darkness, resting in the slimy area in the fatty growth under his chin. I closed my eyes to let the darkness overwhelm me, hoping I would be at peace in this peculiar haven.

Suddenly I lurched upright, with severe pains in my midriff again, but this time it wasn't from any form of sickness but because I knew that I had a creature living inside me and it was fighting to get out. I could feel it punching my skin, scratching my internal organs and feverishly working away at any passage that would lead it to safety and let it lay its eggs elsewhere.

The only way that I could quash this menace was to transform myself into another character, much like Jim Carrey in The Mask. But every time I tried to copy some of his lines or anecdotes all I would be able to muster was a rasping, guttural, "Feed Me" from the back of my throat, because the evil inside had overwhelmed the rest of my bodily functions. It hurt to talk and I felt as if barbed wire was being dragged across my larynx when I tried to do so much as whisper. Finally, and all of a sudden, gleaming sharp swords that would penetrate me forcefully if I tried to move surrounded me. I had to fight it and couldn't allow myself to be eaten to death from within. I therefore struggled and writhed, trying to get the swords to puncture my skin and in the process stab the creature to death.

I was throwing my self against the floor by now and banging my head against the side of the bed until I was saved by a final, terrifying surge of pain in my stomach. I had killed the monster, but to defeat it I had to flush it and all of its eggs out of my system. I made it to the toilet in time and threw up the remnants of the evil within.

Of all the bizarre, frightening, potentially life-threatening situations that have occurred so far in my life, none has ever terrified me as much as that seemingly eternal period. I had no control over my actions, my surroundings and worst of all my fear. The rest of the night and the whole of Saturday was peaceful in comparison, because I was spared the demons and killer Tetris. But the sickness and diarrhoea was repeated every hour on the hour, without fail, until the early hours of Sunday morning.

I was able to get intermittent periods of rest, but for some bastard 'force majeure' they were always interrupted by the dulcet tones of the mobile phone ringing, just as my eyelids were beginning to close. All of the calls were from either the reps or from guests asking the most needless of questions, which further exacerbated my misery. At this moment in time, the last thing I needed was to hear, "What price is the Goan Heritage in the brochure?", "What time is our pick-up in the morning?", "What time is our rep coming, it says 17:30 on the board?" And so forth.

Saturday night was remarkably better in comparison, but there was no way I was in a fit enough state to go to the airport and sweat my way through the ordeal, so I spent the rest of the day in bed. I was only sick five times and actually managed a period of two hours constant sleep as well as managing to get some fluid into my system for the first time since Friday.

The other distressing factor in all of this was the fact that I didn't get to say goodbye to Kate and also wish her a happy birthday, which she was celebrating by flying for eleven hours in a cramped airplane. I felt sad that I didn't get to do so, but it again goes to show how you build up your emotional immune systems and can be so lackadaisical about some very close friendships, which Kate and I have, despite a few differences of opinion earlier on in the season.

Kate, true to form, finished as she had carried on all season, by turning up at the airport blind drunk, having only recently packed with clothes hanging out of her suitcase. She too threw up in the toilets.

THURSDAY – 8TH APRIL

Although it gets me away from the solitary confinement of my room and takes my mind off how I'm feeling, coming into work and completing a ten hour day isn't really the best medicine at present because I still need a few more days of Rest and Recuperation. However I do not have a duvet, a nice house, football and 'Men Behaving Badly' videos and an endless supply of Heinz cream of chicken soup to entice me to stay away from the office.

Plus The Ranch is not, and has never been, the most welcoming of abodes and I am almost frightened to spend long periods in my room at present, because nothing positive ever seems to happen in there.

So since Monday I have reluctantly make the short ride into the office to distract myself and keep in touch with the rest of the world, whilst surviving on a diet of water, tomato soup, some glucose concoction I bought at the chemist and Lassi, which is a yoghurt drink and is supposed to be good for settling the stomach. The hippies also use it to put dope in and increase the effects of their 'high' in a drink called 'Bang Lassi'. So mentally I am aiding my recovery by working as well as adding to the levels of amusement to the office boys who have fired a barrage of questions at me including: "You look white. You sick? You sweating a lot. Why you have spots? Who bit you?" As well as tolerating this inane banter I have to contend with Goa itself, which isn't the easiest of places to recover from any illness.

The temperatures are now at one hundred degrees and the humidity has reached ninety percent, with the rainy season fast approaching. The streets are even dustier than ever, with dirt and germs being omnipresent and I'm also convinced that there's a fault with the office air conditioning system, which is blowing more germs than clean air into our breathing zones. Then there's the food, which has heaps of coriander on something as mundane as dried toast and has debilitated my appetite completely, apart from the constant cravings for a bacon sandwich that is. But this still means that my posterior is permanently raw and I dream of the day that something solid moves through my behind.

So with the inability to recover as I would like, the fact that I still have to be on call twenty four hours a day and that Goa can be annoying at times, I have recently found myself screaming at people, sometimes at strangers and other times at friends, for no apparent reason.

I'm not the only one to suffer temper losses at the end of a season here, because the constant stream of infuriation that is suppressed over a period of seven months, mounts up until you have no option but to release it. The Indians do not help matters, principally because they are the cause of this build up of frustration. They are fantastically warm, kind, generous and intelligent people, but they have no common sense as we all frequently lament. They have very odd working systems, the red tape and bureaucracy is irritating, they can be rude and unaware of other people's feelings, they often do not listen and very frequently, they can be odd. At times this is amusing, but after a season of reception staff not being able to find a guest's name or room service boys knocking on your door at 07:00 it all accumulates until you can take no more and something small just triggers you off.

This is one of the single most, alarming differences between long haul and short haul repping and dealing with the locals and these feelings is a key to the success of a season. You have to overcome the irritation, work with it and still provide an excellent service to the guests as well, whilst all the time they are feeling some of those anxieties with you.

Some people thrive amongst these attitudes, as I generally do, whereas others, who could ordinarily be excellent and vastly experienced short haul reps end up tearing their hair out and leaving after only a few weeks. But with the season now seven months gone, I'm feeling sick without any visible sign of recovery, my body is weak and my mind is tired. Consequently I have been reacting to some of the most innocuous of circumstances. These reactions have only been for very brief instances until I realise what I am doing, but they are also very frightening, because for a second I lose myself. Recently I have found myself screaming at people who walk out in front of my bike and yelling at someone who might push in front of me in a shop queue, but on Wednesday I think I suffered my worst and most uncharacteristic reaction in a while.

I was watching the TV in the lobby of The Ranch, when Savi the receptionist came over and changed the channels to watch the cricket. The television is for the residents use only and the hotel staff have been banned from watching it, because otherwise they would spend all day watching the cricket and wouldn't get any work done. The other stupid factor is that I also wanted to know the cricket score, but I can't abide bad manners and the guy didn't even ask or look at me. He simply walked up to the screen and pressed the relevant button as if I was invisible.

"What the F*** do you think you're doing you rude f***ing bastard! I was watching that program and you come over without even saying 'excuse me' and change the channel. Where the f*** are your manners?!" I blurted, my face burning with rage and my fists tightly clenched into balls, ready to unleash further fury if he wound me up even more. I wasn't really in control of my anger and I wasn't aware of who was listening or what I may do.

"But you see, I am wanting to watch the cricket," he nonchalantly explained, oblivious to what I was getting at because his logic says that if he wants to watch the cricket then he shall watch the cricket, irrespective of what anyone else may think. His head was rolling, which for some reason stirred up my emotions even more.

"I don't care if you want to watch the cricket. I was watching the other channel and you don't just come in and change channels when someone is already watching one."

And then he did what is usually charming when you watch guests have arguments with hotel staff, but heightens your annoyance when it happens to you. He looked me square in the eye, rolled his head some more and laughed.

"Don't you laugh at me! Now change the f***ing channel over NOW!!"

And he carried on laughing, obviously seeing a European lose his temper for the first time, because he called over two of the other boys, said something patently amusing in Konkani and pointed at me. They all then laughed at me.

"And you bunch of f***ers can stop laughing as well, before I tell your boss you were all watching TV all day long and not doing any work!"

At this stage and with that threat, which was enough to lose them their jobs, Savi realised I was serious and not acting. He promptly changed the channel back to what I was originally watching and then strolled back to his reception desk without apologising. Although I was calming down as quickly as I had lost control of myself, I couldn't let that pass.

"Aren't you going to apologise for being so rude?"

"But you shouted at me so you must apologise to me also."

"Okay."

"I'm sorry mister Ceri, but I only wanted to watch the cricket." He explained.

"F*** off!" I exclaimed ridding myself of any remnants of rage that were still lingering and much to the chagrin of Savi. I was still shaking a little, but as I was coming down I was also unbelievably frightened at my sudden outburst and loss of control.

"I'm sorry" I muttered to a forgiving Savi. "I'm so, so sorry."

We never got the cricket score.

TUESDAY – 13TH APRIL

I woke up with a big cheesy rep's grin on my face, only this time it was entirely genuine, because I had an easy half a day's work ahead of me. I was heading down south in the early afternoon and I would eventually end up spending a lazy day off on the sands of Colva Beach, recharging my batteries, ridding myself of the last remnants of my illness and ensuring that I was still fresh for the final two and a half weeks of the season. I'd even paid for Toni and Sharon to have rooms in the Leela Palace hotel for one night each, to thank them for their efforts, whilst Lester was getting a room in the Taj Holiday Village in the North. All of which was courtesy of our slush fund and there would still be enough left over for a team lunch on our final liquidation day together.

As I got out of bed I made it to the bathroom without banging my shin, and I could swear that my usually flat baritone was in tune for once when I was in the shower. The sun was shining, birds were chirping, flowers were blossoming outside my window and all I had left to do was iron my shirt and drive to the office. Everything was perfect, the most immaculate of plans had been laid, I couldn't wait to get away for a couple of days and have my first beer in ages and nothing could feasibly go wrong, unless you work in this industry.

I should have learnt years ago never to tempt fate by assuming that nothing detrimental or disruptive will occur and that every time I prepare myself for a joyous occasion, I should in turn be preparing myself for anything untoward. This time it was my damned humble abode. Whenever things are starting to go well at work, we've always been able to rely upon The Ranch to bring us crashing back down to earth and start a snowball effect with minor disasters, all of which are quiet easy to keep under control as separate entities, but as they gather strength with their combined numbers, they serve to disrupt and destroy routines and the best laid plans. Today The Ranch brought me crashing back down to earth with two hundred and twenty volts, which coursed through my right arm and faintly through the rest of my body.

I received my fourth electric shock of the season when I was ironing my shirt, which I know was entirely due to the faulty wiring in my plug socket. Every one of the shocks I've had I have diligently reported to the hotel staff and have received pretty much the same offhand response every time.

The first shock occurred in November and when I told the guys behind the reception they just laughed. The second time in early December, they blamed it on my iron, which I was initially prepared to accept. But they still changed the burnt out socket and then laughed. The third time was when I had returned to the hotel in February and on this occasion the staff ignored me completely, obviously tiring of my persistent pedantry over everyday hazards which are commonplace in the hotel. Then I heard them laughing behind my back as I returned to my room. So on this occasion I went direct to the hotel manager, who sneered and then laughed at me.

It took an hour to try and get my case across that it couldn't possibly be the iron, because my first two shocks were in November and December, but then for the two months that I was in the SJM I didn't receive one single shock whilst using my iron at least twice every day. Then I return to The Ranch and I start to receive the electric shocks again. I also tried to explain that the hotel has some very irregular power surges, one of which nearly blew my stereo up at the beginning of the season, and they still continue to play havoc with the ceiling fans. Some nights I can have my fan on full but it won't move fast enough to disturb a feather, but then the next night it whirls so fast my bed sheets are almost flying off the bed.

The manager's response was to sneer again, blame it on my iron, refuse any help and tell me I wouldn't receive a penny from him, which is not what I was looking for. I merely wanted some acknowledgement that there was a problem and that they would look into the wiring to ensure that it was safe for us to use our simple appliances. At the end of the day I didn't want to burn to death in my sleep.

I didn't receive a single, 'sorry' or 'are you alright?' As usual the guys in the hotel didn't listen and didn't want to know and responded with their usual riposte of, 'it's not my fault' and 'you're white you can afford it.' Afford what? I don't really know, but it's their safe response to anything a European may say. I am pleased to say that I managed to keep my calm, mainly because I still had such a good couple of days to look forward to, and I didn't react when I heard the manager chuckling as I left his office.

With the bit between my teeth now though, I was desperate to prove that it was the fault of their wiring system and not my appliance. So I took the iron to an electrical shop to get it checked out and then headed to an immaculate office, with not a single piece of paper out of place and not even the merest hint of a backlog. I also walked into a deluge of phone calls, where travellers were desperately asking for flight seats, which just don't exist.

At this stage of the season my main function now seems to be the selling, or rather the non-selling, of flight seats. There are no guests in the Majorda Beach and I only have a handful of content Billies in the Cidade De Goa, so I spend the majority of my time in the office and deal with any problems that may come our way and of course provide a back-up for the reps. However, the reps don't need any more training or for me to tell them how to do their jobs with three weeks to go, the numbers in the hotels are dropping and the hotels in turn along with our local agency are running just fine, so I don't need to make too many work oriented visits out and about. All of the excursions are winding down and I have the office gleaming with perfection, so in theory I should be having an awful lot more time to myself. But no; I have now taken on the role of a telephone answering machine that constantly repeats, "I'm sorry, we have no flight seats available."

In the midst of this plethora of telephone inanity I received a call from the manager of the Alphaville hotel. One of our guests had gone down sick, was allergic to all forms of medicine and her alcoholic husband was panicking. Because he didn't know what to do, he logically panicked, became more inebriated and in turn less helpful. Thankfully the hotel manager is fantastic and he gave me all of their insurance details, so that I could get some advice from them, and he called out a doctor who was actually more astute than the guests had counted on and was able to help her.

The doctor put a lot of the problem down to the reaction of the drink sodden husband and he confirmed what we have been predicting for the past few weeks. With the added heat and humidity more tourists are going to suffer the effects of dehydration and/or heatstroke, which was the case with this lady. But in dealing with a drawn out case of melodrama I wasn't able to leave the office until 18:00, four hours later than I had originally planned. I did manage to get down south for 20:00 and had to swap a luxurious bath for a shower, which was the biggest disappointment of all, because I haven't had a bath in over eight months and that is now high on my list of cravings along with the desire to chew on a bacon sandwich.

I also had to forfeit watching a classic black and white movie on the satellite television, but I was compensated by a trip to the Pasta Hut bar and copious amounts of conversation about football, proposed changes to the LBW rule and a debate over who is better, Kylie or Kournikova? It was a delight to round off my day by consuming large amounts of glycerine-filled beer, chatting up some overweight hippy women and riding home drunk on my moped to the Holiday Inn, where they have huge comfortable beds, room service and a casino.

And staff that don't laugh at me behind my back.

FRIDAY – 16TH APRIL

We had a couple arrive on our last full Manchester flight today, who happen to be the epitome of the type of holidaymakers we should be expecting at this bargain bucket stage of the season. This flight signals the last fortnight of the season and the guests were booked into the Goa Renaissance hotel, which is a deluxe five star by Indian standards. One of our local reps, Lyndon, took the guests from the airport to the hotel, to receive their customary cocktail, hot towel and warm greeting, whilst I returned to the office to tie up any loose ends.

As I opened the doors to the office, which in itself was stinking like a prostitute who hadn't washed for a week because we have had no water supply for two days so the toilet cannot be flushed, a phone was shoved into my face before I had a chance to add to the stench myself. As this happened I was told that a guest wanted to speak to me, which is indicative of the local attitude at present of letting one of us do any form of work that they can reasonably get out of.

"We're disgusted with this hotel. It's a dump, the rooms are crap and it's disgusting!"

"Okay madam" I said trying to slow things down, because I was dying to go to the toilet and hadn't had a chance to catch my breath yet, "where are you staying?" *Bloody SJM,* I was thinking, *here we go again.*

"The Goa Renaissance!"

"What?! Are you sure? You can't be?" I have to admit that although we should expect the unexpected and that nothing really surprises me any more, I was well and truly gob smacked. I was so surprised that for a brief second I had dropped my usual professional veneer and failed to keep all feelings of shock out of my voice.

"Yeah, the Goa Renaissance. We was in the Holiday Inn last year, which is miles better than here and we want to move there. So I'm telling you as our courier to move us now!"

Ordinarily if someone shouts at me or demands something without being reasonable I would be less inclined to assist them. But I was still reeling from the shock of her saying the Goa Renaissance and I had to gather myself a little, so I endeavoured to try and get her off the phone and buy myself a little time. Plus I desperately needed to go to the toilet.

"I'm sorry if you don't like the Goa Renaissance, but I think you'll find it is far superior to the Holiday Inn. However, if you wish to move I'll call the Holiday Inn to see if they have any rooms available for you. Oh and incidentally it's tour operator, not courier."

"Right. We'll be in reception and we're not budging."

I couldn't get over this. The Renaissance is an excellent hotel with very good standard rooms, superb facilities and we've brochured it one hundred percent correctly. In the last three years, as far as I am aware, there has not been a single complaint about the hotel. The Holiday Inn on the other hand is a good hotel and we've rarely had a complaint there either, but it's certainly not in the same league as the Renaissance. It would be like comparing Wales as a football nation to Brazil. The Renaissance would win hands down every time.

I actually wanted to act in the best interest of the guests here and stop them making a mistake for their own sake, which is something that would probably cost me a lot more time trying to calm them down and bring them around. I also knew that if I could get them to stay in the hotel for just one night, then they would most definitely change their minds and begin to have a fantastic holiday.

I quickly called Werner, who is the manager of the hotel to explain the problem. After a brief conversation between the two of us he agreed to go and see the guests personally, buy them a drink and see what he could do to persuade them to stay. He also agreed with me that they must be tired after a long day's travelling and were obviously a little excitable, so if he could manage to help convince them to stay for just the one night then in the light of a new day they would more than likely have a completely different opinion.

I also checked with the Holiday Inn to find out their levels of availability and they unfortunately had plenty of rooms available, which meant that I would have to move the guests if Werner couldn't persuade them to stay. It would have been much simpler if the Holiday Inn were full, because the guests would have no option but to stay and that would most likely have been the end of the discussion.

After stalling for twenty minutes, to give Werner a chance to work his magic with the couple, he called me back. He'd bought the couple a drink, shown them around the hotel and offered them a complimentary upgrade from a standard room to a superior, but they still insisted on moving. He also confirmed my worst fear that he was duty bound to charge a cancellation fee of three nights accommodation per person, which amounted to a total of £184 between the two of them. Seeing as the Holiday Inn works out at £110 less per person in the brochure and I would be asking them for an extra £184 I didn't expect them to be too happy. They weren't too happy. The general response was that they're not f***ing paying that extra amount and put that extra profit into a couriers coffers.

I explained that the money goes to the hotel, which would still be losing eleven nights worth of business, and not to us. Also we'd fulfilled all of our contractual obligations, had marketed the hotel 100% correctly, so we were not going to bear a substantial loss because they chose not to like the hotel. I also explained that we are a tour operator and not a courier.

Apparently I'm rude, unhelpful and a waste of space and they demanded to speak to the manager.

"I am the resort manager." I politely and oh so sheepishly explained, which put them back on their heels for a second, before telling me that I don't know what I'm talking about.

"Well madam," I countered as patronisingly as possible because not once had she been civil and she was beginning to wind me up, "I've been in the package holiday industry overseas, for over seven years and I have worked in Goa for a combined total of nineteen months, so I think I have a fair idea of what I'm talking about."

"Huh you would say that." She stammered and I thought, *Actually I did say that because it happens to be the truth,* "In fact you seem very well rehearsed at this. I bet you get this problem every time with this hotel."

Now that was a bit of a rash statement from the Billy and she was obviously clutching at straws, which suited me fine because I had no intention of backing down and letting them get a free move on a very flimsy whim. I had also been prepared for most eventualities of this conversation having experienced one or two of them in various resorts over the years, which is why I had our complaint files from the previous three seasons sat on my desk.

"Actually madam, I am well used to dealing with these situations, because as I mentioned to you I have over seven years experience in this industry and it is physically impossible for every single guest to be happy. Because of this our companies feel it is prudent for us to be legally aware of the implications of any such situation, which is why I know what I am talking about and cannot offer to pay your cancellation fee for you. As for receiving complaints about this hotel in the past, I have got a copy of our complaints for the past three years in front of me as we speak and we have received not one single complaint about this hotel in all that time."

This was not what she wanted to hear and my forthright tones had annoyed her a little bit as well. However, I have been at breaking point with a lot of the locals recently, often unfairly, and it was about time someone who deserved it more felt a sharper edge of my tongue. This is why I was shaking a little bit, because I was trying to keep my fraught emotions in check before I unleashed enough fury to lose me my career.

The guests on the other hand were oblivious to any one else's point of view or any form of rational conversation, because they were looking for a complimentary move and were prepared to fight rather than reason. They therefore demanded I speak to someone superior about my decision and I in turn gladly called Dean Smalltown in overseas operations, instead of Stelios George, hoping that I would receive some back up.

"We've sold the hotel correctly Ceri," he told me after I had explained the situation to him. "It has been brochured one hundred percent correctly, which means we have fulfilled all of our contractual obligations. We have done nothing wrong and have not acted in any untoward manner or against the spirit of a holiday booking and if the customers wish to move because of a personal preference they are more than welcome to do so, but they will have to bear any additional costs. i.e. the cancellation fee. We are not legally bound or obliged to reduce our profits because of a personal whim."

And I could have hugged him. The easy way out is to give the Billies the move for free, because it would save us an awful lot of time and hassle, but why should our company suffer financially because one couple haven't followed the age-old rule of Caveat Emptor – Let the buyer beware.

The miracle is that it has taken seven months of a long season before someone in the UK offices has provided us with instant, efficient and total back up, which we need to run an effective programme. I gleefully relayed this response to the guests who blew their tops, called me all manner of none too pleasant profanities, threatened to sue the company, sue me, sue Werner, were going to contact The Sun and Watchdog and stated firmly that they were leaving and were not paying the cancellation fee. I on the other hand remained polite and calm initially, despite an overwhelming urge to return their volley of abuse, but they weren't worth the effort and I was beginning to see the funny side of it all. Instead I replied, "I'm ever so sorry, but I am not paid enough money to be spoken to in that manner, so I shall now wish you a good day" and put the phone down on them. They called back and called me even more names and I put the phone down on them again.

Twenty minutes later they called back, just as I was coming off the phone to the manager of the Holiday Inn and they were slightly more civil, but were still insisting that they were going to move to the Holiday Inn and were not going to pay the cancellation fee. This meant that we were at a very awkward stalemate. They hung up on me.

I presume this was in a childish effort to get their own back on me because they called me back two minutes later, repeating the same demands over and over, where all I could do was repeat the same response over and over. If they had said they were not going to pay the charge and were going to make pigs fly on a circus trapeze in Leningrad, I would still have given them the same answer, but gradually they became more abusive and even more insistent that they were moving.

Eventually the lady yelled that they were leaving and had a taxi booked for the Holiday Inn and there was nothing I could do about it!

"Fine madam," I said as sweetly as possible because I had been expecting this too, "but I think you'll find that the Holiday Inn will charge you their full nightly rate, because I have informed the manager that we will not be paying them our contract rate until the Goa Renaissance receives its cancellation fee."

"You bastard!" she yelled and put the phone down on me again.

This whole matter had by now dragged on for over four hours. I'd been up since 06:00, it was now 16:00 and I hadn't eaten a thing all day long, primarily because of these Billies and I was becoming more fed up, more irritable and almost desperate to the degree that I could have paid the bloody cancellation fee myself, just to get them out of my hair.

Five minutes after the lady had put the phone down on me I rang Werner again, just to chat about the situation and see how his staff were doing.

"So. What's happening?" he asked.

"Well, the long and the short of it, mate, is they're not moving unless they pay the cancellation fee. End of story!"

"You're not going to cover it?" he asked a little too hopefully.

"No way, mate." And I proceeded to explain in detail why not, for what seemed like the thirtieth time.

"So we're stuck with them?"

"Yeah, looks like it" I replied with a long shot rapidly forming in my head, "so you'll have them there for two long weeks, moaning, groaning, complaining about everything, spoiling the rest of your guests' holidays, looking for the tiniest little detail to complain about, which we both know they will and such are the British courts at the moment, they'll probably get a lot of compensation, which will be more than the cost of the cancellation fee, which we'll legally be able to claim back from you guys. Thank God I've only got them on the phone for just today, whereas you'll have them for two whole weeks and you'll probably lose a load of money into the bargain as well. Rather you than me, pal."

"Ceri, I need to speak to the G..M. a second. Call you back. Bye."

Five minutes later he called back to say that he was waiving the cancellation fee, just to get *the miserable bastards*, as he called them, out of his hair. I duly, and ever so reluctantly, informed the guests, without receiving a single word of thanks and moved them to the Holiday Inn.

The lady's final words were as cutting as ever and not particularly conducive to generating warmth or instilling in us a desire to provide them with a good service.

"I still think you're a useless company and we're never travelling with your courier ever again!"

"We're a tour operator!" I corrected.

SATURDAY – 17TH APRIL

I received a phone call from Werner at the Goa Renaissance in the middle of the morning, just to inform me that the guests from yesterday have changed their minds and have moved themselves back into the Goa Renaissance. Four bloody hours I spent dealing with those ungrateful idiots yesterday and they go and change their damned minds, without so much of a word of thanks, apology or recognition of the work they inflicted on us unnecessarily.

Miserable bastards!

SUNDAY – 25TH APRIL

I spent all of Saturday typing out my end of season report and finishing off the majority of the paperwork in time to put it in the mailbag for this week's flight, because today saw the departure of our final Sunday morning charter of the season, which was also the penultimate flight of the season to boot.

There are no arrivals to be seen any more, only departures, which have included a dozen or so reps from various operators, thus making the resorts seem like ghost towns. This also means that today was the very last time this season that I had to get up at 04:00 to go to the airport; this is the last potentially problematic flight and with only forty guests left in resort, who are due to depart this coming Friday it means we've done our last welcome meetings; dealt with what should be our last complaints and problems of any kind; have done our last arrival transfers and this week we'll do our final liquidation; fill in our final expense claims and hand in the final remnants of paperwork for the season.

The flight left on time without the merest hint of a problem, as it should be with the extra flexibility that is afforded to the airlines on the Outbound leg, and we were able to spend the rest of the day celebrating in whatever way we wanted because we didn't have to think about work for twenty-four hours.

Some of the reps spent their time on the beach, others in bars getting slowly drunk and reminiscing about the season and I chose to spend my time in bed sleeping.

The season is now officially winding down; we can relax a little, have a few beers at night without worrying too much about the following day, spend the afternoons on the beach and prepare for an almighty party next Friday when the last charter leaves at Midday.

Five days to go and we are almost there. We can all see the finishing line and are desperately hoping we can hold on to enjoy the inevitable celebrations.

What could go wrong now?

THURSDAY – 29TH APRIL

That's just about it. We did the final liquidation of the season today. I collected the last segments of the paperwork jigsaw from all of the reps and gave them all a small bonus from the 'flight seat slush fund'. This only worked out at about £50 a piece and £20 each for the local agency staff and we all then disappeared for a huge lunch at a nearby Mexican restaurant to fill our faces and celebrate the end of the season.

The past week has been ridiculously easy, because the office has been in pristine condition for ten days or more and everything is in its rightful place ready to be utilised the following season. All of the reports have been sent to the UK and duly filed in their respective areas, not a single iota of work is outstanding, all of the information books and boards have been collected and everything is now neatly stored away for a summer's hibernation.

I felt a feeling of sadness overwhelm me when I sat in an empty office at 19:00 with no people, no noise and no unnecessary clutter of paper strewn all over the desks and this emptiness brought home for the first time the fact that I'm leaving very soon, after completing a gruelling, both physically and especially mentally, eight months or so.

Lester has been coming into the office and is lost without any work to do or without any of his customary frantic dashing in between hotels, to the point that he is almost annoying. Now he just sits at my desk and doesn't stop talking about his bloody girlfriend and their wedding, which is planned for next December. The office staff are really taking it easy at this stage and out have come the packs of cards, scrabble and monopoly, which will be played on a nine to five basis, six days a week, for the next four months until the preparations get under way for a new season. They are paid their measly salaries and are retained throughout the summer, but have nothing to do, except sit in the office and count away the days until the likes of me return.

Sharon has been dashing about like a mad March hare. She's going travelling around India for a couple of months with her boyfriend and so she's been sorting out train schedules, flight details, flight costs, hotel availabilities, prices for everything under the sun from sunhats to medicine and she's been ringing her father at home to arrange their insurance. Thankfully she only has fifteen guests in resort, so has plenty of time to do all of this without it affecting the service they are being given, but this also means she has plenty of time to ring the office and disturb our games of cricket by requesting all manner of variations on transport arrangements and itineraries. She also hasn't stopped going on about how glad she is at not having to get up at 04:00 again this season, a sentiment I thoroughly endorse, but do not feel that I should mention out loud for fear of tempting fate in any way, shape or form.

Despite the fact that she is unbelievably annoying, her enthusiasm is a little infectious and I'm also quite proud of her for sticking the season out and surviving her own dark periods in March, when it would have been easier for her to quit and go home. She will be a better rep for it and I expect she'll be back here next year and will do an even better job.

There have also been quite a few late night parties in Tito's and West End and all I've had to show for them are a renewal of my friendship with Prop forward stomach, furry mouth syndrome and a jack hammer pounding away in my head, without a single woman in sight who may even have remotely come close to turning my head. Gina is very glad about this and I suppose I am too, and I hope that we can catch up in the coming months and see where we can take our obvious attraction for each other.

On the subject of parties though, we have an almighty one planned for tomorrow afternoon, once the flight has departed for the final time this season. There will be almost a dozen staff from various tour operators left in the resort and we have all agreed to bring our swimwear to the airport, together with towels, cigars, camera's and beer money before heading to Bogmalo beach for a swim in our uniforms and a day of drunkenness and debauchery next to the surf. The work has been all but finished, the guests will be gone and for once we'll be able to relax and not worry about the mobile phone ringing or wondering what our guests might think. This is just about it!

FRIDAY – 30TH APRIL

My first inclination that something may have been wrong was when I drove into the airport with one of the office boys and saw a horde of coaches sitting empty outside International Departures, when they should have all been returning to Panjim. This was quickly aided by the look on Sharon's face as I entered the building. She's never been one to hide her feelings and her face was flushed red with thunder and her eyes showed the annoyance she was experiencing.

"It's F***ing delayed twenty-four hours!"

"Okay Sharon, guests are watching us so let's at least look as if we know what we are doing. In the meantime I'll go and check with the handling agent to see what's happening." And I left her fuming and emitting the worst kind of messages to any observant guests.

True enough, the flight was delayed. I don't know where she got twenty-four hours from, presumably the old industry rumour mill working overtime again, but it did still look as if we would be there for a while to come. How long we would never have been able to predict, but as events panned out, far longer than any of us would ever have imagined in our fiercest nightmares.

What had happened was that there were two charters arriving that morning, one coming in from Gatwick and the second arriving in from Manchester shortly afterwards. The Manchester flight, as it transpired, arrived bang on time, but the Gatwick flight was held up in Bahrain for technical reasons, but because the airline desperately needed an aircraft back in Gatwick, they made the decision to switch the planes around and delay the Gatwick flight by forty-five minutes and the Manchester indefinitely. The fault with the aircraft was a generator failure, which means the plane can still fly, but there would be no heating, air conditioning, food or P.A. system. For obvious reasons they were not allowed under UK civil aviation guidelines to get the aircraft in the air. We also knew that this meant the delay would be for a minimum of three hours, which meant that we were obliged to provide snacks and soft drinks, which in turn is virtually impossible to do within the confines of Dabolim International Airport.

An announcement was made to the passengers, coaches were already waiting outside and we bussed them all to a nearby hotel for a buffet lunch. As the guests were making their way to the coaches, we received a mixed response of comments ranging from, "This is f***ing ridiculous!" and "This always happens with you lot." to "Excellent. I hope it's one that lasts three days and we get a couple more days free holiday!"

Sharon, Lester and Lyndon went with the guests to the hotel and I remained behind at the airport to monitor the situation and keep them up to date. Once the plane had taken off from Bahrain and been in the air for thirty minutes, I went to the hotel to inform the others of the welcome news and to plan our belated parties for that afternoon and evening. At this stage it all appeared to be running along nice and smoothly, what with six different tour operators having seats on the flight and all the staff coming to the airport for one big send off. It meant that there were almost as many reps as there were guests, which thankfully provided an overwhelmingly efficient service to all concerned.

I had a number of thoughts that darted about my brain as well, which were: I was glad that the delay had occurred on a Friday and not on a Sunday, because it meant we had three reps for forty guests and not three reps for two hundred and ten guests. I was also relieved about the timing of the delay, in the sense that it is better for it to occur at the very beginning or the very end of a season. This is because logistically it is much easier to deal with at this stage than in the middle of a very busy season, where the flight would have both departures and arrivals affected as well as there being over three-hundred guests in resort who would need looking after. Now we only had to worry about the guests who were leaving. I finally felt a smidgeon of pity for a mate of mine, called Tim, who originally had a ticket for the Gatwick flight, but swapped over with another rep and ended up on this delayed one instead, which must rank pretty highly in the list of the repping world's most ill-informed decisions.

Each of these points also had a significant standing with the following piece of news that we were to receive. At 14:00, just as we were about to take the passengers back to the airport we received a phone call from the handling agent informing us that the plane had been forced to return to Bahrain for the same reason as before and would now not be departing until 08:30 on Saturday morning, almost twenty-four hours later than scheduled. So much for our parties and well done Tim!

We reluctantly informed the guests of this latest development on the buses back to the airport. We felt it was the easiest way of getting the message across clearly and in a manner that we could ensure everyone would receive roughly the same news, thus cutting down any possibilities of Chinese whispers coming to the fore. They were taken down to Arrivals to collect their suitcases, which had already been checked in, whilst we frantically worked alongside the airline to arrange rooms for them in nearby hotels. A sobering thought is that if this were peak season, there wouldn't be enough rooms in any hotel to accommodate a fraction of the guests involved.

We managed to secure rooms for all of our guests in a good standard three star complex only thirty minutes from the airport, with comfortable rooms, superb health and safety standards and excellent service, which means it will be an upgrade for the average Goan holidaymaker. Two other companies also managed to fit their entire allocation of guests into the complex as well, which had its pros and cons.

One of the operator's guests are noticeably more downmarket than your average customer, which may cause an element of resentment amongst some of our more distinguished members. However, it did mean that Sharon's boyfriend was staying as well, because he works for one of the other companies, so we would have a relatively happy team of staff on hand to give the guests an excellent service, despite the limitations enforced by the airline. They were also prepared to provide a room for Sharon and her boyfriend and also Lester and myself.

On the whole the guests reaction was fantastic, because at our end we'd dealt with the situation efficiently and they'd be receiving a free days holiday, in a decent hotel, with all meals, soft drinks tea and coffee included. In fact I only recall one couple who complained, because they had just spent a fortnight at the Goa Renaissance and they wanted a similar standard of accommodation.

In theory they should go wherever the airline decide to place them, but I knew rooms had also been arranged at the Holiday Inn, so I begged, pleaded and called in a few favours and managed to get them transferred there and allowed Lyndon to take them down and look in on them. It was only when I was looking at the flight charts later on in the evening that it registered in my fatigued little mind who they were. Two weeks back they had provided me with untold amounts of abuse over the standard of the Goa Renaissance, and if I had realised that at the time they approached me

I'm not so sure I would have been so accommodating in calling in favours for their ungrateful souls. But looking at the situation with hindsight, I am glad that they were kept apart from the rest of our guests.

The passengers were all in their respective new accommodation by 16:00 and after I'd helped Lester and Sharon check them in, I headed back to the office to write an interim report to the UK, to keep them up to date and also to deal with the logistics of the situation. Sharon and Lester did some sterling work and remained with the guests in the hotel. If all goes to plan they should leave Goa by 08:30 in the morning.

SATURDAY – 1ST MAY

Why did we have to rejoice at never having to rise at an abominable hour anymore, for a ridiculously scheduled flight time? I should have learnt by now that you never ever tempt fate in this industry. It has a sadistic habit of coming back to haunt you and I now had to pay my penance by stumbling out of bed at 04:00, to get into the office for 04:30 and to receive a mini shock that jolted me out of my sleepy eyed reverie.

"Hello. Mr. Ceri." Prasad screamed at me just as I was walking in the door. I jumped out of my skin, hit my head against the side of the door and tripped over the step, which for some reason is just inside the door. After recovering a little and asking Prasad what on earth he was doing there, I made my way upstairs to the phone. He traipsed behind, scrambling into his trousers and hurriedly explaining that he'd slept in the office all night, just in case there were any phone calls. I was deeply impressed.

We'd received no calls or faxes, which I took as a good sign and I perked up even more when I called the airline to hear that the flight had left Bahrain at 04:00 Goa time.

"Thank Christ for that!" I thought out loud, because it meant that hopefully the guests would get away this morning, be out of our hair by 09:00 and we could resume our waylaid plans for a beach party.

We drove to the airport to find a profusion of coaches waiting outside and over six hundred people trying to squeeze into the departure area, because two other flights were leaving that morning as well. This caused even more chaos than usual, but we somehow managed to get all of the guests in, made some sense of the varying queues that were lining up and crossing paths, and the guests checked-in with a maximum of hassle.

At 07:00, half an hour before the flight was due to land, I was called into the agent's office along with the managers from the other five tour operators, to be told that the flight had returned to Bahrain for the same reason, yet again. To say the atmosphere was tense would be a dramatic understatement of Shakespearean proportions. In fact some of the language would have embarrassed Roy 'Chubby' Brown. It was then that we found out that the airline had had an opportunity to get another charter aircraft out to Goa the day before, but instead opted to try and repair the generator on the cheap in Bahrain, where incidentally they do not have the necessary parts available to carry out the said repairs.

The atmosphere in the office was also hindered by the lack of space and the godforsaken hour of the morning. We also had three local reps from another small operator who were hiding from their guests, together with a drunken Billy, who had to be kept apart from the other passengers because he was causing a few unwarranted fights. For a while there was a lot of shouting, heated discussion and voices struggling to be heard over their neighbours and a lot of frustrations were released with a succession of cries like, "I don't f***ing believe this!" and "Who the f*** do you think you are?" to the most sensible one of the lot, "Those poor guests!" The agency staff took a lot of unnecessary grief, but it was more out of frustration from a dishevelled group of managers trying to make sense of things. Eventually a general aura of calm reasoning prevailed as we put our heads together and decided on what had to be done.

The airline finally confirmed that they'd have an answer on whether or not the flight would leave today, or not as the case may be, by about 08:00. Therefore we all agreed that an announcement would be made to confirm the temporary delay of the flight and advising the guests that we would update them comprehensively at 08:30. I went out to join the reps to tell them the news and to help them deal with the guests, who were loitering with an element of frustration coming to the fore. Dealing with the guests was not pleasant however, because they were obviously tired from the early start and quite rightly fed up and annoyed, especially seeing as we couldn't provide them with any concrete answers.

To our immense relief and good fortune, the industry rumour mill had broken down, which must be a first, and thankfully no outrageous pieces of misinformation were distributed. Lester, Sharon and Lyndon were excellent. However, I did have to have a couple of quiet words with Sharon to calm her down and make sure she looked as if she was in control. My principle worry was that she may take her pent up anxieties out on the locals, or worse still the guests, but she held up very well and she did herself proud. It wasn't long before it was confirmed that the flight wouldn't be leaving at all today, so it was a case of transporting all of the guests back to the hotels.

This was none too pleasant, because they were still very tired, nerves were fraying and by now a handful of severe problems were coming to light, such as passengers needing to get back to start a new job on the Monday; Single mothers who needed to get back to see their children; Self-employed workers with businesses to run, who were doubly affected by missing out on the bank holiday trade; house deals that needed to be finalised and people who needed to be back for weddings, christenings, birthdays etc. If the information we were given by the airline is correct, one couple actually drove up to Bombay in just under fifteen hours and managed to purchase seats on a British Airways flight later in the day so that they wouldn't miss a wedding.

This time around we had a further eight guests who had been in five star hotels during their holiday who insisted on having a similar standard of accommodation for this one extra night. After more begging, pleading and calling in the last of my airport favours of the season I somehow contrived to secure a room for them all in the Holiday Inn. I also reserved one for Lyndon who did a fantastic job, staying with them all throughout the delay and having a wonderful time to boot, because he never imagined in his wildest dreams that he would ever stay in a hotel of the calibre of the Holiday Inn. His enthusiasm certainly lifted my spirits, because I was desperately clutching at anything remotely positive.

The whole process of arranging coaches and collecting suitcases again took quite a while, but by 10:00 every guest was accounted for and back in their respective hotels. This time I remained at the hotel with the guests after checking into Lester's room, so that I could be visible to the guests and also support the staff, who were holding up very well. About an hour after the guests had checked-in, had another breakfast and made their complimentary calls home, they seemed to settle down to a day of relaxation by the pool or beach and for a while it almost felt like a normal days work. I let Lester and Sharon go home to collect a change of clothes and toiletries, because they'd had the same clothes on for twenty-four hours, obviously not expecting the delay, and I visibly hung around the hotel until they returned in the late afternoon.

In the early evening we were again told the flight was scheduled to leave at 08:30, although we weren't too sure if it was going to be the original aircraft or not, so we left that bit out when we told the guests of the arrangements. Yet again the wake-up calls, buses and breakfasts were ordered for an abominable time in the morning. The guests were so good about the whole ordeal that we even had a few drinks with them in the bar and once the last of them had disappeared, we ribbed Tim mercilessly about swapping his flight for this one. When we left for bed, just after midnight, it was decided that Janice and I would wake up earlier than the others and head to the airport so that we could advise on any developments the moment they occurred. Surely nothing could go wrong for a third successive day.

SUNDAY – 2ND MAY

As it transpired we didn't need to go to the airport, because they called us. Janice and I were awake and in the process of getting ready to head off early when the handling agent came on the phone just before 04:00 to say that the aircraft would be late taking off and was not due into Goa until 09:30. Therefore they wanted the guests to be at the airport by 09:00, which would have given them plenty of time to check-in and head through Immigration Control, for what would have been the third time for some of them.

We rang each of the reps and told them the news and they in turn rang every one of the guest's rooms to pass it on and told them to stay in bed for an extra couple of hours, which doesn't make a lot of sense does it, waking guests up to tell them to go back to sleep? I also called Lyndon at the Holiday Inn to inform him of the situation and to his credit he had already heard and had told all of the guests with him. I then ambled down to breakfast in the previous days clothes to find the majority of the guests there and tucking into their fried Goan sausage and eggs and surprisingly, for that time of the morning, in quite an upbeat mood.

At 06:30 the agent called us again and told us that the plane had taken off, but that it was the same aircraft as before and it was now due in to

Dabolim at the aforementioned time of 09:30, so could we have the guests there at the airport at 09:00 as originally discussed. At this stage it was still only Janice and I who knew this and because the plane had only just taken off and we were suffering from thrice bitten, fourth time shy syndrome, we decided to keep the news to ourselves until we knew for sure that the plane was going to land in Goa. This we found was nigh on impossible because we were constantly bombarded with a whole plethora of questions such as:

"Any news yet?" or "What's the latest?"

We so desperately wanted to give both the reps and the guests some good news. However, we knew that if we had told everyone to be ready to leave in a couple of hours and then we again turn around and tell them that it isn't coming yet again, some of the passengers would be devastated.

For the first time in the two days that this had been going on, we started to hear some discouraging remarks as the scaremongers started coming to the fore, and this is something that sadly we Brits are very good at. All of a sudden, just after 07:00 we started to hear rash statements along the lines of' "It's because of the NATO strikes!", "CNN has announced that all UK airports are closed for a week!" (That particular gem came from Sharon's own lips), "It's a military airport in Goa and you can only leave on a Friday, so we'll be stranded here for another week at least!", "The plane has been attacked by Saddam Hussein!" and most worryingly of all, "If it's the same aircraft as before, then there is no way that I will be getting on it!" which to be frank we all had every sympathy with.

By 08:00, just as everyone was starting to become more than a little restless and frustrated in their desperation to hear some news, in fact any news be it good or bad, I received a phone call in reception. All of the reps gathered round, which didn't really help because the guests obviously knew that something was up, but at this stage who could blame them, as the news I was given by the handling agent was written all over my face. I went deep red through anger, my eyes blazed for a second and my hands shook as I gripped the receiver with a furiousness that would have turned stone into dust.

"It's turned around and gone back to Bahrain for the same reasons as before," I remember telling the gang. I could see their faces drop, bodies sag and then they all went through much the same sense of anger that I had, before we all composed ourselves to face the onslaught that we knew was inevitable. Our body language must have been plaintively obvious to most of the watching guests and we could hear one or two mutterings over our shoulders. At this stage it was scant consolation for Janice and I that we were right to withhold the earlier information we were given.

I was able to get some information out of the handling agent, which I repeated to them all, in that it was delayed for a further twenty-four hours and the airline would be sending out a replacement aircraft, which was due to arrive the following morning. The guests were to stay in the hotel on the same Full Board and soft drinks basis, with an extra two phone calls per room and a confirmed update would be given to us at 18:30 later that evening.

We quickly composed ourselves and decided on the exact wording of what we were going to tell the guests, so that we could ensure that we were all singing from the same song sheet and then Sharon was elected to inform the bulk of the crowd in the lobby. We elected her unanimously, which she was secretly quite thrilled about, because she has the most dominant voice, is very thick-skinned and a little simplistic, which is what is required. We knew there was no way that she would embellish on anything.

I went and told the guests who were still in the restaurant and the others went around the poolside and rang the rooms to ensure that every guest was aware of the situation. The groans that reverberated through the hotel went round like a Mexican wave of doom, traversing from one area to the next and I'm sure they could have been heard as far away as Bahrain itself. And who could blame them?

That was one of the hardest parts of the season, because we all felt the same way that the passengers did and we were the ones who were left to inform them of the bad news. Instead of telling them how we felt and explaining that we were tired and fed up too, we had to be strong, informative, disciplined and also distant to a degree, which was becoming harder to do. It did make much more sense for us to tell them however, because the guests had seen us working on their behalf so they had a smidgeon of sympathy for us, as opposed to some cold official from the airline who would have caused a mini riot. But for me this was one of the toughest moments of the ordeal so far and I can safely say that we certainly earned our basic wage.

The initial couple of hours after that were manic, with an endless stream of questions dealing with the reasons for the delay again, clarifying a lot of finer details and generally going over the same old ground that had been repeated over the past forty-eight hours. The more positive of the passengers then started asking questions about the south of Goa and where they could go and what they could do for the rest of the day, which was very encouraging.

It was also mildly amusing hearing some of the phone conversations. The guests were only entitled to a maximum of three minutes a piece to get their urgent messages across, but because the delay had reached such farcical levels, a lot of people were having problems in being believed by their families at home.

"Hi mum it's me." I heard one lady say almost cheerfully, "Listen, I've got to be quick because I've only got a couple of minutes......Yeah, I'm fine.... And Steve's fine as well. Look mum be quiet please because my times running out............ no I'm not home yet I'm still in Goa!

"Yes mum I'm in Goa................no really I am.....................Mum I swear to God the plane's been delayed again, we're still here................Yes I know it's unheard of that planes get delayed for two days, but it really has happened and I'm still in Goa................No I'm not joking, we're really here in Goa!....................No I'm not at home...................No I'm not at Nan's either I'm still in Goa. How many times do I have to tell you? And my time is running out quite quickly mum................Never mind my sister wanting some perfume from duty free, can you please call work and explain the situation to them please?........Yes I'm really in Goa. Look my time is definitely running out, because they only give us three minutes. I've got to go now, bye. Love you. Bye.................YES I REALLY AM STILL HERE IN..." and she was cut off.

After the initial burst of mayhem died down and things started to settle down a little bit, I called Lyndon to make sure he was okay again and then I took my turn to head back to Panjim to get some toiletries and a change of clothes. In fact I was very grateful that I didn't throw a lot of my uniform out as I had originally intended to. While in Panjim I spent a couple of hours in the office trying to get hold of the UK to keep them updated and was disappointed to find that the only way I could do so was by fax. I couldn't locate anyone in the UK offices. I presume this was because it was a bank holiday weekend and that everyone was out having a mini break, but even so there should have been someone available to help assist with any potential emergencies. I tried calling operations, the switchboard, Stelios George, Paul Rodrigues, and even our Managing Director's direct line, but they all just rang out and didn't even have their answer machines switched on. I also tried the emergency mobile number but could get no response from that either, so if in the event of a real emergency occurring on a weekend or bank holiday we'd have no back up or assistance and would just have to muddle through as best we could. I didn't find this to be the most reassuring element of service from my own company and I made a mental note to include this in a report I was planning on how we should move into the twentieth century, before we depart it.

I arrived back at the hotel at 16:00 and spent ages on the phone, first to the handling agency staff, then Lyndon and finally the girl who was co-ordinating matters at another hotel to see if there were any further updates or news of which there was only one. The airline had definitely confirmed that they were sending out a replacement aircraft and we'd be given confirmation of flight times at 18:30.

I went down to the reception afterwards and joined Sharon for a coffee in the restaurant, to see a pair of glum faces that were both looking tired. Apparently while I'd been away the handling agent had come down to the hotel to visit the guests to tell them that a new aircraft was on its way this evening and they also increased every guests board basis to all-inclusive. This meant they all had free alcohol twenty-four hours a day now and in turn meant the more miserable and rowdier of the passengers had been taking advantage of this since midday. As a result their macho bravado was creeping to the surface of their personalities and their fertile imaginations were working overtime. By now all manner of stories were floating around the pool and of course one or two passengers had started mouthing off to Sharon, who in her fatigued state had understandably taken it quite personally.

Then to exacerbate an already fragile situation, the airline's customer relations department in the UK sent through a fax, which was given to every single guest in the afternoon, stating that the original aircraft would be coming into Goa, which of course wound the guests up even further. They also made us look stupid, because the guests automatically assumed that we were giving them misinformation. Or as the more inebriated ones succinctly put it, "The whole f***ing disaster was our f***ing fault and we're a bunch of lying toe rags!" At that stage the airline were not very high on my

Christmas card list.

We were able to hold onto our sanity until 18:25, when the airline remarkably called us five minutes ahead of schedule. They confirmed that a new aircraft would be leaving Manchester in a couple of hours time and would be landing in Goa at 07:30 the following morning and departing an hour later. They also faxed this information through to the hotel as confirmation, which we in turn photocopied to give out to the guests to prove that we weren't making the whole thing up. At last, we had received some positive, believable news for the first time since the delay had first occurred. Now all we had to do was make the breakfast arrangements, book the wake up calls and order the coaches and of course give the guests the good news.

At exactly 19:06, Sharon stood in front of an enraptured audience in the lobby of the hotel and made the big announcement to the expectant congregation. She gave the exact information and no more and apologised for the inconvenience. She then thanked the guests on behalf of us all for their patience, understanding and for being unbelievably well behaved. They had restored ten-fold our faith in the average Brit abroad. To our surprise one lady stood up and thanked all of us for our efforts, to which a chorus of 'hear-hears' circulated. Amidst the applause a rather inebriated gent exclaimed that he was very disappointed, because this whole scenario hadn't been like anything he'd seen on the television before and we'd done such a good job in looking after the guests at our end that they couldn't find a single thing to complain about!

That's a typical British statement that we hear from time to time, because it indicates that nowadays the tourists are actively looking for things to complain about. But I let it go and called on Lyndon to find that he had informed his guests and that he was still having a great time. We all went to bed cautiously positive. Lyndon was disappointed that it would all be over in the morning.

MONDAY – 3RD MAY

I hardly slept at all during the night, constantly fretting over whether or not the plane would actually make it and also worrying over my ability to rise, yet again, at such a godforsaken hour. By 03:30 I was wide awake, and like the rest of the reps I was nervously willing the plane to come into Goa.

Janice drove me to the airport at 04:30 and we both had a little time to reflect over the past couple of days, as well as over the whole season. After months of indifference and generally avoiding the other's company, we had suddenly been forced into a situation where we were almost in each other's pockets for eighteen hours a day. This was one of the big benefits of the delay for me, because I realised I still valued her friendship, and I think she agreed, so we arrived at the International Departures in relatively good spirits and on speaking terms again. By 05:30 we'd had confirmation that the plane was on its way and we duly relayed this to the hotels and told the reps to get the guests to the airport by 07:00, to allow them enough time to check their luggage in and make their way through Immigration control.

As it again transpired they had plenty of time to do so, because lady luck had one final dig in the ribs, when she delayed the flight for a further two and a bit hours; but what's a couple of hours in seventy?

At 11:23 a group of holiday industry staff were stood on a wall overlooking the runway at Dabolim International Airport. We were all wearing the same clothes we had on the day before; we were drenched in sweat and wilting from a combination of fatigue and the heat; we were holding hands, frightened to speak and our ties were at half mast, shirts were creased and our hair dishevelled as the aircraft finally edged its way ever so slowly to the beginning of the runway.

The guests had checked in without any hitches, we'd gone through the goodbyes with Tim for a third and final time, but this time they meant all the more because our friendships had grown stronger and closer as we shared adversity over the past three days. The plane pulled onto the runway, we collectively held our breaths and as it started its run towards take-off we all blew instinctively, helping its wings lift it off the ground and take it clear into the sky, without a hitch. A huge cheer could be heard from inside the aircraft and an equally loud one from the group of reps standing on the wall, holding hands and some crying with relief.

The *** 4331 eventually departed seventy-one hours and forty-two minutes late on Monday 03/05 and created a new record for a delayed flight for that particular airline.

SRI LANKA
TWO YEARS LATER

23 MARCH – 12.00 MIDDAY

I'm still shaking a little. My mouth is still dry and I'm only just starting to lose my nervous sweat, which has been racing down my armpits, missing my loose T-shirt and bouncing off my tennis shorts and leaving tiny, yet brief, 'Lilliput' size puddles in the sand below me.

I've just ordered a glycerine filled Lion beer and as I sit with my bare feet in the soft white embers on the Sri Lankan coastline, at the beach side bar of the Club Palm Garden, I'm trying to take in the events of this morning which have turned me into this wreck. I can't help but reminisce over what's happened since we finished the season in 1999, after that three day delay.

By what I've said here, it sounds as if I've never been back to the place, but nothing could be further from the truth because I've virtually made Goa my home and there have been some odd adventures and lots of changes, mostly for the better, along the way.

After finishing the season and having plenty of time at home to recharge my batteries, gather my thoughts and nearly find some semblance of direction in my life, I eventually came out to Sri Lanka in June 1999 as Head Rep for a few months, before returning to Goa again in September of the same year. This time it was in the exalted position of Destination Manager. I was pleased to be promoted, although yet again it involved one of those long round trips, from home to the office and back again to be given news I could have received over the phone, by fax or now that I have entered the 21st century, by email. But it has renewed a lot of lost energies and a great deal of my old dynamism has reappeared, which has certainly helped me like myself a lot more.

Sri Lanka passed relatively uneventfully and to summarise the stint in general, I'd conclude that I didn't make much money, but learned an awful lot. I gained some great experience, saw some awesome sights, gave up alcohol for a couple of months and thus regained some of my old fitness levels to go with my new found energies and made some great friends. I had to put up with Janet on a couple of occasions, seeing as she was my direct boss but being based in the Maldives didn't actually do a lot. I had a wonderful time and I failed to get laid.

The following winter in Goa, with me being in absolute charge saw a few changes, which were evidently for the better. I changed a couple of the paperwork systems and made the office more efficient, which certainly assisted the Reps and they were able to provide a good service and thus generate further sales. We were most definitely assisted by the departure of Stelios George, who handed in his notice just before I was about to hand mine in, and we were certainly aided with the introduction of Dean Smalltown and Kathy Rodrigues who have taken overall responsibility of our area and they have introduced new standards of professionalism and integrity. This I have most definitely appreciated and the resort has most certainly benefited from. One of which, was the eventual introduction of email into the office, which has saved a fortune in time and money and again helps us provide a better service to the clients. Another was the cancelling of all contracts with the dreaded SJM hotel, which has made the reps' jobs easier and again we were able to concentrate on service and sales.

It was still a topsy-turvy season, with as many highs as lows. We still had some staffing problems and I'm sad to say they were with a UK rep and not one of the reliable locals. At the end of the day we almost halved the number of complaints compared to the previous season and increased the revenue generated from excursion sales by 60%. So my first season as manager will be regarded as a success on paper.

I kind of lost touch with Gina, but that is typical of this industry when you are so far apart. But I was able to take solace in a number of arms, most regularly with a Norwegian Rep who was quite happy to teach me even more dirty Scandinavian words.

But if Goa was a success, then the following summer was an unmitigated disaster, because I swapped sides and joined our parent company for a season. The only benefit I could say I gained was the knowledge that I want nothing whatsoever to do with them again and that my days in this industry are limited. The reason for this drastic mood swing is that I spent the summer as Supervisor 1 in Zakynthos and had the worst time of my professional career.

I was lucky to make some good friends and have another troubled relationship, this time with an attractive red haired rep. But I found the island had no history or character, the locals were abusive and obsessed with money, and the new reps had no sense of professionalism, energy or desire to learn the job. The company's methods of operating I found to be unprofessional, with no regard or care for the customer, even though they're supposed to have improved over the years and the area manager was the least inspiring person I have ever encountered. I went with grand ideas of a huge future in the industry and left in mid-September a very relieved man, desperate to come back to the welcoming arms of my beloved company and the warm bosom of Goa for the fourth time in five years.

This season has gone very smoothly with very few complaints and increased sales yet again. The only staff problems I've had with British reps were a severe bike accident on Christmas Day for one, a drink and drug dependency for another and I had to spend three nights in hospital myself. My intestines had swollen and were seeping blood through every available orifice. Things have gone so well though, that I have been allowed my first week's holiday since June 1999 and I am happily sunning myself with some old friends on the island of Serendipity. I am tanned, relaxed, rapidly discharging my stress, have decided to do just one more season and I am shaking like a leaf.

About an hour ago, I walked along the beach about twenty metres to the neighbouring Neptune hotel. I hadn't slept a wink all night and in the morning I couldn't decide which T-shirt and shorts combination to put on. I decided against the grunge look of diver T-shirt and cut off denims and said a curt 'no way' to a formal check shirt and tailored shorts and was instead, in mild agreement with my 1958 short sleeved Brazil jersey. It is a neutral blue, looks quite smart, but not too smart which would say this is planned and uncomfortable, and gives off a slight air of intrigue and mystery. My shorts are for tennis and are a green comfortable fitting knee length, so they match the top (if you know anything about Brazilian football you'll know they do), but still look casual enough to make it appear that I've thrown the whole ensemble together without thinking about it.

Because I went across the beach I opted for rugged and masculine barefoot, as opposed to some geeky sandals, which I hope has exuded a slight air of danger and excitement. These days my head is shaved, having given up the battle with receding hairline quiffs. I've got a goatee beard and day old stubble and I've also put on a slight hint of Calvin Klein Escape, even for that early in the morning.

I held my stomach in as I walked through the entrance of the Hotel Neptune snack bar, past a crowd of people sunbathing on the grassy verge. I was convinced they were all staring at me, because I was nervously sweating, my mouth was Sahara dry, my legs were like lead and I was finding that this walk was taking forever. It was even more daunting than the first time I ever walked across the tarmac to a waiting McDonnell Douglas airbus, which was to transport me to the beginning of this whole big adventure.

I walked past the guests, alongside the pool from where I could see the reception above and a prominent lime green notice board. Then I went through the restaurant downstairs, only bumping into the one table, feeling even more uncomfortable as the waiters all stared at me and sniggered, which made me sweat a little more and my mouth became even drier. I tried to muster some spittle, but found it impossible to do and then stumbled up the open stairs because my sunglasses had misted up and I couldn't see where I was going.

Just as I turned the corner to go into the reception, I questioned myself for the thousandth time. I really couldn't answer why I was doing this. Did I really want to be doing this for all the right reasons or was I just in the process of exorcising another ghost? I hoped it was the former, but in truth I really didn't know at that juncture.

And there she was, sun shining behind her, big smiling brown eyes, glossy hair which had grown to her shoulders since I last saw her and the cutest little body, which could never sit still.

This was it. One of those big life-defining moments, the kind that Brad Pitt and George Clooney carry off so well. This was my chance to make this big impression and alter our destinies forever. I opened my mouth to deliver one of my well rehearsed lines, when she looked up, smiled as if I were just another 'Billy' and then a second later realised who this older, balder man, with the goofy grin was, staring right back at her. I breathed to compose myself, took off my misty shades and said, "Mmmpf, grhbwlbrmn guhb nrbrm!"

"Oh my god! Ceri! You've come for me! I always knew this day would come!"

I heaved a huge sigh of relief, glad to see that my feelings, hopes and fantasies were being reciprocated and replied:

"Hello Gina."

EPILOGUE

Two months later she dumped me again.
Janet's toe still hurts.